CW00376599

How ᴜ

There is an unfortunate gap between those who do extraordinary things and those who are able, or even willing, to tell us about them. This important book by Dr Stuart Evans bridges that divide in that it is a bold, no frills explanation of precisely what it's like trying to save lives in some of the most dangerous and poverty stricken parts of the globe.

Dr Evans resigned from a safe job as a British GP to brave the bullets, land mines and sheer grinding hardships of countries like Uganda, Cambodia and Haiti, to join Médecins Sans Frontières as a doctor, trying to save lives in conditions sometimes too appalling for most comfortable Western minds to contemplate.

But as well as letting us into the gruesome details of such travail, Dr Evans pulls no punches in his criticism of how the system itself, one that is supposed to bring aid and relief, is actually often unwittingly culpable in causing chaos. It's rare for a piece of work to be so candidly written and, for someone who has so selflessly devoted their adult life to helping others, to examine whether what he and others have done is of any real value.

This is a precious piece of work, not just because it chronicles one man's contribution to the sum of human compassion, but because we can actually learn something from it. If the reader understands the situation even a fraction more clearly from having encountered this then it will have been a triumph in itself, but since the book also offers the chance for someone to actually act upon the errors that are highlighted and fix them, then Dr Evans should rightly feel that his life has been one of extraordinary value.

Muriel Gray
October 2003

First published in Great Britain 2003

All rights reserved. No part of this publication may be
reproduced, stored in a retrieval system, or transmitted
in any form or by any means, electronic, mechanical,
photocopying, recording or otherwise, without the prior
permission of the authors.

Copyright: Stuart Evans and Carol Tweedie

ISBN: 1-898654-15-8

www.howcanihelp.org.uk

Printed and bound in Great Britain by
Bordersprint Ltd, Selkirk, TD7 4DP

Photographs
Front Cover: Howard Davies, Exile Images
Back Cover: Stuart Evans and Andrew Tweedie

How Can I Help?

*Reflections of a
Humanitarian Aid Doctor*

Stuart Evans

*with
Carol Tweedie*

To Boy

Contents

Thanks to Andrew, Hilary and Bill

Preface

I spent time searching for a successful opening gambit, something that would work both for myself and for the patients. In Britain, General Practitioners (GPs) are allocated a limited amount of time for their consultations, meetings that may involve complex, even desperate need. Of course, all too regularly it's just another cold, but even that may be an excuse to talk about some underlying fear. So I needed to get it right. Each short time-slot must include welcoming pleasantries, the patient's explanation for the visit and any diagnosis and advice that I might be able to offer. A good start was essential.

In the early days, I tried, "How are you today, Mrs Smith?" Polite people simply responded, "Fine thank you doctor," smiling silently and waiting for my next attempt. Clearly, a more direct question was necessary, to obtain a more revealing answer.

"What seems to be the trouble?" inferred to some patients that I expected a self-diagnosis, one that would let me off the hook. It was also a negative start. Trouble was not always why people came to see their doctor.

As time passed, it became clear that many of the ills in my surgery were social problems, issues which medical science alone could not be expected to cure. Patients presented with ailments, which often masked more fundamental issues. Sometimes we both knew that there was no real hope for a "cure", but a GP is one of the few individuals in the community, who makes unconditional appointments to speak with people. Regularly, patients wanted something different from a simple medical diagnosis, with its accompanying prescription of possibly ineffectual drugs.

So I progressed to, "How can I help?" That appeared to be my role and this question allowed patients to state their needs, whatever they were. Furthermore, it enabled me to listen. Listening, was a much more important aspect of my work than I had been taught.

Moving into the field of humanitarian aid, with scant thought for what it would entail, I knew little about the Red Cross, Oxfam and Save the Children and nothing at all about Médecins Sans Frontières. The sum total of my information came from television, with images of emaciated babies, or broken bodies receiving treatment amidst the ruins of an earthquake. Naïvely, I supposed that the aid world would be simpler, more "rewarding". This was not to be the case and I was to find humanitarian aid work complex, even at times quite baffling.

The question "How can I help?" remained, although assessing the right sort of help became even more challenging. Despite the fact that treating patients with sleeping sickness, malaria or cholera can be immensely satisfying professionally, I now discovered that perplexing social, economic and public health issues were often related to such diseases. Gradually, I came to accept that these could not be viewed separately from the work itself. And finally, I began to question the efficacy of some of the help that was being offered.

Although humanitarian work may appear to be straightforward in a crisis situation, a surprising amount of aid does not in fact deal with emergencies. It was this aspect that was to prove most puzzling for me. I had become involved in the world of Non-Governmental Organisations (NGOs), groups that blithely venture into sovereign countries with the avowed intention of helping.

NGOs are organisations, which work in various parts of the world, trying to achieve "desirable change", while remaining independent of external controls, to varying degrees. Some are very powerful and influential players on the international stage. Each has its own, independent agenda, yet there is little overall control of what these organisations do, in the countries where they work. The fundamental objective of most NGOs is helping people, but understanding all the issues and finding the best solutions is not easy. Furthermore, NGO activities are affected by a wide range of factors, including funding sources, multi-national and local politics, economics, socio-political issues, the need for media prominence and, of course, their own specific objectives.

NGOs attract large numbers of volunteers, all with the very best of intentions, often with little or no training, far less knowledge of the global issues they may be attempting to solve.
I know. I was one of them.

In the West, we still arrive at wrong answers to our own problems, despite our superior technologies and apparently sophisticated philosophies. Yet, somewhat arrogantly, we are quite sure that we can help others to resolve their predicaments. We need to think more carefully, when we ask the question "How can I help?", remembering that economic constraints, trade-barriers, international arms-trading, drug-trafficking and political duplicity will inevitably preclude a simple answer.

Now, I wonder if conventional aid is the answer to anything other than emergency situations. Medical organisations seem to have mastered emergency work, but even this "band aid" can be confused by wider, often political issues. For the more complex problems, we need to find different solutions, ones that empower developing countries to resolve their own social, economic and environmental issues. Only then will we eliminate poverty, dependence and the continuing need for "help". As yet, despite decades of non-emergency projects, more than a billion people in the world do not even have access to clean drinking water, far less adequate medical care.

CHAPTER ONE

A leap into the dark

I watched Luc with a mixture of anxiety and resignation, while he chewed steadily through his plateful of steak tartare in the Café Rotonde, close to Bastille. It was June 1995 and we were in Paris, where I was receiving the briefing that was intended to prepare me for Cambodia, a country about which I knew almost nothing. I had recently been accepted as a volunteer with Médecins Sans Frontières (MSF), a French organisation that provides medical aid around the world, both for emergencies and for longer-term projects. My first "mission" was to be in the East, somewhere up the Mekong River and the briefing was being conducted in French, one of the official languages of Cambodia.

After the first forty-five minutes at MSF headquarters, about the only words I had understood were, "On va manger" which appeared to mean, "We can talk as we eat". This I knew was a bad idea, since my understanding of French was at best rudimentary. Under restaurant conditions, what with the noise of other diners talking and the inevitable music, it was bound to be a complete debacle. My pick-up rate would probably be down to one word in three! In everyday social interaction I used facial expressions, gestures and concentrated guess-work to fill in the gaps, in an effort to avoid appearing overtly moronic. I knew from experience that busy French restaurants dramatically reduced my ability to comprehend and this encounter was much more important than a chat with friends, where it would not matter in the least if I missed some detail of who had done what and to whom. Here, there might just be some information, which it would be best not to miss. I was anxious to grasp anything of substance about my new job, or for that matter about Cambodia itself.

It was worse than I had imagined. Luc ate and talked at the same time, filling his mouth with bread and then bending his head over his meal, so that he could more intently examine the contents of his plate. Each time this happened, I lost more of his message. The obvious solution would have been to ask that he speak in English, but Marie-Jo, the young, blonde nurse who was sitting beside me was French and as well-versed in my language, as I was in hers. One of us would have to lose out, so I decided to be the gentleman and muddle through. A less honourable motivation for keeping quiet about my deficiency was the fear that if they found out how poorly I spoke French, they might change their minds about me. I need not have worried. I was to find out later that MSF was very short of doctors at that time. Even with my poor grasp of the language, I was better than nothing.

The lunchtime briefing lasted for an hour and a half and Luc seemed not to notice that I contributed almost nothing to the occasion. Perhaps it was not unusual for "first mission" candidates to be reticent, but surely they didn't all just nod and smile like idiots, failing to ask anything about what the future might hold for them? Finally it was time to leave the restaurant, with me little wiser about what lay ahead, just relieved that my shortcomings had not been exposed. I never found out what Luc thought about this new recruit he was sending to wave the flag of French medicine in foreign climes. Just as well, perhaps.

We now returned to the MSF office, a modern building tucked incongruously down a back street, off Place de la Bastille; a forest of antennae on the roof, alerting you to the fact that this organisation has contacts all over the world. These, together with an appropriate, ship-like structure and a coating of grey paint, convey the impression of a vessel about to set sail for foreign parts. Inside, the offices are grouped around a central glass atrium. Through the glass wall, you can see a small, enclosed garden, with a strange sculpture; a brown plastic tree trunk about two metres high, with a fringe of twenty human feet sticking out from its base. No doubt this signifies some complex aestheticism about humanitarian aid, but to this day, it quite escapes my understanding.

We, however, had no time to indulge in artistic appreciation, for Marie-Jo and I were immediately directed towards the departure staff, whose job it was to arrange all the practical details for our trip, such as air tickets and travel connections. As we made our way past the reception desk, I glimpsed a collection of backpacks and lumpy bags, their owners presumably about to set off for, or arriving back from, exotic foreign missions. We passed groups of people, all bustling around purposefully. Some were rushing, as if to an immediate and desperate emergency, while others would glimpse friends and stop to embrace them with characteristic French cheek-kissing, as they loudly caught up with one another's news. The place was buzzing. It was alive. This was just the sort of organisation I had wanted to be a part of, in total contrast to what I had done in the past.

Zouina and Natalie (the Bureau de Depart girls) rushed around energetically, confident of the dramatic effect of their neat figures, short mini-skirts and striking hairstyles. They were very pretty, very friendly and very busy. Telephones rang constantly and each seemed to be doing three things at once, but despite the apparent chaos, we were eventually issued with our standard kit of MSF tee shirts, letters of authorisation and identity cards. Mine stated boldly, "Médecins Sans Frontières recommends Stuart Evans to all Military and Civilian Authorities and will be grateful for any assistance they extend to him". It amused me that the words so resembled those written in my British passport. Equipped with both, surely I would be invincible, whatever South East Asia had to offer.

Then there were various health insurance documents and unexpectedly, six condoms. I glanced at Marie-Jo and considered making a joke like, "these won't last us very long", but then I decided that with my poor French, I might make a hash of it. Worse still, I might make an indecent proposal! Also, I wasn't sure about her sense of humour. It was a good decision—she didn't have one, or at least not of the British variety. I'm still not sure where I stand with French humour and I regularly get it wrong.

Finally, we were handed the magic plane tickets, for London, Bangkok, and Phnom Penh, the last two names proclaiming the fact that I was beginning my journey towards a new and different lifestyle. The name "Phnom Penh" reeks of the exotic. So with virtually no preparation, I was off to work in a strange language, in a strange country, full of strange illnesses. The idea was both exciting and a little daunting.

All formal arrangements completed, I said, "A demain" to Marie-Jo, agreeing to meet her back at headquarters at eight thirty the following morning. There, we would pick up the parcels of supplies that MSF wanted us to transport to Cambodia, along with our own baggage. Before leaving the building I visited the library, in an effort to find out a bit more about Cambodia and, more importantly, the mission itself. The MSF library is extensive, maintaining a detailed catalogue on all the countries it enters, together with relevant information about most of its missions. An hour was more than enough, however, to convey to me that my understanding of written French, was possibly even less proficient than my aptitude for speaking the language. So I packed up and set off for my last night in Paris, that amazing city of culture and sophistication. Perhaps I should make the most of it, before my leap into the dark. I still wasn't exactly sure what I was expected to do, or to become, in the new world I was about to embrace.

These problems engaged my mind throughout the ten-minute walk from the MSF offices, up Rue Sedaine, to the hotel arranged by Zouina and Natalie. It was the first time that day when I had not been expected to listen to, read or speak French and it was a relief to be left to myself, to sift through what I had been told, or what I thought I might have been told. It was even more of a relief to find, that what I had learned to date, seemed to make sense.

My hotel was built on the Parisian lighthouse principle, a very small footprint, but seven storeys high. Of course my room was on the sixth floor, accessible only by climbing dark, narrow, circular stairs, which still bore some remnants of an ancient, red carpet. In true French style, the switches, which controlled the corridor lights, allocated just enough time to move from one level to the next, before casting you back into stumbling darkness. I've often wondered how the less agile manage in such places. Perhaps they know the system and take a torch?

The room had clearly been part of a larger one, at some time in the hotel's less seedy past. Now, it was reduced to a space just three metres square, with a bed, a tiny wash-basin and a shower in one corner. In the corridor there was a toilet, to be shared with the occupants of the other six bedrooms. None of the doors fitted very well, the locks being more symbolic than practical and the general impression was decidedly second-rate. So much for my final night of Gallic sophistication. But perhaps this is the calculated way MSF prepares its employees for imminent culture shock? Or perhaps they don't want to waste cash on luxuries, when they have so many more important commitments for their money?

The hotel manager, a big, blond woman of about fifty, was accustomed to being a mother hen to all her MSF children. She smiled and chatted a lot and despite the fact that she spoke no English, I felt quite at home. Thanks to her, I managed to find a decent place to eat my last proper meal in France, but it seemed wiser to give the fleshpots a miss. I had a feeling that an early night and a clear head, would serve me best during the following day's travel.

I was up and ready by 7am, my few belongings stuffed into my rucksack. I went down to the basement dining room for breakfast, taking time over the fresh coffee and crusty baguette, thinking that whatever else the isolated mission would provide in Cambodia, a boulangerie was extremely unlikely. As I walked towards the MSF offices, I absorbed the sounds and sights of early morning Paris, aware that unlike the rest of these people hurrying to work, this evening would find me somewhere very different indeed. At that hour, there were few people about; a road sweeper pushing his cart and a tramp in a doorway sandwiched between an old mattress and a large sheet of cardboard.

When I reached headquarters, Marie-Jo was waiting and we became instantly embroiled in the matter of loading into the taxi the numerous packages for the mission. In the forty minutes it took us to get to Charles de Gaulle Airport, there was no further time for reflection, since I had to concentrate intently on keeping up with the conversation. At last my journey had begun and from this moment on it would all unfold relentlessly, whether I could cope or not. So I settled back to enjoy it.

CHAPTER TWO

Chugging up the Mekong

During the interminable, twelve-hour flight, Marie-Jo and I began to get acquainted. My colleague for the next nine months was a qualified nurse from the South of France, blonde, very pretty and extremely petite, weighing perhaps only forty kilos. Because she had already worked with MSF in South Sudan, she had been given the responsibility of being Field Co-ordinator for the project and this was clearly weighing heavily on her mind. I tried to reassure her that we would sort out any problems together, but whatever it was I said, it didn't seem to make her feel any better.

In retrospect, the reassurances of a novice aid volunteer, especially one who could barely communicate, were unlikely to engender much confidence. Furthermore, although still enthusiastic, I was beginning to consider the demands of my own job in greater detail. I had doubts, both about whether I knew enough tropical medicine and how I was going to improve my French sufficiently, so that sick people could rely on me to understand every nuance of their described illnesses. Despite what the public may think, medicine is an imprecise science (or art?) and both the unknown and the unexpected are always lurking in the wings, waiting to intervene. In the course of my career in Britain, these two factors influenced results with as much regularity as either logic, or certainty. In Cambodia, it would probably be worse.

Tired and preoccupied, we landed in Bangkok ten hours later, with a further four hours to wait for our connecting flight to Phnom Penh. Thanks to the notorious traffic jams, sightseeing was not possible, so here I was, in one of the most interesting locations of my life, sitting in an airport lounge! We were exhausted, both by the travelling and by our attempts to communicate in a mixture of French and English. So, as we waited, we relapsed into a reasonably comfortable silence.

Once in Phnom Penh, we cleared customs easily enough and with our rucksacks and miscellaneous parcels, struggled out into the Arrivals Hall, where we were relieved to see a man carrying a large cardboard notice announcing MSF. To our surprise, our driver spoke almost no

English and very little French, so we learned almost nothing from him, as he drove us into town in a large, white Land Cruiser, with the MSF logo painted on its side.

Phnom Penh was hot, busy and extremely humid. Quite silent now, Marie-Jo and I tried to take in as much as possible, as we weaved through traffic that was entirely different to anything I had seen before. There were bicycles, hand-carts, people on foot and a few cars, all jostling for the same space and the resulting mayhem was fascinating. Eventually we arrived at the MSF house, situated in what appeared to be a residential suburb. Here we met Isabelle, the MSF doctor who worked at Kom Pong Cham, a town midway between Phnom Penh and our project village of Kroch Mar. She was about thirty-five years old, short, stocky and friendly. To my relief, she switched comfortably between English and French, depending on whom she was addressing. While she talked, she constantly moved around, giving the impression of being both dynamic and competent. As she pointed out all the things we needed to know about the house, she explained that it would be two days before we went on to Kroch Mar. We must first have a briefing with Pascal, the Head of Mission.

"As usual, he isn't here to welcome you, but you will see for yourselves," she said enigmatically. I looked questioningly at Marie-Jo, in case I had missed something, but she seemed as nonplussed as I at this cryptic statement. However, since no further illuminating detail was proffered, I decided to change the subject. No doubt we would find out more about the internal politics of the place, as time went by. I was old enough to know there were always workplace politics. It would be naïve to think that an aid organisation would be in any way different, just because it was well-intentioned. Anyway, for the moment, I had other priorities.

"I don't know about Marie-Jo, but I need to get some sleep for an hour or two. Is it all right if I look around the city later on?" I asked. I was exhausted, thanks to the heat, seemingly endless travel and lack of sleep.

"Yes, of course. There's no driver at the weekend, but you can reach the commercial area on foot, when you wake up," Isabelle told us. "You'll find restaurants, shops and a park, all close by. But don't go far from the main roads, as it's easy to get lost in the narrow streets and you won't be able to ask for directions. It takes time to find your way around properly," she warned us. I asked her how long she had been in Cambodia.

"About ten months and that's enough," she replied. She seemed less than enthusiastic.

I was later to realise that Isabelle was a classic example of someone who had been too long in the humanitarian aid business. She had not found a real niche, a cause to which she wanted to commit the rest of her life and was instead trapped in an endless cycle of short-term projects, which in themselves did not give her enough job satisfaction. The longer she left it before returning to France, the more difficult it would be to find work there. In modern medicine, you have to strive to keep up to date with all the changes and although it is possible to catch up with new fashions and innovative therapies, alienation from your culture and friends can be a more difficult issue to address. Perhaps that is one of the reasons why MSF encourages a constant turnover of staff, happy that people leave the organisation for a while, or move on, to find a more stable lifestyle.

"There's no-one else in the house with you, until Monday morning. I am staying with friends this weekend. Help yourself to food and drink from the fridge. Denise, the admin, has left you a little money to see you through the weekend." Then, after ensuring that we had no further questions, Isabelle set off on foot, leaving two very tired and bemused new recruits to explore the house, which appeared to serve both as a guesthouse and office. It was surprisingly large and comfortable, with solid, concrete walls and several balconies on the first floor. I had expected everything to be very basic, but each room had two or three beds, mosquito nets and air conditioning. It all seemed quite civilised. And what a relief to stop moving.

"I'm going to have a snooze. See you in a while. Perhaps we could eat together, later this evening," I managed to mumble to Marie-Jo, before finding myself a bed and climbing under the mosquito net. I fell asleep immediately, all worries about language, new colleagues and stressful medical issues totally forgotten.

When I awoke, it was ten o'clock the following day and extremely hot and humid, as I had not bothered to switch on the air conditioning, before lapsing into unconsciousness. Outside, it was even hotter, but less oppressive, so I decided to go for a walk, as there was no one else around the house. Isabelle's clear directions quickly led me into town. On the way, I passed through expensive looking suburbs, whose houses were totally surrounded by high fences, all covered with brightly coloured flowers. Then I found myself in a busy, main road, full of street vendors, small restaurants and all manner of tradesmen, who squatted on the pavement while they plied their trades. Barbers, tailors, joiners, welders and all the rest, were busily working side by side. The noise, bustle and colour were almost overwhelming.

Overhead, there hung electrical and telephone lines, like nothing I had ever seen before. On each support pole, the wires were tangled and twisted, like enormous balls of knitting. They reminded me of huge accumulations of mistletoe, parasitically clinging to old apple trees. I had the feeling that public utility regulations and health and safety, were much less of an issue in Cambodia. It looked as if everyone simply added another strand of wire, as and when the mood took them, and the thought of trying to repair such a line if something went wrong was mind-boggling.

Life underneath these wire fluff-balls was no less chaotic, since the Cambodian traffic was totally anarchic. There were few cars, but thousands of bicycles and Honda 50 motorbikes darted around, careering in all directions, with little obvious sense of the rules of engagement. As I stood transfixed, the traffic seemed to be involved in a form of stylised mortal combat. Even the smaller motorbikes had between three and six people on board and I felt that there must be a significant death rate at this junction alone. God knows what the statistics must be like for the country as a whole! But as I continued to watch, mesmerised, there were only a couple of near misses and these excited hardly any response from either party and certainly no reduction in speed. The general flow was momentarily interrupted and then the river of traffic closed around, as if nothing had happened. Incidents, I discovered, were seldom of sufficient note to persuade people to dismount and discuss. I realised that my Anglo-Saxon tendency to order and discipline might need to be adjusted, at least while I stayed in Phnom Penh.

That evening, I met up with Marie-Jo and we ventured a little further into town, opting to eat in a Vietnamese restaurant. It was small, with perhaps a dozen tables, only half of which were occupied. We were entertained by the two young men next to us, who ordered their meal and then produced a half-bottle of whisky, which they drank as they ate. Later, I was to discover that this habit was accepted practice in Cambodia. Although my menu had an English translation, this was so obscure that I couldn't recognise any of the dishes and was about to stab randomly at something, when Marie-Jo advised me, "Je crois qu'ils sont les crevettes," (I think they are prawns) when she saw my finger pausing over one of the items. They were, spicy and excellent too. If this was a sample of Cambodian cooking, at least food was not going to be a problem.

Next morning, well before 10am, Marie-Jo and I presented ourselves at Pascal's office, for the all-important briefing that would, we hoped, help us to cope with our new jobs. The delay in our travel plans was making us impatient, but we were keen to learn anything that would help us in Kroch Mar. As we waited, we were surprised to discover that there was a boulangerie in Phnom Penh and it was a ritual to buy croissants for the office every morning. French colonialism had left its mark.

Pascal arrived punctually at 10am, dressed in the regulation MSF tee shirt, khaki shorts, heavy hiking boots and clean white socks. With his suntan and long pony-tail, I had the impression that he had stepped straight out of some novel, or film and that his character was a flamboyant mixture of Indiana Jones and Easy Rider. The pair of us listened attentively, as he described what MSF had been doing in Cambodia to date, along with a little detail about the country's history. He also gave us a list of do`s and don`ts that were intended to keep us safe. We should be careful at night and never stray from busy, well-lit streets. When we went out for a walk, we should always tell someone our destination. Motorbike taxis should be avoided and we should remember that AIDS was very common, particularly amongst prostitutes! I began to feel like the new boy at school, not an experienced, forty-seven year old doctor, but at least I was able to understand much of what was being said. If nothing else, this fact instilled some confidence.

My ignorance about Cambodia was an embarrassment, considering I had been hearing its name since the Vietnam War. I remembered that the United States had secretly invaded and used it as a bombing base, but for the life of me I couldn't put together much else, except that I recalled the infamous Pol Pot and his "killing fields". Pascal told us that the country had been given its independence from France in 1953, but following a short period of calm, it had endured decades of war and violence. It became involved in the Vietnam conflict, when first the Vietcong used positions in Cambodia to shell the South Vietnamese and then the Americans moved in, to try to oust the Vietcong. By this time, many Cambodians supported the Khmer Rouge, their own brand of Communism, since their government (led by Prince Sihanouk) was dishonest and ineffectual. Prince Sihanouk was finally overthrown in 1970, when the Republic was proclaimed, headed by Marshal Lon Nol, but he in turn was incompetent and corrupt, so many Cambodian people were in favour of Pol Pot, when he seized power in 1975.

Nothing could have prepared them for what followed. Pol Pot engineered a dramatic Marxist revolution, restructuring the society on an elementary, co-operative basis. Everyone was immediately moved out of the towns, since a rural economy was seen as the best way of creating Utopia. There was instant execution for any infringement of a huge raft of new rules, while education and healthcare, together with all aspects of traditional culture, were eliminated. In time, the Khmer Rouge became overwhelmed by its own incompetence and corruption and the country was scourged by famine, so that many of its remaining citizens became refugees, existing pathetically on its borders. Between 1975 and 1979, it is estimated that approximately three and a half million people died (out of a population of eight million), from fighting, famine and on Pol Pot's infamous killing fields. Almost all professional people perished, or fled.

In response to this disaster facing its neighbour, a Vietnamese army invaded in 1978, driving Pol Pot and his Khmer Rouge from much of the country. They installed a new government, which together with some international relief, enabled Cambodia to recover slowly, but it took until 1989 for the UN to organise the withdrawal of Vietnamese forces. Even then, there were still four warring factions to contend with. Following a hugely expensive UN peacekeeping operation in 1993, an election was held, but corruption and violence continued to occur sporadically throughout the 1990s. Now, in 1995, MSF was one of the many NGOs trying to get the country back on its feet. Pol Pot was still alive and his group of rebels, no more than about two thousand strong, were only able to cause occasional damage in isolated areas.

Pascal explained that our village of Kroch Mar was on the bank of the Mekong River, about one hundred kilometres north of Phnom Penh. There, in the east of the country, the Khmer Rouge were reported to be relatively inactive. I briefly considered the words, "relatively" and "inactive", while Pascal went on to say that Khmer Rouge territory began four kilometres to the north of our village, but there had been no trouble for years. Yet, as he spoke, four kilometres suddenly didn't seem all that far. It didn't help when he continued, "The United Nations' peace-keeping force has just pulled out, so we are waiting to see if the country will remain stable."

The potential for armed conflict, was a small detail that I was sure Paris had omitted to mention. There again, perhaps it had been part of that initial briefing, the one which I had not fully understood. Since I tend to be fatalistic about most things, I decided that if other people were there, it was probably all right. If not, I could always leave.

"How long does it take us to drive to Kroch Mar?" I asked.

As I waited for Pascal's response, it occurred to me that it might be easy to get lost and accidentally travel that extra four kilometres—into Khmer Rouge territory. In this job, precise map reading might be a more important skill than I had imagined.

"There are no roads beyond Kom Pong Cham. After that, you travel by boat. It takes four hours to go upstream and two hours to come back, as the current is quite strong. But remember, although the Kroch Mar area is peaceful now, you should on no account leave the main roads. There are still many land mines in the area." He said this quite calmly, as if he was warning of rough terrain, or some other feature that might cause you to sprain an ankle. I quickly quashed any thoughts I might have had of exploring the backwoods.

Pascal at last moved on to discuss the programme we were here to implement. It was my turn first.
"Your tasks are to improve hospital care in Kroch Mar, strengthen the tuberculosis (TB) programme and teach the local doctors all you know about tropical medicine."

I hoped Pascal couldn't read my thoughts. In order, they were: I worked as a GP, not a hospital manager; I don't know what a TB programme is; I have never seen a case of malaria and it's twenty-five years since I slept through the tropical medicine lectures at Edinburgh University. To be truthful, even then, there were not a lot of practical examples of any of the diseases we discussed. All I knew came from pictures in old textbooks, some of which were remarkably grotesque. The image retained by most British doctors is from a book of surgery, where an African chief is depicted, suffering from elephantiasis of the scrotum, which organ he carries around in front of him, in a wheelbarrow. Somehow, I didn't feel this knowledge would be all that useful.

Marie-Jo was charged with improving the pharmacy system and training the local nurses, which seemed to me to be a much more achievable target. Pascal had now arrived at the end of his briefing and asked if we had any questions. Marie-Jo managed to come up with one or two issues, which I guessed were pertinent, since the replies took a while.

When my turn came, I considered, "When is the next flight home?" but decided instead to settle for a confident, "No. I'm ready to start now. I'll ask questions after I've seen the situation in the field." Luckily, Pascal seemed pleased by this assertion. Then, just as we were about to leave, I thought of something.

"Why are we working in this particular village, in such a remote area, when you seem to suggest that TB exists on a huge scale everywhere in Cambodia? What makes Kroch Mar special?"

"The choice of MSF projects can be influenced by many things, such as a government request, a particular need, or even the presence of a combat zone. Or it can be a mixture of all three things."

"And what are the specific reasons for choosing Kroch Mar?" I pushed, not really any the wiser from this answer. Unless someone had not told me something, this wasn't a combat zone, so what was the particular need?

"MSF likes to be in touch with the population, not just the authorities. The Regional Health Director asked us to work in Kom Pong Cham, but we wanted a remote area, so that we could really work with the people and understand their needs. Eventually we compromised, so Isabelle is in Kom Pong Cham, while you are in Kroch Mar. Anyway, MSF cannot solve the country's problems alone. We have to make choices and Kroch Mar is our choice."

To me this answer was unconvincing. My work in an increasingly bureaucratic NHS had been more or less ruled by Needs and Priorities, so this decision seemed to be less focussed, less reasoned, but I decided to leave it for the moment. Perhaps in the fullness of time, all would be revealed? After all, I was hardly an expert on Cambodian health needs. What did I know about where to locate an aid mission?

The following morning we loaded our bags into the Land Cruiser and set off with Isabelle, who was returning to Kom Pong Cham, where we would leave her, to catch our boat north. I was relieved to find that she was working on the TB programme at regional level, so there was someone experienced in the vicinity, who could give advice. Isabelle seemed to radiate confidence. It occurred to me that in Britain there had been a feeling of frustration in a safe job where I knew lots of the answers, while here I wasn't even sure I would understand the questions. On reflection, I didn't even know how to buy a loaf of bread in Cambodia, far less do my job. There again, I had wanted a challenge.

It took about forty minutes to leave behind Phnom Penh's seething, suffocating chaos of traffic. In complete contrast, the countryside was startlingly green and calm. Under a vast blue sky I began to relax and enjoy the view, as we passed through a flat landscape, rimmed by a circle of impressive mountains ten, or fifteen miles away. The ground was intensively cultivated, with palm trees planted around the edges of flooded rice fields. There were people everywhere. They worked in the fields, walked on the roads, rode on bicycles or perched on loaded produce carts, pulled either by oxen or small motorbikes.

The entire scene appeared almost too perfect and I realised that I had never seen so many shades of green at once. Dusty-green palm leaves, lime-green rice plants, huddles of darker-green trees and lush, bright, emerald-green walkways all merged together seamlessly. As I contemplated this quiet, rural scene, it was hard to imagine that these were the infamous killing fields, but there was no time to dwell on the past as Isabelle now began to give us more details, both about our village and the project itself.

She explained that Kroch Mar was a district of the Kom Pong Cham region, whose capital was the town of Kroch Mar itself, (sort of New York, New York). The town was a narrow strip of habitation, that followed the River Mekong for about fifteen kilometres. It supported approximately ten thousand inhabitants, making it a fairly hearty village by British standards, rather than a capital city. Our project had started eighteen months earlier, at the request of the local authorities, who had asked MSF to repair the ruined hospital and upgrade it to a regional referral centre. Pascal mentioned that the previous team had abandoned the project after eight months, saying that the people were "too difficult to work with". Now, after a year's gap, we were to try again. I began to wonder what "too difficult" meant. Then I asked myself how the local staff might have viewed the MSF team and whether they had also considered them, "too difficult to work with". Who knew what tensions and conflicts were buried behind such an expression?

Our team would consist of Marie-Jo, myself and Eric, who was an experienced logistics officer, (known as a "log" in MSF). Eric would spend about half his time in Kroch Mar and half in Phnom Penh. His job was to co-ordinate the non-medical part of the work. In Kroch Mar, this activity was mainly the rehabilitation of the hospital, which had started eighteen months previously, stalled and then restarted three months before our arrival. It appeared that much of the time the MSF team would consist only of Marie-Jo and myself. That would certainly make her role as boss less arduous, I thought to myself. I wouldn't be difficult to manage. Of course, I conveniently forgot that colleagues in the UK had not always found me "easy".

"Hospital staff are often difficult to begin with," Isabelle went on, "but once you have built up a relationship, they are okay".

"If that's the case, why did the first team give up?" I asked, quite logically I thought.

"That was a problem of personalities, between the hospital director and the field co-ordinator. I'm sure it will be fine this time."

Isabelle was off-hand and not very specific. I guessed that there was more to it than she was telling.

We arrived in Kom Pong Cham around midday, spending the afternoon relaxing and looking around the town. It was smaller than Phnom Penh, but not all that different, with a good selection of shops, a few bars and some restaurants. Then we explored further and discovered a major port, including both a commercial wharf and a passenger terminal, the two stretching for about a kilometre along the river bank. Marie-Jo and I spent that night at the MSF house with Isabelle and the next morning we were up early, packing our bags enthusiastically. We were anxious to move on to the last stage of our journey, to stop travelling and to get on with our new jobs. After saying our goodbyes, we piled our stuff into the MSF car, which took us to the landing stage and left us standing in front of a magnificent boat.

It was like nothing I had ever travelled on before, a wooden craft of about eighteen metres, with a small cabin near the middle, through which protruded a black funnel. My first thoughts were of "The African Queen", but here there was no Bogey poking around the deck and certainly no Katharine Hepburn languishing in a long white dress. Underneath a flat, awning roof, there were several hammocks, in one of which sprawled Eric, the log.

Eric was tall and thin, with very deep-set eyes and an easy smile. I suppose he was about thirty-five or so, but with thinning hair he looked older. Lounging casually in bare feet, he explained that the boat was our security, "in case we need to leave in a hurry, if there's trouble". There it was again, another of those slightly disturbing references to our potentially precarious position. More prosaically, the boat also served to transport the building materials required for the hospital's reconstruction, which explained its size. It could carry up to twelve tons of stuff at a time, although Eric explained that most of the essential, structural material had already been delivered. This part of the work was well under way.

As soon as we were safely on board, one of the crew-members leapt over the side to push us off the mud. Suddenly we moved into the current, with the diesel engine throbbing rhythmically and reliably under our feet and as we pulled out into midstream, I was surprised at the huge width of the Mekong. The opposite bank was about a kilometre away and there were numerous islands, and secondary channels leading off the main river course. We moved north, gradually becoming aware that the captain was steering us carefully in and out of these islands, always staying as close to a bank as possible. He constantly searched for any still water, that would allow him to make the best progress. All around the boat, small canoes were doing the same thing, desperately trying to avoid the strong currents. Without engines, they clearly had a much more difficult task.

After thirty minutes of just standing and staring, I retreated to a hammock, spending the rest of the trip watching the amazing scenery unravel and swinging gently with the motion of the boat. Sometimes, as we changed course, these oscillations became more pronounced, threatening to throw me out onto the deck, but a very slight effort of my foot against the stanchion counteracted the motion. As the sun beat down ever more fiercely, I lay watching an amazing film-set unfold, the flat landscape intensifying an impression of endless sky.

When the town buildings quite disappeared, they were replaced by a steady procession of curious boats, passing at a snail's pace upstream, or rapidly downstream. Powerboats passed at breakneck speed, with a watchman on the front, to scan the water for debris such as cows and logs, not to mention small canoes. There were fishing boats and others built like Chinese junks, piled high with cargo: wood, charcoal, cars, boxes and animals. Women cooked on open braziers on deck and fluttering washing lines were strung fore and aft. Water was collected by throwing a bucket on a rope into the thick, muddy flow and anything else that fell in, disappeared instantly below the brown surface, never to be seen again. This river was a community, providing accommodation, transport, food and water for its residents. It was all fascinating.

Occasionally, we encountered amazing vessels, reminiscent of submarines. Eric explained that these provided a public transport service. They moved through the water in a manner reminiscent of the Nautilus, in the Hollywood version of "Twenty Thousand Leagues Under the Sea". Completely enclosed metal tubes, they had portholes along the side, just visible above the water line. Later, when I used one of these contraptions myself, I discovered that their massive engines generated powerboat speed, with a corresponding level of noise. Once entombed, I found the racket intolerable, although it seemed to trouble the locals not at all. This engine noise was augmented by a video-player, blaring out extraordinary, Vietnamese gangster films, full of gunfire and kickboxing. Almost as soon as I began my first voyage, I felt obliged to climb outside, on top of the hull, where I sat out the rest of the trip in quieter, more scenic discomfort, along with those who couldn't afford an "inside" ticket. I didn't see anyone fall off, but in Europe, such transport would have been banned as suicidal.

The river never failed to enchant me, on this or on succeeding voyages for as well as the fascinating traffic, we passed a string of small villages, set against a backdrop of cultivated fields. From the boat we could see local people occupied with their daily routine, of cleaning clothes, fetching water, fishing with small hand-thrown nets, mending boats and even washing their cows. Children played at the water's edge and all waved enthusiastically. Three of the bigger villages boasted temples, multicoloured and garish to my Western eye, but with an exotic form that was surprisingly compatible with the landscape.

With my hammock swinging gently in response to the motion of the boat, I relaxed and marvelled at the dramatic changes that I had experienced, since leaving Britain.

CHAPTER THREE

Discovering Cambodia

The sequence of events that led me from my life as a General Practitioner in a small English town, to my current prone position on a boat in the Mekong River, was neither completely accidental, nor completely planned. After fifteen years, I had become restless. Even though I had diversified a bit, running a peer education system for fellow doctors and doing a little bit of consultancy work, I still felt vaguely unfulfilled. Was this it? Would I follow this prescribed path all the way to my pension? Of course the work itself was both rewarding and useful, but life had begun to feel very repetitive, with fewer challenges than before. This is the sort of mid-life crisis that hits many people in their forties, when they have the time to stop, to assess where they are going. At work, I saw plenty of patients experiencing similar feelings, people who presented with illnesses both physical and psychological, to support their dissatisfaction.

After much thought, I came to the conclusion that I wanted a complete change. I didn't know which direction I wanted to take, but I did know that there were all kinds of worlds I had not seen, worlds less privileged and more challenging than the one I inhabited. At that time, it wasn't so much that I wanted to travel abroad. I was just keen to learn something new and tackle something unfamiliar.

When I announced my decision to resign from the Practice, colleagues and friends displayed what I saw as a strange mixture of responses. Many of my co-workers in the newly changed NHS had expressed similar discontent with their lot. Yet as soon as I had taken the first step, a number of them expressed resentment, even animosity, at such decisive action. I felt quite puzzled. But I knew that it was the right thing to do, because suddenly I felt liberated. There were fears of course, of the unknown, of failure, of the fact that I might regret my decision, but there was also exhilaration.

Although my wife was quite happy to go along with my decision, taking the chance to alter her own work patterns, we found that our

15-year-old son, Michael, was not so relaxed. In retrospect, I can see that his parents' lifestyle changes were destabilising news, at a time when he was not sure of his own future. With the wisdom given to all parents after the event, I realise that I should have spent more time discussing our plans with him. I think he understands now, but at the time it was difficult.

So, with no real idea about my future, in 1990 I cheerfully launched myself into a variety of medically related activities, such as training and consultancy. For a couple of years I worked hard, but did nothing that really changed my lifestyle in a fundamental way, probably because I was still based in the same town, with many of the same kinds of experiences. As part of my quest for new horizons, I enrolled in 1992, for a course in Business Management with the Open University, a part-time correspondence course, which could readily be combined with whatever work I found. By now, I was considering returning to the NHS as a manager in the new Thatcherite semi-market environment and I thought that such a qualification might be useful. In fact, the Open University course did change my life, but not quite in the way I had imagined.

I found the second year of this programme quite difficult for a number of reasons, not the least being the break up of my marriage and decided that the next year should not be so hard. Since Michael had now left home, I was no longer tied to the town we had lived in for twenty years and if I gave up my business interests, I could move away. But where? While considering my options, I attended an OU summer school in Holland and was embarrassed to discover that all the other students were multilingual. On a whim, I decided to spend a sabbatical year in France, to complete the OU course, while learning French. The OU doesn't mind where you study and it was possible to attend the requisite seminars in Geneva, so why not work in sunny France, rather than wet, gloomy England? As long as I had some sort of base, my son could visit and this temporary relocation would give me time to reflect on what it was I really wanted to do. Detached from the security and certainties of small town life in Britain, I might see my future more clearly.

So, I packed a caravan with a few things from my old life and headed for a friend's apartment in the French Alps. After three months skiing and studying, I decided that on balance I should prefer a warmer climate, and moved closer to the Côte d'Azur, finding a pretty village and renting a cheap apartment. However, when my course work was completed and it was time to return to England, I was not ready to go.

The desire for a career in NHS management had now disappeared, but I was not sure what it was I wanted to do next. What's more, my French was still less than fluent.

I bought a small apartment in the village, one that needed quite a bit of work and settled down to study the language seriously. The home improvements however, made better progress than the French. Like many expatriates, I fell into the trap of spending my time with other English speakers, improving neither accent, nor vocabulary. After a while, I decided that the way to learn properly was to work in France, as this would force me to immerse myself in the language for several hours a day. I began to search for employment, studying the "offres d'emploi" in the newspapers each morning. Anything would do.

It was after two months of rather haphazard job searching, that I saw some television publicity for Médecins Sans Frontières (MSF), asking for volunteers for its worldwide, humanitarian aid work. I had never heard of MSF, but on impulse rang the office in Marseilles, to enquire both about the nature of the work and my eligibility. To my surprise, an appointment for an interview was offered in ten days time and since I had no other plans for the moment, I accepted. After all, I could always say no, if presented with something I didn't want to do, and it might be interesting to move away from the regime of traditional medicine. From the television publicity, Médecins Sans Frontières (Doctors Without Borders) seemed to offer aid to people all over the world. Whatever else, it sounded like an attractive alternative to working as a manager in the new NHS.

Without considering if I really wanted to have this unknown job, years of exam taking instinctively made me prepare for the interview, for as usual, I wanted to "pass the test". Since my French comprehension was questionable, I decided it would be best to talk a lot, preparing a summary of my CV and memorising it in French. Then there was a list of answers to likely questions. Whatever else happened, I would be prepared. The interview went surprisingly well and when Regis (the interviewer) asked, "Do you have any preferences about the type of work, or country?" I was relaxed enough to quip, "Anywhere, as long as it's hot and French speaking."

And that was that. Regis assured me he would be in touch and assuming that this was the first stage in months of negotiation, I returned to my apartment, relieved that I had managed to answer all the questions. Perhaps my French would improve, if I simply applied endlessly for work?

But after five days, Regis rang to offer me the post in Cambodia, due to start in a couple of weeks. Strangely, it didn't seem like a difficult decision and I immediately accepted. A little later, I felt somewhat embarrassed to realise that I did not know precisely where Cambodia was. Much later, I was to discover that many MSF people will, if questioned, admit to the same ignorance and embarrassment. So here I was, four weeks after my initial telephone call, in an MSF boat on the Mekong River, heading towards Kroch Mar and a new life.

After four hours, we found ourselves heading towards the right bank. A long way above our heads, we could see several houses peeking out from trees and Eric explained that the river level was low at this time of the year, so there was a bit of a climb up to the town. Then we bumped gently to a stop beside the muddy bank and I watched curious villagers, watching us. The boat secured, we all jumped ashore, to be faced by a steep, slippery slope. Aided by the captain and the engine boy, I began to climb, hoping that I wouldn't slip and look foolish, in front of an audience of potential new patients.

By good fortune, we all reached the top safely, where we gathered our belongings and began to follow Eric to the house. Within a few steps, the wooden planks that constituted the jetty came to an end and we found ourselves in a muddy street. Entering the village, I could see to my left and right many wooden buildings, haphazardly crouched together, mostly shops or storage areas on the ground floor, with living quarters above. There were one or two small motorbikes, but no cars at all. Men and women were dressed similarly in sarongs, worn at the waist by the men and around the chest by the women.

Then we turned into a narrow alley, where houses on stilts loomed above us. It was quite dark as we passed under and between them, even though it was early afternoon and the sun was high. Here, all the space underneath the houses was used for domestic animals, storage, or household tasks like washing and cooking. The path itself had become really muddy, developing eventually into a series of large, unavoidable puddles that lurked in a barren, plantless gloom. To add to our problems, small pigs snuffled about in the mud, occasionally removing rubbish right from under our feet. At times it was possible to walk on scattered branches, but my shoes were soon both covered with, and finally full of mud, so I gave up worrying about them, concentrating instead on keeping up with Eric and not falling down. At least I was carrying my belongings in a rucksack on my back, so my hands were free to help me maintain my balance. I really didn't want to arrive in my new home, coated in mud from head to toe.

As we walked, Eric explained why the houses were built so high on their stilts. The Mekong River rises an extraordinary fifteen metres in the rainy season, invading settlements and dominating the villagers' lives. In some low-lying areas, people are forced to move around their communities by boat, for several months of the year.

The MSF house was situated on the main street and like all the rest, built on two levels, with a roof constructed from wooden tiles, with a decorative dragon's head on each corner. I hoped that here the river was not a problem, since the caretaker and his family lived beneath, while MSF staff occupied the first floor. Our total space was about fifteen by twelve metres, divided into one large living area and four small bedrooms, separated by thin plywood walls. These were built to a height of two metres and not up to the high ceiling, to enable good air circulation. The flimsy, open, construction provided excellent acoustics; you shared any type of noise you made with everyone else living in the house and they returned the compliment fulsomely! Soundproofing and privacy are not widely recognised in Cambodia.

The furniture was locally made of hard wood, which resists both damp and termites (at least for some time) but after just three weeks, all my clothes were covered in mould. The worst problem was leather goods: shoes, belts and even my wallet, which was soon covered in a fluffy, white fungus. I had never encountered such humidity before and it took time to adjust to the feeling of everlastingly being wrapped in an invisible, warm, damp blanket.

All around the MSF house and throughout the village there were endless varieties of trees, none of which I recognised. This was my first experience of jungle and despite knowing the word from books and films, nothing prepares you for the experience of living in the middle of the real thing. Except in the wider clearings, trees up to thirty metres high obscured the sun for most of the day. This absence of sunlight meant that our "garden" was just a patch of bare earth, swept clean at least once a day by the housekeeper. Our main room had a balcony on the front, where we could sit at dusk, watching the birds settling for the night (providing of course that we remembered to replenish our stocks of insect repellent). Mosquitoes flourished in this environment.

Eric introduced us to the house staff, the husband having the role of guardian, his wife that of cook and housekeeper. There were three children, aged seven, five, and eighteen months, who stared at us with curiosity, but without fear. These MSF employees catered to all our daily requirements and although this brought much needed income into the community, I found it oddly luxurious and uncomfortable to have servants.

Once we had stowed our gear, Eric took us through some important points concerning the workings of the house. We used river water for washing, cooking and drinking (after passing it through a filter!). The toilet was a "squatty", the classic hole in the ground, with positions indicated for the feet. I found it takes a while to learn how to aim correctly and I never overcame the problem of things dropping out of my pockets, to fall down the hole, into the fermenting, black oblivion.

During my time with MSF, I came to realise that we in the West have a most conservative attitude to waste disposal. Some years later in Africa, when I emerged from a similar toilet, complaining that this time I had lost my glasses, I was astonished when one of the workers enthusiastically offered to reach down into the hellish orifice, to see if he could find them for me. Needless to say, I refused to allow him to try, but I am sure he thought I was quite mad.

In Cambodia, our sink waste-pipe was without the protection of a safety grid or U-bend, so that it instantly devoured any items that were carelessly dropped. Since this also drained into the black mess of the septic tank, the loss was accepted without question. On one occasion, our guardian retrieved my toothbrush, which had been thoughtfully wiped and then formally returned. Although I thanked him profusely, I was forced to find a way of hiding the horrid thing. I didn't want to offend him, but nothing would have persuaded me to put it back in my mouth.

Not everything was quite so basic. Electricity came from a generator that ran between 6pm and 10pm and charged a system of car batteries, used to run the office computer and a high frequency radio. We had daily contact with Phnom Penh at 7.30am and 5pm, with the possibility of a third transmission at mid-day, should security conditions warrant it. But it was hard to take this potential need for assistance seriously. Lush green vegetation, brightly coloured flowers and vast numbers of exotic butterflies seemed to refute any suggestion of potential danger.

I hoped that I would remember how to connect the inverter, to provide AC current for my electric razor. During the next five years with MSF, I only once failed to find a supply for my razor and that was in Brussels, when I forgot my adaptor.

Next morning, I was awake at 5.30am. I had no choice — World War Three had started, right beneath my bed! At first I was quite disorientated, totally unable to comprehend what all the noise was about. Then I remembered. This was Cambodia. Gradually I began to recognise elements of the horrendous cacophony: cockerels, pigs, a donkey, assorted unknown birds, a motor revving up, the radio at a volume worthy of Led Zeppelin and two hundred Khmer terrorists, screaming as they cut the throats of the entire village. But no, I was wrong. There were no terrorists. It was only a normal day's start-up in Kroch Mar, with neighbours enthusiastically calling out, "good morning" to each other. The sound came directly up through the open, slatted floor, which allowed circulation of air, noise and mosquitoes, in equal measure.

At 7.30am, sweating profusely from the humidity, we left for the hospital, travelling on two small Honda 90s, the most suitable form of transport in the dry season. Eric and Marie-Jo shared one, while I rode the other. In the rainy season there is no suitable form of land transport, as the mud is knee deep and the river can rise up and invade the road. Today however, we could drive slowly along the small path that wound between trees, in and out of unfenced and ill-defined gardens, along the side of the Mekong. Bushes rose up to three metres high and huge palm trees and hardwood giants blocked out the sun, so that we passed repeatedly from light into shade. The flowers were spectacular reds, oranges, yellows and even blues and on a hibiscus bush I glimpsed a beautiful, black butterfly. It was a botanical dream and I tried to take in as much of the scenery as possible, while staying on the bike.

Mostly, our route kept close to the riverbank, although at times we were forced to take detours, where sections of the path had been ripped away by the fast flowing current. In one place an immense hardwood had fallen into the water, but its roots were still holding and the local timber merchant was attempting to haul it up onto the bank. I didn't fancy his chances, since the tree must have weighed many tonnes. I still had no idea what the work would be like, but I certainly didn't mind the commuting.

Kroch Mar was unlike any hospital I had encountered. We parked our mopeds and walked slowly up the drive. There were three buildings: the Main Hospital, the Outpatients' Department and the Tuberculosis Unit, which was set to the rear. The Main Hospital (circa 1950) had a central, colonial style section, with a wing on either side. Eric explained that the left-hand wing was designated the main ward, with twenty beds. The right-hand wing was divided into maternity (three beds), paediatrics (six beds) and the laboratory, while the central part constituted the store, pharmacy, office and meeting room. In all, it was the size of a large English house, yet it was intended to be the medical facility for a population of perhaps fifteen thousand people. The structure was concrete, the windows had no frames or glass and there were no ceilings, only the pitched roof. The Outpatients' Unit was the same design, but it had only two rooms, each about fifteen metres square. Everything looked decidedly dilapidated.

As we came closer, we could see that there was building-work in progress. Wooden scaffolding embraced several sections of the hospital; the left-hand wing was devoid of patients and full of workers. I asked Eric to explain what was happening.

"We rehabilitate one side at a time. Luckily the hospital is not too busy just now, so all the patients can be housed in one wing. We're not doing anything major, just repairing the ravages of time and inattention. Our policy is to try to provide a structure that is both appropriate to existing services and to the capacity of the authorities to maintain, once we leave."

This was my first contact with the principle of matching an aid organisation's work to a country's existing level of development. It was also my first experience of the shocking contrast between medicine in Britain and what exists in the Third World. There were no beds, no electricity and a limited water supply. Cooking was done in the wards and the laboratory was equipped with only one "school" microscope.

"We concentrate on shelter, a water supply and facilities to enable the staff to carry out standard activities," Eric continued.

As we walked, I saw that in places the roof had collapsed and the outside walls were blackened from cooking fires. Then I noticed the bullet holes—all over the place! In the improved, left-hand wing, the floor was being re-cemented, the roof strengthened and the walls whitewashed. It was better, but it still had the look of a warehouse, rather than a hospital.

"Where does the water come from?" I asked, looking around for a tap. Surely you couldn't have a hospital without a single tap!

"Same as us — from the river," came the depressing reply. "They carry it up here in jerry cans. Obviously, not much is wasted on hand washing when it's so awkward to acquire, so one of our projects is to construct a well, with a pump. We'll build a reservoir, so that the hospital can have a permanent water tap, to encourage basic hygiene. That tower in the garden is for the reservoir," Eric added proudly.

Later, when I realised that the plan really was to have just one tap for the whole hospital, I suggested that improvements in hygiene would be much easier to achieve, if there was a tap in each ward.

"They will only waste water, if you give them too much," was I felt, a rather odd response. "These people are not used to a lot of water."

"But how will there be progress, if we don't try to improve things? Surely hygiene will be no better with one tap, than it is with jerry cans," I protested.

"You have to think about what will happen here, in the future," Eric explained. "We are installing a hand pump as well as a motor pump, because when we leave, it is highly likely that the hospital will be unable to afford the fuel. With a hand pump, they won't be able to lift so much water, so they won't have enough to feed lots of taps. But they will have one tap, a reservoir, clean water and a well. Progress here is made in small steps."

"What will happen when the water tower deteriorates?" I asked.

"With luck and without maintenance, it should last twenty years at least. By that time, things may be very different in Cambodia."

It took me a long time to adapt to this sort of thinking, but Eric had mastered it. I later found that this approach is not always followed, either by MSF itself, or by other agencies.

"Where do the workmen come from?" I asked, changing the subject. "Are they local?"

"They're Vietnamese. We use them, because they are more reliable and have better skills. The local people are not too happy about it, especially since they lose all their dogs," Eric explained.

"I don't understand," I said, puzzled. What could the Vietnamese use dogs for?

"They eat them of course," smiled Eric, watching my face for the expected grimace.

So it was with a very different attitude, that I began my introductory round of the hospital wards. I realised that everything here had different rules and different parameters. I must try to learn what they were, make an effort to adjust—and be careful about what I ate.

Although there were beds in the paediatric ward, elsewhere "beds" was simply a figure of speech. It seemed that in Cambodian hospitals, people are happier to sleep on the floor. In time, I discovered that it certainly makes things easier when you have a busy spell. Everyone just edges up a bit, to make space for the newcomers.

Eric now led us through the rest of the hospital, where we met most of the local staff, Dr Duong and Dr Nol, Madame Chi, the head nurse and Jean Baptiste, the pharmacist. The hospital superintendent, Dr Lun, was working in his private clinic in town. This, I was told, was often the case. Dr Duong began to outline the hospital's problems.

"We have no water, no drugs, no electricity, no equipment, no books, not enough staff and more importantly, a total lack of confidence from the public."

Rather selfishly, I found myself thinking, how am I expected to work with nothing? Then it occurred to me that these people had been working with nothing for ages. It was immediately obvious, that the nature of the medicine I had practised at home was light years away from what was possible here. This place epitomised back to basics, with a vengeance.

At first, I was overwhelmed by the difficulties, wondering what I could achieve here, in a relatively short period of time. Then, slowly,

I began to adjust. I saw that here, just as in Britain, the fundamentals of medicine remained. The relationship between doctor and patient, together with the clinical diagnosis, are the basis of medical care everywhere. In my practice in England, I had become convinced that one way of improving the quality of care was to use fewer drugs, ask for fewer tests and refer people less often to specialists, who so often fail to communicate and may even make matters worse, by seeing only the illness and not the patient. In my view, current medical practice in the West tends to impose too many useless drugs and too many pointless tests on patients, raising false hopes about what the medical profession can achieve. Here, I would certainly have the opportunity to practise what I preached! I have to admit, that within three months, Kroch Mar revealed that there are limits to my theory and there are most definitely times when access to "high tech" and modern drugs can be useful.

But on that first day, as we continued our tour and Eric revealed more and more difficulties that accompanied medicine in Kroch Mar, there seemed to be no end to the list of things that we did not have or could not do.

"Dr Lun, the Superintendent, has been seen as a bit of a problem. He is rarely here and a few of the medical staff have suggested that he uses some of the hospital drugs at the private clinic, where he spends most of his time. The previous MSF toubib (doctor) challenged him about it, so relations with MSF went from bad to worse."

Now the penny dropped.

"Was that why the mission had closed?"

"Partly, but there were also cultural problems. The previous team were young, female and very forceful. Cambodia has a culture that values hierarchy, politeness and men, so whatever anyone did, it was almost bound to end in tears. Two young girls who seemed to barge in, telling the staff how to run the hospital, were never going to be well received, even if what they had to say was quite correct."

I made a mental note to try to avoid being outspoken in my initial comments, for the last thing I wanted was to ostracise myself from the staff. Of course, I had the advantages of being older and male, with 10 years involvement in the teaching of other doctors, as well as my years of practical medical experience. I hoped that these factors might counterbalance at least some of the cultural differences. Then I remembered Isabelle mentioning that Cambodians often "bought" their degrees, or qualifications. I wondered how the three doctors in Kroch Mar had been educated. It was hardly something I could ask outright. What if these doctors had little genuine training? The idea was suddenly very disturbing, although if the doctors were poorly qualified, my role would be easier, for at least I would have plenty of scope for teaching.

Later, I asked Doctor Duong to give me some idea of what had happened to medicine in Cambodia during the Pol Pot years, to help me to understand the extent of the problems. He explained that almost all of the educated people had been massacred, or had escaped into neighbouring countries. When all the doctors had been eliminated, health care found itself in the hands of young revolutionaries, people with little or no medical training and, of course, no drugs. Instead, they relied on "folk remedies," with predictable results, although there was no recording system and thus no precise figures. The regime had left behind a desperate shortage of qualified people, so it was hardly surprising if training was rushed through, with little time to consider either selection or quality. Dr Duong assured me that his degree was genuine, but he could not vouch for his two colleagues. I guessed that if I asked, I would get just the same reply from the other two. In time, I would find that whatever their qualifications, their medical skills and training were not up to European standards.

I decided to make a positive beginning with Doctors Duong and Nol, preparing a little speech that I hoped would make me sound like someone with the same interests as them, rather than someone who had just come to interfere.

"I have been asked by MSF to come to Cambodia to help. I know very little of your country and I have never worked with many of your diseases, but I have quite a lot of medical experience none the less. How do you think I might help in the hospital?"

I avoided saying that I really knew nothing of their medicine, their beliefs or their local systems, as I didn't want to appear a complete idiot. Total honesty brings its own problems. To my relief, these doctors were responsive to my initial approach, saying that they were happy to learn from me.

"We need updated information on Western diseases, like high blood pressure, strokes, cancer and heart attacks."

I thought to myself that these were probably the last things they needed, as life expectancy in Cambodia was just a little over forty years, but I was delighted that they were interested in areas where I was confident. This would give me a good base and I was sure that we could move on from there, to look at the diseases that represented 90% of their workload.

The first three weeks passed very quickly, as I established a pattern of working. In the mornings I made ward rounds and met outpatients; in the afternoons I had the opportunity to read intensively because there were practically no staff to be found in the hospital. Everybody worked in their private clinics in the afternoons and evenings, leaving patients to rely on their families to fill in the gaps of nursing care. This situation I now know exists in many Third World countries, but to someone from the West it takes a bit of time to accept.

The spare time that I gained from this unusual timetable, gave me the opportunity to supplement my limited theoretical knowledge of local diseases. Ignorance is hardly a good basis for any teaching, so I read voraciously for three months, becoming more and more fascinated by the bewildering array of pathological names from my student past. I suppose you have to be a doctor to find magic in names like kwashiorkor, typhoid, syphilis, dysentery, schistosomiasis and of course malaria. Since I didn't want my colleagues to find out just how little I knew about diseases that were so common here, I devoured the entire MSF library in Kroch Mar (two large text books) within a few weeks. Unfortunately, my application to Paris, for more medical literature was turned down. I never understood why.

Over these first few weeks, I found that my credibility was protected by the fact that my training in the UK had been particularly wide-ranging. I had a lot of experience in all the minor subjects, like eye diseases, obstetrics, ear nose and throat problems and my speciality, dermatology. Slowly, the local doctors began to consult me about some of their difficult cases. In return, they were happy to answer my questions about the various tropical diseases that I was encountering. Everybody was learning and a positive relationship was being created. Although my remit was primarily in the tuberculosis section of the hospital, this work was not very demanding, so I was pleased to join the local doctors in some of their general consultations.

One morning, Dr Lun invited me to look at a man who had come into the outpatient clinic. Dr Lun had begun to ask me about dermatology cases, an area in which he had no training, but considerable interest. This particular patient had a very marked rash on his hands, which was unusual by not being itchy. Having examined the man, I was unsure of the diagnosis, but I explained to Dr Lun that there were only two known causes of this kind of rash. It was either a reaction to a common antibiotic, or syphilis, which to be honest had not presented itself regularly in my rural practice in England. I asked if the man had been prescribed ampicillin in the last two or three weeks. The reply was positive, but Doctor Lun said that he thought it was syphilis. I wondered if there was some special way of recognising the disease, one not covered in my training and asked him how he could be sure.

"Well, his wife works as a prostitute in Phnom Penh and she comes back here every weekend, to be with the family".

"Then I think you're probably right," I agreed.

As at home, the patient's situation is vital to the diagnosis.

Part of the long-term plan for Kroch Mar hospital, was that it should become a referral centre for the district, including improved surgery, X-ray and laboratory facilities. A wide range of surgical cases presented themselves, so I understood why expansion was necessary and gathered information for a report on the level of need. This would enable MSF to plan an appropriate response. Currently, we had to refer surgical cases to Kom Pong Cham, but they rarely arrived, since the patients knew they would be asked to pay for the treatment, unlike our own establishment, which was free. Since they had little spare cash, it was a waste of time and effort to ask them to make the journey. I began a limited review of my patients' monthly incomes at the TB centre and although I didn't expect a very reliable picture, I was surprised to discover that many of the patients never used money at all. They fished in the river and grew rice. For items like plates, or buckets, they bartered food. It was quite impossible for these people to purchase health care.

I particularly remember one patient whom I had been trying to treat for weeks, a man who finally needed more care than we could offer. When I explained the necessity to go to Kom Pong Cham, he refused politely, saying,

"I know you have tried your best, but we have no money and I would like to die at home ".

His family took him away the next morning and we heard later that he had his wish. It was heartbreaking and it left me feeling helpless.

Lack of money was not the only problem. One evening, following the customary meal of famine-stricken chicken in a gooey, yellow sauce, the three of us sat down on our balcony to enjoy a couple of Tiger beers. Then a child started to scream. I had become used to increased noise levels in Cambodia and crying children are not unknown in the West, but after a few minutes I was really uneasy, as the intensity of this screaming was unusual. Certain that something was amiss, I got up and looked down to the courtyard below, where I could clearly see our neighbours. The parents were holding down their six year old son, while a man I did not recognise, pressed what seemed to be a heated coin repeatedly on to the child's forehead.

"What are they doing? I think we should go and help," I said to Eric, agitated by what was happening.

"No, you can't. You would be interfering. It is their way of treating certain illnesses; it is traditional medicine. The habit is widespread and accepted by everyone as being a good treatment. Don't you recall seeing adults with circular scars on their faces? That's what makes the scars," he explained.

I was torn between the heartrending screams and Eric's view that I was not here to meddle with Cambodian beliefs. I knew these parents. They were good, kind people, who were doing what they felt was best for their son. Fortunately, the torment ended after a few more minutes and the coin doctor packed up and left, leaving the rest of us upset and uncomfortable.

It was only later that I thought of a British equivalent of this "barbaric ritual". Regularly, during my work in dermatology, I had been confronted by a dilemma, when children were brought to the clinic to be treated for warts. Removal of warts is a painful process, the most popular procedure (in the profession, not amongst the children) being to freeze the warts off with liquid nitrogen. My policy, after some months of giving this treatment and witnessing the children's distress, was to do my best to persuade the parents that the warts would eventually go away without intervention. Occasionally, when parents were very insistent, I would comply, until eventually I could no longer stand to inflict pain, for what is a cosmetic, self-limiting condition.

Giving vaccinations and inserting intravenous drips for children also upset me at times, although at least I believed they were, "for their own good". I only hope I was right in some of the things I have done to children. Unfortunately, many treatments that doctors give in good faith are subsequently proved to be useless, even harmful. We have all heard about "later studies", that discredit popular treatments, which have been trustingly prescribed. It is a misconception to consider all medical actions to be unquestionably right. People just do what they think is appropriate at the time and that was what these parents were doing with their hot coins.

As I came to terms with general medicine, Kroch Mar style, I had more time for the tuberculosis programme and my intensive reading schedule filled in the gaps in my knowledge. TB is a bacterial infection, but the germs are very slow growing and usually the disease is correspondingly slow in its deadly effect. Patients may have the condition for months, even years, without it progressing. Indeed, only about 10% of infected people actually become ill. In Europe, TB was largely eradicated after the Second World War, as a result of new drugs, improved nutrition and better living conditions. It is now re-appearing all over the world however and is increasingly difficult to treat, because the bacteria are becoming resistant to an increasing number of antibiotics.

The treatment of TB using standard drugs, costs as little as twenty dollars per patient, but resistant cases can cost many thousands of dollars, because new, very expensive drugs are required. Standard treatment must last at least six to eight months, to ensure that all the bacteria are killed and this need for a lengthy programme, together with the fact that complicated combinations of drugs may be needed, means that most TB patients are treated in specialised units, such as we had in Kroch Mar. Here, we could isolate patients and allow the staff to become completely familiar with the programme. The Unit was generally a happy place, as patients often arrived in very poor condition and the majority improved within a few weeks. Most went home after two months of care, continuing their treatment as out-patients. In Cambodia, there were not very many "resistant" cases, but we did have a few who failed to respond and all we could do for them was to watch as they deteriorated and died, since we did not have access to the more costly medicines.

So why did MSF not buy the expensive drugs, those that would have saved just a few more lives? At first I accepted the message that it was hugely expensive and beyond their means, but in time I was to learn that the issue was far more complex. To diagnose antibiotic-resistant TB germs is technically more difficult than diagnosing a simple infection. Furthermore, in order to limit the numbers of germs becoming resistant to new antibiotics, you must only treat cases that are proven to be resistant. So it is not only a matter of expensive drugs but also a matter of setting up expensive diagnostic techniques, if you want to keep the resistant germs out of the general population.

MSF, like most aid organisations, has a policy of using the cheap and simple products, as classified in "The Essential Drugs List". This is a small book, which comes with simple, therapeutic notes and has been translated into five or six languages. Purchases are made from approved suppliers and there are rigorous quality control procedures, providing a reliable range of drugs of proven efficacy, available under their generic names (not trademarked), for all common conditions. It may surprise the layman to find that this policy results in a list of only about one hundred common drugs, out of the many thousands that are available today. Although the list is regularly updated and deals with the majority of situations, unusual cases and increasing resistance to antibiotics, ensure that dilemmas regularly arise.

Neither aid organisations, nor the Third World countries in which they work, can afford to purchase and distribute all the expensive drugs that are currently available. Like most aid organisations, MSF has a policy with regard to using them for resistant cases and there is an approved procedure for doctors who wish to use drugs not on the main list. But the essential problem remains; if you are setting up health structures in a Third World country, for the host government to adopt, it must be affordable. Western standards may raise expectations, which can create both distress and disappointment, if not maintained.

MSF is beginning to re-examine its policy towards TB, as antibiotic resistance is becoming common. MSF Belgium has started a pilot programme of treatment in Siberian prisons, where the percentage of TB resistant cases is especially high. Sadly, TB is not the only illness to present the problem of drug resistance, or to pose the moral dilemma of rationing expensive treatments. Drugs used to treat AIDS are notoriously costly and recent international campaigns, supported by organisations like MSF, have arrived at agreements which are aimed at reducing the price of drugs sold to Third World countries. Whether these prices are sufficiently lowered, to fall within the reach of the truly poor nations, remains to be seen. Expensive medicine is not only an issue for the Third World, however. Even in the UK, local authorities sometimes have to limit the prescription of specific drugs or treatments.

Fortunately, in our TB unit in Cambodia most of the patients were cured, so there was, on the whole, a very positive atmosphere. The programme was not complicated medically, but it required a lot of attention to detail. Since the staff were competent, we had good results and soon the only innovations I could offer were minor ideas, like putting up a notice board to display their successes. This was good both for staff morale and for the patients, who were encouraged to keep coming back for treatment.

The TB centre had a visiting leprosy health worker, who used our hospital as a base, but saw his few patients in their own homes. Officially I had little contact with this programme, yet I was curious to learn a bit more, for I wanted to be sure of recognising the disease if someone presented with its symptoms. Leprosy is a fascinating illness and since Cambodia has one of the few remaining leper colonies, I was anxious to visit, although a little nervous of turning up uninvited, in case I was thought to be a ghoulish tourist. But our driver assured me that there would be no difficulty, as we would be in the MSF car. "They don't mind medical people."

The village was like any other. Luxurious vegetation grew between the huts and there were no formalities on entering. First we went to the medical unit, where I explained my clinical interest — the fact that the TB programme had links with leprosy. We were made most welcome and shown around; the staff were clearly proud of their work and pleased to have a professional visitor. Today, the policy world-wide is to treat leprosy in the community, so that people stay with their families, collecting their tablets every month, as they do for many other diseases. The bacteria behave in a similar way to tuberculosis, but they are not very contagious and grow slowly. In itself, leprosy is not fatal.

Medically, it is both interesting and complex however, with several different forms, ranging from slight changes in the colour and texture of the skin, to the classical lion face deformity and a loss of fingers and toes. The main problem for sufferers is that their nerves are damaged and they have no sensation, no sense of touch. If they burn their hands, they are unaware of what they have done, until they smell the burning flesh. Manual work can lead to loss of fingers and during my visit to this colony I was dismayed to see many of the lepers working as breakers of stone. They sat in front of a huge pile of boulders, painlessly breaking them down into gravel for building work, the worst imaginable occupation. Most had lost several fingers and for some it was remarkable that they could still hold a hammer.

The treatment for leprosy is expensive and lasts for many years, often just controlling the condition, rather than curing it, or removing the hideous deformities. In this village an international organisation was paying for the drugs, so the programme was secure, yet I wondered why the colony still existed, since it was now policy to treat people in their homes. The nurse in charge explained.

"This is their home, the only one they've known since the Pol Pot years. There are few new cases, but the people live here contentedly and have no desire to go away. Where would they go? Anyway, since they live with their families, fewer than fifty percent of the people here are lepers and we hope this will eventually fall to zero. It will simply become another Cambodian village."

I was again reminded of the Pol Pot legacy. For many, there were no homes to return to at the end of it all, no childhood memories of an older, more stable Cambodia. A few days earlier, my translator had told me about the day he returned home from working in the fields, to find that his whole family had been killed, during an attack on his village. He had managed to reconstruct his life, but he assured me that he could never forget the utter horror of that time. And there were thousands like him. So as I watched the patients coming into the consulting room for treatment or advice, I was aware how gratifying it must be for everyone, that some stability now existed.

One weekend, as a break from our routine, we organised a visit to a famous Buddhist temple, two hours from Kom Pong Cham. The party was to include Marie-Jo, Isabelle and her friend Madame Buna, who would translate and explain the historical background. The long, hot journey gave us time to observe details of Cambodian rural life.

I was intrigued by an unusual form of commercial transport, the motorbike and trailer. 150cc motorbikes were used to pull flat-bed trailer units, about three metres in length and one metre wide. These taxis might have ten or twelve passengers perching precariously on the flat surface, clutching, or sitting on baggage. Alternatively, there could be four or five enormous live pigs, each with its feet tied together and all covered with foliage. I was told that this particular greenery gave off a chemical that tranquillised the pigs, which was just as well, since those beasts could have made a mess of things if they had decided to get awkward. I wondered if the plant was cannabis and if farmers got the pigs stoned, before persuading them on board. It was an appealing idea. Fortunately the land is flat, since many trailers are loaded with more than half a tonne, a lot for a small bike to pull. When they stopped to pick up new passengers, they needed help to get moving again and it was entertaining to watch the more able pushing the vehicles off for a few metres, before hurriedly jumping back on board.

Eventually, we arrived at the foot of a small hill, that looked just like a dumpling, plonked down in the middle of the rice fields. It was about one hundred metres high, with a temple perched on the summit. By now, even climbing out of the car caused us to sweat profusely in the hot, sticky air, so the ancient stone steps circling from the base to the top, turned us into dripping, wet rags. Madame Buna recounted more of Cambodia's history as we climbed. From the summit, the view was stunning, a huge blue sky framing endless, lush green rice fields, each bordered by sentinel palm trees. To our relief, an enterprising boy had carried some cold drinks up the hill. The price he charged for a Coke reassured me that the future of the country was economically sound, if he was an example of the next generation. His grasp of supply and demand was faultless.

This particular Buddhist temple was relatively intact and surprisingly modest; a place for people to gather. It had no elaborate architecture, no tombs, and no ostentation, only a few naïve religious images, and many bullet holes. On balance, I think I prefer such simplicity, in contrast to the great and ornate Gothic cathedrals of Europe, with their priceless paintings and heavy gold plate.

We broke our homeward journey at a crossroads, a regular resting-place for businessmen and travellers. Our guide recommended a local drink made of fruit juice and milk, mixed together and served cold. It was thick and delicious. I enjoyed the drink, but could not bring myself to try the nibbles that went with it — completely black, deep fried spiders, each about three inches across!

CHAPTER FOUR

Trouble in paradise

Just as I was growing more comfortable with my new life in Kroch Mar I became aware that in contrast, Marie-Jo was not finding her life easy. She spent the first few weeks arranging the pharmacy to her satisfaction, but once this was in order her next task was less obvious. Eric was always busy, coming and going between Kroch Mar and Phnom Penh, where he had other responsibilities. Since she now had insufficient work, Marie-Jo began to accompany him, to Phnom Penh, or to Kom Pong Cham, where she spent time with Isabelle. Gradually her weekends lasted from Friday mornings, to Monday nights, so that we had little time to speak. Although my role, as designated by MSF, had not proved arduous, I had found lots of other things to take up my time, not recognising that our lack of communication had become a problem.

One morning over breakfast, Marie-Jo began to complain that we didn't talk enough any more. I thought briefly about suggesting that she sounded rather like a worn-out wife in a television sit-com, but almost immediately suppressed the idea. This was no time for levity. I could see she was upset.

"I think you are right. What should we do to improve things?" I congratulated myself on my positive tone.

"We need to discuss the programme more. I have no idea what you are doing and I'm supposed to be in charge."

"That's true. I have been rather pre-occupied with trying to sort out what I should be doing, not to mention reading up on all the local ailments that I've never met before." I tried to sound reasonable. It hadn't occurred to me that what I was doing might be a problem for Marie-Jo. As a GP, I had become accustomed to taking decisions on my own behalf.

"That's all very well, but you do things without telling me. I have to discuss the project with Pascal in Phnom Penh, before we make any changes". Her voice rose, "I need to know what you're doing. You can't just make decisions by yourself!"

"If you were here a bit more, perhaps we could discuss things, but you're always away somewhere or other and I never know what you're doing either," I snapped back, losing the advantages of age and experience, almost at the first hurdle.

However, my outburst broke the ice and for the first time I realised that Marie-Jo did have genuine anxieties. What's more, I think she now realised that I had simply become bound up in my own work and that I wasn't trying to usurp her position. She hesitated for a moment and then began to tell me about some of her problems.

"The staff say that the head nurse, Madame Chi, is Dr Lun's mistress and since he's never here, she's the one in charge. She's taken over the pharmacy from Jean Baptiste, who's too frightened to say anything, for fear of losing his job. There are no nurses in the hospital after 11am. How can I run a hospital, when there are no staff for twenty hours, out of twenty four?"

By now she was nearly in tears and I realised that the responsibility of the mission was getting to her. Her six months experience with MSF had not been enough to prepare her to cope with such a complex situation. What's more, now that I considered what she was saying, I could appreciate her difficulties. Like me, she was expected to spend part of her time teaching the staff, but since the nurses (like the doctors) were only present for three or four hours every day, we could hardly suggest that they each undertook an hour's study with us. The short time they were on the premises, had to be devoted to the patients. At least I made contact with my colleagues on ward rounds and during outpatients' surgeries, while Marie-Jo had to work harder to keep in touch with the nursing staff.

"Nursing care isn't the same here as in France. The nurses only do injections and dressings. Relatives of the patients do all the washing, lifting and helping, so the nursing role is much reduced and no one really wants to change it. I hardly see the doctors at all, since they all rush off early in the afternoon to work in their clinics."

I recognised that she was feeling uneasy, because her training in France had given her a perception of a nurse's role that was quite different from what it was in Cambodia. Given the short time that the nurses were in the hospital and their satisfaction with their role, she found it difficult to achieve the things that Pascal had suggested.

I felt constrained in what I could say to help her, not least because of the language barrier, but I made an effort.

"We have to try to understand how the system works here. I don't think the doctors and nurses are lazy, or dishonest." I began. "It's just that they have different customs."

"They are employed by the government, so they should be here to see to the patients." Marie Jo was not ready to give in.

"But the doctors are only paid fifteen dollars US a month and they need about one hundred dollars to live reasonably. I think they are quite conscientious to take any hospital work at all, since they really earn their living by working privately. If you look at it from their point of view, they are reducing their private practice opportunities, every time they see a patient in the hospital. It's the same for the nurses. There isn't the tradition of public service here that we have in Europe.

"But what about charging the patients for their drugs? Hospital care is supposed to be free."

Marie-Jo introduced a new argument.

"I know that seems strange, but some of the patients request drugs not provided by either the government, or MSF, so they have to pay for them. I don't think the doctors charge more than the going rate for any of the drugs they sell. We have to try to understand and be flexible," I suggested.

Unlike Marie-Jo, I spent quite a lot of time with my colleagues, who had explained their position to me about selling drugs to patients. It was different, but I understood their point of view.

"But most of the drugs are provided by MSF. It isn't right to hand them over to the hospital, if the staff are going to pocket the money. I've decided to organise the pharmacy, to make it quite clear what MSF is providing. 95% of the drugs come from MSF, but at the moment it's difficult to see which are ours, so we can't be sure what they are selling."

"Look, I really don't think the doctors are charging for our drugs. It's just that some patients want things that MSF doesn't provide. That's what they're probably selling."

Then I began to wonder. Surely my colleagues were not selling MSF drugs? But how would I know? Perhaps Marie-Jo was right and I had not noticed. I resolved to try to give her more support. However, despite the fact that this discussion cleared the air a bit, I was to find that things did not really improve between us. It didn't help that I was totally immersed in my own work, fully exercised by all the new diseases and a complex new working environment. The job itself was not demanding, but at the start, there was so much for me to learn. Marie-Jo's situation was much less satisfying. She did not have enough to do and it gave her too much time to think.

I resolved to work harder at communicating with her and a few days later, I took the opportunity to have a chat.

"How are things going?" I began, as we sat on the verandah at the end of the day.

"The new pharmacy system is organised and we have re-arranged the supplies, so that it is easy to see which are the MSF drugs and which are the government ones," she told me.

"Are you happy about the way the pharmacy is running now?"

"No, not completely. We still run out of things and doctors are always requesting items that we don't stock. I think that is the biggest source of tension. All the private doctors seem to use different drugs in their own practices and the patients know this, so they think these drugs are better and request them from the hospital. But you know the MSF list. I can't change that."

I decided to talk with Jean Baptiste, who was now working well with Marie-Jo, to see if he could shed some light on the issue. I asked her to join us, not wanting her to think I was interfering in her territory. The pharmacist seemed pleased to talk and I began.

"In your opinion, what exactly is the problem over hospital drugs?"

"You must understand that we used a different system, before MSF arrived. At that time, there were no drugs in the hospital at all. The authorities in Kom Pong Cham were supposed to send us stock every three months, but for several years this was incomplete. Sometimes nothing arrived at all. All the good medical staff worked full-time in their own clinics, because they received no pay from the government. So the local population thought that the hospital was somewhere to go, only if you were destitute. The staff in hospital were considered to be not good enough to have their own private clinics, so people just bought their drugs from the market as required, or consulted a private doctor, if they could afford it."

"But now there are doctors and nurses in the hospital, at least in the mornings and MSF provides free drugs. The government also sends a small allocation, so there shouldn't be a problem with supplies," I said. "We should always have enough drugs to treat our patients and everyone should know that the hospital will look after you properly."

"In theory, yes," Marie-Jo interrupted, "but I understand that there has been no drug contribution from the government for a year, so there are still shortages."

"I suppose that the government thinks that MSF will pay."

I wanted to hear Jean Baptiste's explanation, hoping he would realise that I was not simply criticising.

"Perhaps they're desperate for money, so they send what supplies they have elsewhere?" I suggested.

For a moment Jean Baptiste was uneasily silent, then he spoke quietly.

"No, it's not just that. No one knows where the drugs go, but we see that some people get very rich, both in Kom Pong Cham and Phnom Penh. Someone along the line is probably stealing drugs and selling them in the local markets. It's this, that leaves the hospitals short."

Now, I realised that this was not just a local problem. It was an issue for all of Cambodia, something too big for Marie-Jo to tackle on her own.

"Look, I can ask Pascal to clarify what each party is supposed to contribute, but for the moment, we need to carry on ordering enough drugs, so that we don't run out. People will never build up confidence in the hospital if we don't have all the ordinary drugs, the ones we need to treat people every day. We can't have people buying what they think they need from the market place. Apart from anything else, they've no idea what they should be taking and they can't be sure of the quality, or even if there's anything in the tablets except sugar and chalk."

I knew that the local markets stocked many products not on the MSF/ WHO (World Health Organisation) approved lists. Now, I understood that the local population thought that these were the best drugs, the ones to buy if they wanted superior treatment.

Marie-Jo reminded me of a recent case, where drug availability had been an issue for us both. A ten year old girl with typhoid fever was not getting better, after two weeks of standard treatment. Dr Lun felt she had resistance to the conventional drugs and recommended the use of Rosafin, a more modern product that we did not stock. What's more, it was available in the local market. Would I authorise its use and save the girl, or stick with MSF's policy and risk her dying? If I bought black market drugs, I was encouraging the idea that this was acceptable, although for the girl and her parents, it was indeed the right thing to do. Then I decided that if it was my child, I would want the drugs, so I decided to buy them the next day, but luckily her fever broke and she began to improve.

"What do you think of the quality of what's for sale in the market?" I went on to ask Jean Baptiste, for this was another important issue.

"Some of the packages that I've seen are dirty and broken. They are often past their expiry dates and the market people know nothing about their effects, or the indications for their use."

The pharmacist was clearly aware of the risks, but the biggest concern about people self-medicating on sophisticated drugs, is that they contribute unwittingly to the growing, worldwide problem of drug resistance. I decided to visit Kroch Mar market, to see the situation for myself and to talk with Pascal and the other doctors, the next time I was in Phnom Penh

So the following Saturday, I wandered round the market with Jean Baptiste and Marie-Jo. The traders were selling an assortment of odds and ends, in no particular order and mostly in very poor condition. When I picked up an unfamiliar packet of tablets, already open at one end, I did not recognise the name, so I asked what it was for. The man was about to reply, when he saw Jean Baptiste.

"I don't know," he muttered, but I had the impression he would have told me differently, if the pharmacist had not been there. Kroch Mar was a small place and Jean Baptiste was well known. Here, I had seen enough to convince me that we had to educate the local people.

I made up my mind to launch an information campaign and set about discussing my plan with as many people as possible: doctors, nurses, lay people, patients and especially Marie-Jo. I wanted to achieve the desired result (quality drugs accessible for all) without damaging local social and economic structures, which had been necessary during the difficult years of the civil war. It wouldn't help matters if I simply alienated the local traders, whose livelihoods depended on their drug selling. When a form of words was agreed, I arranged to have some posters printed. Since these were in the Khmer language, I was aware that I had to trust that the message was correct:

- *Only buy drugs from qualified health staff*
- *Consult a health professional about drugs you want to use*
- *MSF provides free drugs for hospital patients*

This message was simple, but it was a start, although some local people said I was very brave to risk the wrath of the market traders. For a while, I was slightly uneasy about going out at night.

With the coming of the monsoon, life changed dramatically in Kroch Mar. The rain was torrential and warm, with the roads and gardens flooded to several inches, in as many minutes. It was spectacular and exciting to watch, from the safety of our terrace. At night, alarmingly close lightning frequently illuminated the jungle and after each storm the vegetation would steam. One of the more disruptive aspects was that the rainy season put an end to our use of motor-bikes and from now on, we travelled by boat, or on foot. Using the boat seemed incredibly wasteful, but the alternative was an uncomfortable slog through thick, sticky mud, a journey, which could take up to ninety minutes. If you slipped, which you were more than likely to do, it meant arriving covered in filth, with wet clothes that never dried. The dampness seeped into everything we wore, everything we owned, everything we did.

Early in July, it was a welcome surprise, when Dr Lun invited us all to his house-warming party. We had heard rumours that he was creating a sumptuous new home, built Marie-Jo assured us, from the profits of his alleged drug-dealing, even though I reminded her that with the amount of time the man spent on his private practice, he could well have earned his money legitimately. However parties were thin on the ground in Kroch Mar, so Marie-Jo agreed to come along too. We set off at 4.30pm for a ceremony which was due to start at 5pm. Our group was the first to arrive and was immediately asked to sit on the floor. I am not very good at sitting cross-legged for any period of time, so I edged over to a wall, trying to hide the fact that I was using it to support my back and rather hoping that no one would notice. After fifteen minutes of awkward conversation, more guests arrived and settled themselves into the growing circle. Marie-Jo was ill at ease, being the only woman present, feeling and looking conspicuous, with her long, blond hair and blue eyes.

A group of six, shaven-headed Buddhist priests then filed in, all wearing saffron robes, chanting and waving incense lanterns.

"In England, house-warming is usually an alcoholic affair," I whispered to Eric, who had now sidled over to my area of wall.

"It's the same in France," he replied, a little despondently. "I've a feeling this will be very different though, if priests are the centre of entertainment."

They now settled themselves on the floor in a place of honour and the good doctor came in with his wife, both dressed in white ceremonial clothes and carrying a model of a house. A ceremony followed, involving the burning of small pieces of paper and putting dolls into the model house, while the priests chanted continuously. It was particularly amusing, when one of the older priests took a break from chanting, to light up a cigarette and the other five continued singing, as if this was part of the performance. Then, after about thirty minutes, their work seemed to be complete and they sat patiently, while the lady of the house filled their bowls with rice. Finally, they filed out.

There was a slight pause and I wondered if we too should leave. We looked at one another questioningly. But before we could make up our minds, Madame Lun came in and to my discomfort, organised us into a tighter circle in the centre of the room, where we were now all forced to sit, cross-legged. However, when Dr Lun appeared with a case of beer and walked round the outer circumference, depositing six bottles behind each person, I grinned at Eric. Clearly, the cultural divide was not as great as we had thought. Things began to liven up and the men all started talking at once. In about thirty minutes they were all roaring drunk, having finished their beers and our attentive host collected the empties, returning immediately, with replacements. Of course we could not understand the conversation, but the impression was that of a universally recognisable, "chaps night out" at the pub.

At 7 o'clock, Dr Lun suggested that we leave, as it was dark and he was afraid for our safety on the road. Probably just an acceptable way of throwing us out, we told ourselves, not that we cared if there were a hundred brigands out there, waiting to murder us. We were quite drunk. So we said our "goodbyes" and "thank yous" and set off home. Driving a few kilometres by moonlight under such conditions was not easy, but I was the only one to fall off my bike, into the mud. The others laughed a little drunkenly, when I tried to explain that it was nothing to do with the beers. I was just out of practice.

Now that I felt more confident about what I was doing in the hospital and my reading schedule had relaxed, I had free time in the afternoons to explore. On my first expedition, I wandered down one of the lanes that led out into farmland, to the north of town. After five hundred metres or so, the countryside became less organised and the fields quickly turned into grazing and scrubland. I continued along a small path, until I met a farmer walking in the opposite direction. He spoke as I passed, but when I continued, he called after me and waved furiously, indicating that I should return to the road with him. Later, my interpreter explained that land mines were the issue. There are three hundred such accidents a month in Cambodia and the streets of Phnom Penh are full of disabled victims, whose only recourse is to beg for a living. I was rather embarrassed, that I had so quickly forgotten the security rule about staying on well-used roads.

Since I was now under-employed at Kroch Mar, I decided to discuss possible changes to my job description with Pascal, in Phnom Penh. Additionally, I thought he might be able to help me with Marie-Jo, since communication with her was once more a problem. Perhaps she had talked to him, on one of her regular visits to the capital? The problem was, given the hours that the medical staff in Kroch Mar worked, I could not see how we could contribute much more to the hospital. The TB unit was working fairly smoothly and there was little time for the teaching that had been a part of our original remit. It would also be good to meet a few other MSF workers, for I knew they regularly spent their weekends in the capital. Viewed from Kroch Mar, Phnom Penh was beginning to look like the centre of the universe and it would certainly be interesting to find out what the others were doing and if they were meeting the same sort of problems.

The river trip was enjoyable and this time much faster, since we were now travelling with the current. Isabelle met me at the river-side, but said she would not be coming to Phnom Penh, as she was still not on good terms with Pascal. I was quite relieved, as my relationship with her was not great either. She had been very welcoming when we arrived, but since then, I had developed the impression that she and Marie-Jo had become "best buddies" and I was one of their chosen subjects for criticism. Even when I bought her some cigarettes and a bottle of wine, as a gesture of thanks for meeting us when we arrived from the airport, she had replied, "I don't smoke that brand and I don't drink wine; these are no use to me". I was quite surprised, wondering if I had contravened some obscure, French social convention. Or perhaps she didn't like British doctors? I never got to the bottom of it, but it disturbed me. Life is so much more pleasant when you get on with your colleagues.

In retrospect, these thoughts do sound decidedly puerile, but personal relationships can become a real problem in claustrophobic, expatriate communities. I suppose some of the people who volunteer for aid work are liable to be a bit unusual, perhaps even downright eccentric (not me of course), so there are bound to be problems. This is an issue for all organisations, who send small teams to isolated locations. People, who in all likelihood have never met before, must pull together and work positively from the start, something that is not easy.

So it was with some relief that I returned to Phnom Penh, with its new faces and unfamiliar surroundings. Since I was particularly anxious to spend time with other people, I was pleased to find most of the MSF teams from Battambang and Kom Pong Thom were also in town. We ate together both nights but I missed much of the conversation. Those who did try to speak to me gave up after a few minutes, because of my limited French. I did understand one joke however. Kroch Mar, was really "cauchemar", the French word for a nightmare! My language had improved, but I was still very frustrated by my inability to communicate fully.

During that weekend, I discovered the Foreign Correspondents' Club, situated on the waterfront. This old colonial building, with its large balcony overlooking the Mekong, accommodates a bar, restaurant and billiard room. Slow overhead fans and black-suited waiters evoke the nineteen thirties. The majority of the patrons were expatriates, so the ambience was privileged, if not actually smug. However, it was relaxing for me to speak English to a few people for an hour or two, as I enjoyed a cool drink. Photographs hung on the walls, depicting the reality of the violence, during the Pol Pot era. There were illustrations of amputations performed under primitive conditions, the dead and wounded lying where they fell. The living stared without expression, traumatised by who knows what. These pictures were an extremely moving, if slightly unusual choice of interior decoration.

The images returned to my mind the following day, when we were driving through rush hour traffic in Phnom Penh, our car windows wide open because of the heat. When we stopped for a few moments, a man approached my window, stretching out his "hands" in a begging gesture. Then I saw that there were only two stumps — both hands were missing. We gave him a few coins and he went on his way, smiling and joking with his friends. I was told that this was quite a common sight, since de-miners, who work with poor equipment and little training, are often injured. Cambodia must try to clear some of the ten million land mines that are thought to remain in its ground — more than one for each member of the population! If only the countries that produce these monstrosities, could see the legacy they leave behind. Long after wars are over, men, women and, above all, children are injured, often beyond repair. Yet year after year, these "perfect soldiers" are still being used.

A later visit to the Club was more unexpected. It was the 14th July, (Bastille Day) when all French foreign embassies have a party, to which they invite local French citizens. In countries with a small French national population, this is usually a friendly affair, with much good food and wine. This particular year, the 14th in Phnom Penh was to be marked by a grand party, because the French Government had just finished building a sumptuous new embassy, costing thirty-six million francs (about five million pounds). There was much excitement during the days leading up to the event, as our team were all looking forward to the luxury of unlimited French cheese, not to mention champagne and I was assured that I would be admitted too, because of my MSF identity card. That evening, we cleaned ourselves up and set off in high spirits for an exuberant night on the town. However, as we approached the embassy, we could see a rabble of people, firmly being kept at bay by a cordon of armed police. The crowd, mainly Australians, were shouting and waving banners. There were several TV and film crews contributing to the mayhem and we discovered that it was a political demonstration, against the French Government's policy of nuclear testing in the Pacific. Naturally, since security was very tight, I was refused entry.

So I spent a peaceful evening playing billiards and watching television, while the rest of the team ate and drank their fill. They had been embarrassed by the whole episode, trying hard to get me into the party, but I understood and was fairly philosophical about it. As I left them at the gate, I had quipped, "I'm off to find a brothel for the evening!"

As planned, during my visit to Phnom Penh, I had a very productive meeting with Pascal, discussing ideas I had developed for extending my teaching remit. I also asked for his advice about the nature of my role. The TB programme required little additional input from me, but the general medicine was unexpectedly proving to be a problem. Although I was happy enough to take some surgeries, because I was "foreign", the local population had decided that I must be better than any Khmer and there was a lot of pressure to see me. I realised that this situation was weakening the local doctors' position and since I still had little experience of tropical medicine, Cambodian culture, beliefs and values, the local people were quite wrong to see me as their preferred choice. Anyway, my function at the hospital was to explain about the alternative ways that we did things in the West, so that the medical team could decide which of our practices and systems they wished to adopt. It helped no one if I took a few clinics and made a few diagnoses, for in a year's time I would not be there.

This is often at the heart of the dilemma, faced by MSF doctors in the field. Appropriately, the organisation believes that contact with the population is the essence of its role. This gives credibility to its work. The bigger agencies, like Oxfam and the UN, are moving to a policy of employing local people as much as possible, but one result of this, is that foreign aid workers spend more of their time in administration, bureaucracy and even politics. Health professionals in Third World countries benefit from seeing MSF in action, discovering what we have learned from our more sophisticated health care systems. I believe that local staff should choose for themselves what they want from Western medicine, and the best way to do this is to let them see what we do.

Pascal agreed that I should no longer undertake duties that the doctors could just as well do themselves. I would continue to work at the TB unit, but any additional time should now be concentrated on teaching. If there was not enough scope in Kroch Mar, I could begin to support another hospital in the same district. Pleased that this issue was resolved, I went on to discuss the subject of drugs. Despite our campaign, people in Kroch Mar were continuing to use unauthorised medicines. High prices, poor quality and lack of expertise in their use were undoubtedly threatening lives.

"Why do we insist on using such a limited range of drugs in Cambodia, where there are locally available alternatives in the market place? Is there no room for flexibility, when people are tempted to buy things they think are better?"

"Yes, but all aid agencies use a similar list of essential drugs, based on WHO recommendations. Each item on the list is of proven efficacy."

"I understand that. Still, there are times when we need alternatives to the essential list, such as when we find high levels of resistance, or when we meet something unusual. Alternatives are available here."

"We are allowed to buy drugs locally, but in Phnom Penh, we can't be sure of the quality. And you need to consider the problem we'd have, if each doctor was authorised to order his own individual favourites. Remember, there are 20,000 different products available in Europe. It would become a logistical nightmare. We buy European drugs, to assure ourselves of quality, but they all have to be shipped and stored somewhere. Then there's the issue of expense, when we are talking about new drugs. It costs 12,000 dollars a year, to treat a single AIDS patient! We don't have that kind of money. The Essential List gives us something reliable to base all our work on, something that MSF can afford."

He was right. I could see the problems from an administrative and a public health point of view, but it was none the less distressing, to be faced with the kinds of dilemmas I had met in Kroch Mar. I was working towards an understanding of the wider issues, but everything was more complex than I had originally imagined. Aid work must be planned and affordable, but it must also adjust to local conditions and local personalities. I left that meeting resolving to try harder on the personal relations front and planned to focus more on helping the local doctors, not their patients.

Then, after only three months in Cambodia, my work was brutally cut short by the news that my mother had terminal cancer and would need medical care during the few months that she had left. Having notified MSF, I packed and arranged to take a commercial boat down river, the first stage in my long journey back to Britain. On the morning of my departure I arrived at the jetty at 8 o'clock, to wait for the 9am boat. By 9.30, I was a little anxious and asked a man working at the dock, if there was indeed a boat that morning.

"It's coming soon" was his confident reply.

I waited anxiously until 11am, when at last it appeared on the horizon.

Unfortunately, it then sailed past without stopping, so I asked my new acquaintance if there would be another boat.

"Certainly," was the reply, "tomorrow. There is a boat every day."

I went back to the house to wait.

Although concerned about my mother's condition, the journey home gave me time to reflect on my experiences. What had I, or MSF for that matter, contributed to the people of Kroch Mar? Why indeed had Kroch Mar been chosen as a mission? Of course, three months is a very short period of time to make one's presence felt and there had been unexpected dilemmas, so I found the questions difficult to assess. My presence in Kroch Mar had been as a supernumerary, not really intended as a normal member of staff. I was meant to be a resident "expert" and I had been able to devote all my time to the project. I was fairly sure that I had imparted a little of what I knew, to the local doctors. Marie-Jo had done her best to keep the pharmacy in order and Eric had achieved much on the building front. In a general sense, MSF had brought relatively large sums of money into the area, in the form of drugs, buildings, transport and local salaries. Yet how had we helped Cambodia in the long-term? Was our presence part of wider plan, one that would help the country to obtain adequate health care for its people?

Cambodia clearly faced a wide range of medical difficulties, resulting from years of neglect and poverty. The doctors' training was no doubt limited. Many of the people could not afford to use the extensive private medical system, or pay for their drugs in state hospitals. And unless something was done soon, the freedom of the rich to buy and use any drugs they chose, would create a dangerous health problem for the entire population. Now that I understood the background, I could see that these were all complicated issues. Even the relatively simple task of teaching the doctors and nurses was challenging, when staff worked for most of the time in private clinics. Yet, the country could not afford to pay its health professionals adequate salaries. Is it even possible to provide a reasonable level of health care, when poverty is endemic?

It was all more difficult than I had imagined. I had thought that humanitarian work simply meant going into a country to offer a bit of medical aid and by doing so, resolve its problems. Already, I could see that a wider, more complex kind of help might be required.

My own ideas were vague and ill-developed when I started to work in

Cambodia, but I could see that MSF could accomplish things, valuable things. In Kroch Mar, I had begun to realise that my original remit had been flawed, along with that of Marie-Jo, but there was scope for something to be achieved. Humanitarian aid was fascinating. I knew that I wanted to work for MSF again, at a later date.

CHAPTER FIVE

Sleepless in Uganda

I looked after my mother until she died, spending what was for me, an unusual amount of time with my family. The funeral was towards the end of December, so in January I found myself back in France, where I allowed myself a couple of months to recover. It had been a strange, sad, unsettling and emotionally tiring time, but after a while I was ready to return to work.

I had never felt any special desire to visit Africa, but when MSF suggested that I might join the sleeping sickness programme, I did not hesitate for a moment. The name "sleeping sickness" ensured that I would say yes. For the average British doctor, this most charismatic of diseases engenders images of Black Africa, straight out of the old textbooks, with photographs of patients lying comatose, dying of what should be a curable condition. True, my lectures in tropical medicine had been twenty-five years ago and after such a long time, the name was the only thing I remembered about the disease, but that fact only added to my excitement. Surely any deficiencies in my knowledge could be rectified by an hour or two in the MSF medical library?

Unfortunately, there was not much information in the library and the only research available, seemed to date from the 1930's! However, I did discover that the medical diagnosis had to be confirmed by a lumbar puncture, which involves pushing a long needle into the base of the spine, to draw off some of the fluid that bathes the brain and spinal cord. It was twenty years since I had any experience of that particular procedure, so I re-read the technique very carefully and memorised the relevant anatomy. The procedure is not difficult and it had been almost a daily event, when I was a junior house officer in the Edinburgh hospitals, but despite my confidence that I would regain the ability, I was not so comfortable with the prospect of relearning the technique, under what were likely to be less than ideal conditions.

The ladies in the MSF departure office were their usual friendly and efficient selves, as they handed over my now familiar kit of goodies, plus a return ticket to Entebbe, Uganda. It was the Saturday afternoon flight from Paris to London and then overnight to Nairobi, where I arrived at 6am, feeling tired and uncomfortable. There were no other MSF staff waiting, to serve as a distraction, so after an hour wandering aimlessly around the airport, I settled down to read, beside similarly dishevelled companions. It's not very exotic, I thought to myself as I perched on my plastic chair in the awkward corridor that served as the departure lounge for Nairobi airport. The connecting flight was not till 2pm and I hoped the time wouldn't drag too much.

Just as the book was getting interesting, a soft, low moan from the person on my left interrupted the flow of words. I had the uncomfortable feeling that this was a noise that I recognised from somewhere and I turned to see a plump woman, perhaps fifty-five years old, slowly toppling sideways in her chair. As soon as I saw her face, I recollected the sound, for her colour was pasty white, fast becoming grey/blue. In fact, her lips were already blue. She had suffered a heart attack.

"Oh shit, she's arrested," I thought, the medical jargon coming back instinctively from my youth. I dragged her quickly off her chair onto the floor and straightened her up, to see what was happening. Then I felt her neck for a pulse and hit her hard on the chest, the standard procedure now universally familiar, thanks to numerous hospital soap operas. Somewhat to my surprise, there were now two men kneeling down beside me, one starting mouth-to-mouth resuscitation, the other clearly searching for a pulse in the patient's wrist. The mouth-to- mouth was certainly a laudable attempt, but as the patient was still breathing, in my opinion it was not entirely necessary. I said in my best, pompous, don't panic manner,

"Don't worry. I'm a doctor."

"So am I!" the two men retorted in unison.

For a cardiac arrest in the middle of an airport lounge, there are not so many things anyone can do, but it's usually best if everyone avoids doing the same things at once. I decided that someone would have to take charge, if the poor woman was to stand a chance. One of the men then said,

"She is my wife and this is her cousin."

Great! Problem solved. Medical ethics recommend that you should not treat a family member, so I could be the one to carry on giving the orders.

"Somebody phone for an ambulance," I said loudly. I wasn't even sure if conventional ambulances existed in Nairobi, but it's what I would have said at home and it seemed to get some sort of reaction. A jolly, fat, black lady, wearing an official-looking uniform and carrying a walkie-talkie radio appeared, assuring us that she would send for an ambulance. All we had to do, she said, was to wait. So we waited.

Fortunately, by now the patient had sorted herself out. Her heart had restarted and she was breathing normally. I imagine that the shock of being dragged on to the floor and jumped on by three anxious people all at once, had done the trick. Whatever the reason, she was returning to the appropriate colour for a live person, so the initial emergency was over.

The ambulance took an hour to arrive. Madam continued to look fine, although she failed to regain consciousness, thus making it a rather uncomfortable wait for the rest of us. Her family were naturally very distressed and constantly checked her pulse, but there was little more I could do. However, I could hardly carry on reading my book as if nothing had happened. Sitting next to an unconscious patient, I had to stay on the case, so to speak. The departure corridor offered no other distractions, so we three doctors began to chat, exchanging details as a start. The two chaps turned out to be elderly, American orthopaedic surgeons, travelling around Africa on holiday. We agreed that all three of us were out of practice at this emergency room stuff, but it had all gone well so far, we thought.

After that, it was a bit awkward. I'm not much of a conversationalist at the best of times, but even I knew it would be a little insensitive to ask how their holiday was going. I smiled encouragingly and we now took it in turns to measure the patient's pulse. Then at long last, the ambulance arrived and I escorted the group to the vehicle, relieved as it raced off to the accompaniment of sirens and lights. I forgot to ask all their names and I have often wondered if the lady made it, since hospitals are dangerous places wherever you are. In retrospect, I reckon that this patient stood a good chance, since she had already got over the high-risk part of her trauma, resuscitation by the enthusiastic inexperienced.

I turned to go back inside the airport, only to remember with a jolt that my belongings, passport, plane ticket etc, were in my bag, under the plastic chair in the departure lounge/corridor, while I was now outside the terminal, with no proof of identity. Fortunately the jolly lady re-appeared five minutes later, managing after some earnest negotiation to persuade the unsmiling customs men, to let me back into the airport. She accompanied me back to my seat, only to find that my bag had disappeared, but my new friend was not in the least perturbed, convinced that someone would have handed it into Security.

"Fat chance" I thought, but with no other option I trailed after her, to discover that it was the security staff themselves, who had picked up my bag. This in itself was a problem, since Security were now preparing to blow up my few possessions and it took more persuasive talking to get my things back, mainly I think, because they were looking forward to a little explosion, to brighten up their day. This small flurry of excitement helped pass the time until my flight to Entebbe. As we took off once more, I reflected that Nairobi had been one of the least boring airports I had ever visited.

The ninety-minute flight was uneventful and as I strolled out of the arrivals terminal, I spotted a man with a placard, bearing the MSF name and logo. He introduced himself as David the driver, explaining that we were based in Kampala, forty kilometres from Entebbe. As we left the airport, I saw the old terminal building and control tower, decorated with the stigmata of the Israeli rescue mission of the 1960's, the spattering of bullet marks evocative of Uganda's difficult past.

I had previously wondered why Winston Churchill had called Uganda "The Pearl of Africa", but the drive from the airport suggested the reason. The countryside is wonderfully green and hilly, with a rich red soil that produces a host of extraordinary, colourful plants. The journey took a long time, as the road was being repaired in several places, but the delays allowed me to take in my new surroundings. Eventually, we were in the suburbs of Kampala, an impressive modern city, built on several hills, with multi-storey buildings dominating the skyline.

"That is the business area and these tall buildings are mainly banks," David told me.

He skirted the downtown area and drove on to a suburb called Kabalagala, where MSF had its guesthouse.

"We are going straight to the house, as there is no one in the office on Sundays," he explained.

He insisted on carrying my rucksack inside, where the administrator was prostrate on a long couch. She barely said hello, when I asked if there was a room free.

"Second on the right, down that corridor," she said, waving her arm vaguely in the direction of a door.

It seemed an odd way to welcome a newcomer who had travelled so far. The house was a dingy, sombre place, despite the hot sun outside, and the three days I spent there were quite uncomfortable.

When he arrived at 4 o'clock, Evan, the Head of Mission, was most welcoming, suggesting that we go to his home to talk. An American, of Chinese origin, he was married to a French nurse and they lived about two kilometres away, in a pleasant three bedroom bungalow. Evan introduced me to Francoise, his wife, their small son and Dominique, the MSF mechanic who lived in an apartment at the back of the house. Dominique's job was to keep each of MSF's fifteen Ugandan vehicles operational. At this point, there were only eight expatriates on the Ugandan team, but he explained that the cars were left over from previous times, when there had been much more activity in the country. One year later, we were to need all those cars and more, when the workload more than doubled.

I was invited to take a seat, which I did, once I had cleared the toys and books from one of the chairs. This was a true family home.

"Welcome to Uganda," Evan began, rather formally. "Yours is a quiet mission at the moment, but things here can change very quickly. Two years ago it was very different, but the country is now relatively stable and President Musaveni remains fairly popular. There are however, rebel groups in the North and relations with some of the neighbouring countries like South Sudan, are not so good, but you will hear more about that, when you go to your village. This area of Africa is part of what is called the Great Lakes Region and it has always been unstable. The village where you will be working is called Omugo. It is near the northern border with South Sudan, about three hundred kilometres northwest of Kampala. It's very isolated and fourteen hours by road from here. Because rebel groups operate in the area, we normally travel by light aircraft. The nearest town, Arua, is the provincial capital, with a population of forty thousand."

Evan was also a doctor, so we spent the rest of the briefing talking about the medical aspects of the mission. Then we adjourned to a lakeside bar, at a place called Gaba Beach, sipping cold beer and chatting about our respective careers, while his son played on the swings. Evan explained that he had previously been a physician in America and now, after two and a half years with MSF, he was thinking of returning to his former work, since he could not see a long term career for himself with the organisation. We talked till it began to get dark and then returned to the house, Evan explaining that I would have a day's grace to look around Kampala, before flying to Arua, the next stage in my journey.

Of choice, MSF flew with Mission Aviation Fellowship (MAF) a religious NGO based in Entebbe, so two days later I took a taxi back to the airport, to join the other passengers at the check-in desk. I did find it a little disconcerting when the pilot offered up a short prayer for a safe landing before take-off, but it worked, since we arrived in one piece. As I climbed out of the aeroplane, I saw a dozen or so assorted NGO vehicles to one side, including an MSF Land Cruiser, with a smiling, blond-haired man standing nearby. At last, transport for my final destination, Omugo! I was anxious to get to the place where I would be spending the next six months of my life.

"Bonjour. Ca va?"

"Ca va."

We exchanged greetings in French, in recognition of the language of our organisation, despite the fact that this was an English speaking country. Alain explained that he was currently the log for the mission, but was due to leave in four weeks time, as he had already completed five months of his contract.

"The two girls, Nadine and Sandra, are on holiday at the moment, so it's just you and me in Omugo for now," he told me. "I have a few things to buy in Arua and then we will have a coffee, before we set off. The full team is a doctor, a lab technician (Sandra), a nurse (Nadine) and a log. Nadine is also the RT (the person in charge of the mission, "Responsable Terrain" in French). You will be replacing the Japanese doctor who left six weeks ago. He developed tuberculosis, after only two months."

As we drove the five kilometres into town, I wondered how I would manage in my role as solitary doctor in a sleeping sickness hospital. I also vaguely wondered about my own resistance to tuberculosis. Then I followed Alain round the market, allowing the new colours and sounds to wash over me, as my companion bought piles of vegetables, which he said were not readily available in Omugo. His purchases complete, we stopped for coffee at the Hotel Continental, where we sat on a tiny, street-front terrace and viewed the morning activity, from behind old-fashioned, wooden palings. Directly opposite was a tailor's shop, where two men were working furiously at foot treadle, sewing machines. Next door, they seemed to sell nothing but crates of Nile beer, which were stacked precariously from floor to ceiling.

"Why do they keep such large stocks?" I wondered out loud.

"Because of the rebels. The shopkeepers need to have enough to keep them going if the road closes. In fact, you can judge the state of security conditions in the area, by the current price of beer," Alain explained. "When the rebels are in control, they cut the road between here and Kampala and the price of beer doubles, or even trebles. But it's been fairly quiet recently," he added encouragingly.

Rebels were the last thing I would have expected in this pleasant, busy street. People were chatting cheerfully as they passed by, either on foot, or by bicycle. Local taxis, that Alain called "boda bodas," were bicycles, with padded planks attached at the back. The drivers were thin, muscular young lads, who seemed in the main to have two sorts of clients. These were either fat business men, with their smart attaché cases and sunglasses, or gaily dressed women, whose plump buttocks hung resplendently over the small seat, while they desperately clutched huge baskets of shopping to ample bosoms. Everyone was smiling. It was hot, busy and comfortable and with the sun beating down from a clear blue sky, I felt quite at ease.

"I read in Paris that Idi Amin was born near here," I mentioned. It was about the only thing I did know about the area.

"No one is sure exactly where, but they say it was in Koboko, about fifteen kilometres to the north. In French, we call him Idi Amin Dada, or Amin Dada. The people around here certainly remember him."

We went on to discuss Uganda's recent history. Idi Amin was another of the 20th century's infamous despots. He seized power in 1971 and there had followed an appalling reign of terror and brutality, until he was finally deposed in 1979. Six years of lawlessness and food shortages, fuelled by a surge of old tribal rivalries, then dragged the country further into despair. Finally, a military coup put Museveni into power in 1985 and although there were still troubled areas that suffered from serious rebel activity, much of the country had now settled, enabling people to get on with their lives.

With an, "On y va", it was time for us to go. We climbed into the car and began the thirty-five kilometre trip to Omugo, passing the airfield, which now stood deserted. The road was rough and dusty, in places little more than bare rock, but the vegetation was green and luxuriant. Alain pointed out mango, palm, avocado, cassava, potatoes, corn and sugar cane. Then, after forty-five minutes, we descended a steep slope that made me glad we had four-wheel drive and Alain pointed to the twin peaks of Liru and Wati, in the near distance.

"Rebels use these mountains for their bases, so we don't go too close," he warned.

As we drove into it, Omugo did not seem to be a place at all, more of a T-junction, with a few buildings scattered indiscriminately around. Then, I realised there were about fifty houses, but it was still not large by anyone's standards. Alain pointed out that the town included a school, a shop (large enough to accommodate two customers), two bars and administrative offices, as well as the MSF facilities.

The most imposing structure in the town was the brick-built, MSF building, painted incongruously bright blue and white.

"It used to be a bank, in the days when there was a tobacco industry here. After the trouble with Amin Dada, the community almost died," Alain explained. "Then MSF arrived. We employ about seventy local people, so we have regenerated the economy. We are very popular."

As we pulled into the compound, most of the staff were assembled. They were a motley crew and within a few days, I began to think of them as the "Adams Family": Harriet was Morticia, Nunu was Lurch and Olema was uncle Festus, all lovably idiosyncratic in their habits, people who were to become my friends as we got to know each other. After the introductions, Alain gave me a quick tour of the compound. The old bank was a square building, with twelve small rooms, set around a central courtyard. In its grounds, MSF had built a workshop for the cars and three circular, straw-roofed tukuls (one roomed huts) to serve as bedrooms. In the centre of the courtyard was a large mango tree, which provided both shade and fruit, not to mention large numbers of ants, which I would discover fell on to our table and into our food as we ate.

I installed my belongings in my tukul and then lay down for a few minutes. The room was in fact quite large, with a bed, a table and chair, plus a piece of string hanging between two beams, to act as a wardrobe. There were shutters on the windows, but of course no glass and up in the grass roof there were a few insects buzzing around, but nothing that seemed too threatening. It was cool, charming and extremely pleasant.

Our domestic arrangements were very basic. A generator ran for three hours a day, to charge batteries for the computer and radio. Water was carried by our water-fetcher on his bicycle, from the nearby well and kerosene lamps enabled us to eat and read at night. There were of course, no telephones and no television.

Now that I had stopped travelling, it was time to face the realities of my job as a doctor for the sleeping sickness programme. Alain had informed me that the previous year, MSF had erected a new hospital in Omugo to treat this specific condition. It was on the other side of the T-junction, about 150 metres from the bank. Nearby, there was a government dispensary, which dealt with all other illnesses, although serious cases were referred to Arua. The hospital was made up of four, long, rectangular tukuls, arranged in a star shape, with a medical station at the centre. Each of these rooms could accommodate thirty patients. There were no doors, no glass in the windows and the roofs were made of straw.

Sleeping sickness (Trypanosomiasis) is a parasitic infection, caused by small organisms, which look rather like the malaria parasite. The infection is transmitted by the bite of an infected tsetse fly and most infections in our area were passed from man, to fly and back to man. In other areas (where the parasite is slightly different) infected cattle can be a more important reservoir for transmitting the disease. The tsetse fly looks like a large housefly, but it has a long proboscis and a painful bite. Weeks, or months after being bitten, patients begin to have headaches, joint pains and sometimes a rash. A few months later, the parasites get into the brain and the patients become "sleepy". Later still, they lose consciousness and die, often from dehydration, as they can neither eat, nor drink.

The condition is 100% fatal, if not treated. At the beginning of the 20th century, much of equatorial Africa was ravaged by the disease. Estimates at that time, were of five hundred thousand deaths. It wiped out whole villages, just as the plague had done in medieval England and it destroyed all economic activity in infected areas. In the 1920s, the various colonial powers introduced control programmes, which almost eradicated the disease, but as the African nations gained their independence throughout the 1960s, these programmes gradually collapsed and the disease began to re-emerge. Sleeping sickness is once again a serious problem in Angola, Zaire, Central Africa, South Sudan and of course Uganda. (The Democratic Republic of the Congo was called Zaire during the time period covered by this book, so this is the name I will use.)

Next morning, I was surprised to find that work started with a security briefing, rather than an update on the medical situation. Alain began,

"Uganda is relatively quiet under the presidency of Yoweri Museveni, but only 80% of it is under his control. There are two main rebel groups waging a guerrilla war in the Omugo area, the West Nile Bank Front (WNBF) and The Lords Resistance Army (LRA). The WNBF are of a military and political persuasion, but they occasionally attack the general population. Their indiscriminate use of land mines is a major hazard for us all. The LRA operate more to the East, but they occasionally cause security alerts, so you should not venture very far on foot. About fifteen minutes in any direction out of Omugo is the recommended limit, but the area towards Liru and Wati in the North, is probably the most dangerous. Up till now, there have not been any land mines on this road, but they definitely exist, as you move north towards the mountains and Koboko. If you plan to drive anywhere at all, you must ask the local taxi drivers if they have any news. If a road seems deserted, stop and ask why. The people living beside the road will almost always know what is going on. Not many of the villagers speak English, so you must have a driver with you at all times, to act as your interpreter."

"But everything's fine, here, in Omugo?" I asked, a little concerned by all these warnings of rebels and land mines, not to mention the fact that a fifteen minute radius would certainly inhibit any plans I might have for walking, or running.

"Sometimes, there are reports of rebel groups moving around this area at night. If that is the case, you should avoid going to the hospital after dark."

Not only was this discouraging, I thought it also unrealistic. Whoever heard of a doctor not going to see his patients after dark? After all, it wasn't as if the hospital was that far away from my tukul. In fact, given its somewhat fragile construction, the tukul didn't offer me any protection in the first place.

That afternoon, I wandered around the village. About twenty houses lay along the opposite side of the road from the bank, with others scattered amongst the trees, a little further off. Some were well-cared for, others dilapidated, but all were very small. Just beyond a roughly marked-out football pitch, was the local administrator's office and in the other direction, down the right hand arm of the 'T' junction was the hospital, where I met Olema, the programme's medical assistant.

Olema was a friendly twenty-five year old, stocky and cheerful. He had finished his training just one year before and this was his first job, but already he had a very sound knowledge, both of the protocols and of the local conditions. (Protocols are the written instructions, which ensure that everyone gets the same treatment.) Olema explained that a medical assistant has a qualification somewhere between a nurse and a doctor. The training lasts for three years and is highly practical, focussing directly on the specific needs of the Ugandan population, illnesses like malaria, pneumonia and typhoid. He introduced me to each of the patients on the ward, summarising their condition and progress; then we spent about an hour going through the treatment protocol in the circular nursing station.

On Monday morning, I started work properly and was surprised to hear that during this first week, I was also to be apprenticed to Harriet, the head nurse. If Harriet and Olema were both able to teach me, why was I here, I wondered? Then I remembered Cambodia and decided to wait and see. No doubt a genuine role would eventually reveal itself, since MSF employed Olema, Harriet and twenty-three other full time nursing staff in the hospital. They would not have additionally sent me to Omugo, if they had not felt there was a need.

Harriet was twenty-six years old and extremely competent. Small and quiet, she had a natural authority, which allowed her to run the hospital effectively. However, she did have a problem with Olema, who was hierarchically her superior and her cousin. Most of the time things seemed to work out well and as I got to know them better, they both complained to me that the other was difficult, but "I can handle him/her", they said, as relations do.

The government dispensary was run by Dominique, another medical assistant. This facility was chronically short of drugs and Dominique regularly came over to ask MSF for supplies.

"You must decide for yourself, if his requests are reasonable," Alain said, when I asked his advice.

After Cambodia, I was extremely wary of handing out MSF drugs arbitrarily, but here the situation seemed to be very different.

"Nadine usually gives him what he asks for," Alain told me. "She has confidence that he doesn't abuse the situation."

In the absence of other information, I decided to follow this precedent.

The main part of my work was on the sleeping sickness wards, where there was usually a complement of about forty patients and I quickly became familiar with the procedures. Because there was a research project being conducted, we followed the standard treatment protocol as recommended by the WHO. This introduced a sense of discipline and gave patients the benefit of the regime, which was considered to be most effective. The presence of a lab technician ensured that the tests and thus the diagnoses were of high quality, an important issue because the treatment was most effective, if it was based on accurate laboratory information. A disadvantage was, that it made the clinical care rather automated and therefore less interesting, as there was less need for decision-making. In time, I found that patients often had two or more conditions at once and this fact dramatically widened my knowledge of tropical medicine.

One embarrassing aspect of my first few weeks in Omugo, was that I could not understand the Ugandan English accent and I often had to ask my French colleagues to translate for me. Everyone else found this greatly amusing. As I began to settle in, I found that the staff all knew their jobs, although there were too many nurses for the number of patients. The programme had been designed to treat up to one hundred patients at a time and this number was never attained.

After three weeks, I was confident in my ability to cope with my duties and as in Cambodia, I began to feel that I had too much spare time. Just as I thought I might get bored however, Olema asked if he could take his annual holiday, since he had been working for twelve months without a break. He had been very happy indeed, to see me arrive! So Olema left and during the next month, I was the only doctor in the hospital. The workload itself was not a problem, but without his support, I was on call in Omugo twenty-four hours a day, in case of an emergency. This quickly became tiresome, not because of what I had to do, but because, even with the extra duties, I found that I still had too much spare time. Omugo's charms were strictly limited.

Then one evening, Alain and I were relaxing under the mango tree, enjoying a goat stew and chatting about his experiences with MSF. It was all highly civilised. Since it was well after seven and already completely dark, we were eating by the light of a small, twelve-volt fluorescent lamp, that we had hung up on the wall behind us. Alain was reminding me that the two other members of our mission were due to return, some time during the next week. That, he promised, would spice up our lives.

"Sandra has been here for more than a year," he told me, "which is why she was entitled to fly back to France for a month's holiday. Nadine has done eight months and has been on holiday in Zanzibar. Actually, Nadine is thinking of leaving as soon as a replacement can be found, but Sandra is still undecided. She may do another six months."

"Who will replace you, when it's your turn to go?" I had started to ask, when several bursts of submachine gun fire shattered our evening. It was very loud, very near and very frightening. Quite startled, I leapt to my feet. Irrelevantly, I wondered how I could recognise this new sound with absolute certainty, as I tried desperately to keep my fear under control.

"Is that normal around here?" I asked, hoping that Alain would come up with some reasonable reply. I'm still not sure what would have constituted a reasonable reply.

Before he could say anything, there was another long burst of firing, much, much closer. Alain now looked as worried as I felt. This was clearly not normal. He switched off the light.

"No, that's the first time I've heard any shooting here."

It was a moonless night and we could see nothing, so we continued to sit under the tree, unwilling to move, silent, anxious; waiting for what might follow.

The next bursts of gunfire lasted for several minutes and now it was difficult for me to say if it was one, or many guns together. There was another lull, then just when we thought it was all over and we could begin to relax, there was a long burst of fire, this time even louder — a deafening noise, which seemed to come from just outside the bank. We abandoned our tree and ran hastily inside, Alain extinguishing all light as we entered, so that we now stood together in the darkened room, terrified. Then my legs began to tremble, so I sat down, unable to think or do anything at all, because so much mental effort was going into forcing myself not to panic.

Suddenly, Regina our cook came running in from the kitchen, crying, "They will kill us all. It's the rebels and they will shoot us all dead."

"Quiet!" said Alain roughly. "Keep still, be quiet and don't show any lights. They may not come in here."

So we waited and waited, hearing more bursts of gunfire for about thirty minutes, until it faded away into the distance. Regina went back to the kitchen and now there was no noise at all.

Unwilling to make our way outside to our tukuls to sleep, we each took a couch in the sitting room and lay down, trying to force ourselves to relax. Nothing had happened, we told each other. We were all right, we said. We should sleep, we agreed. After another hour, I knew that I had to go to the toilet, which was outside somewhere, with the machine guns. I cursed myself for having drunk a pint of beer with dinner and terrified, crept to the shower. The toilet was outside the bank building and I was far too frightened to go there and anyway, this was not the time for social niceties. I returned to my couch, spending a very long, sleepless night, despite the fact that there was no further noise. Once or twice I peered out of a window and saw bright flashes of light, some distance away. Whatever it was, it was continuing.

After a night that seemed endless, the sun rose and I looked outside to see people moving up and down the street, as if nothing had happened. What's more, my own fear had disappeared with the dark. But all was not as it had been before. A rebel group had come into our tiny village, looking for the village leader and intending to release a friend from jail. The headman escaped, so then they went to the police station, where they dragged one of the local policemen outside and blew off half his head. The firing near our building had been a gunman positioned there, to dissuade anyone from interfering with the assassination. I reflected that it had been a very successful ploy.

The morning calm was broken, when the wife and family of the dead man ran up the street, shrieking. I made my way despondently over to the hospital, where about half our patients remained. It's not that gunshot is a cure for sleeping sickness, it's just that anyone who could physically move, had the sense to get themselves well out of the way. The majority had simply taken up their bedding and settled for a night in the bush, along with most of the staff. Gradually, throughout the morning, they returned and I tried to exude complete confidence, while checking to see if anyone had suffered ill effects. Eric, one of the staff, lightened my mood when he explained that he deserved some compensation. He had lost his shoes, when he had desperately run out into the undergrowth with everyone else. His request was accompanied by a huge smile, so that although I knew that on one level he was serious, he did not really expect to succeed with his claim. Like the rest of us, he was relieved to have survived.

Over the next few weeks there was no repetition of the attack and gradually the terrors of the episode faded, although they did leave an unfortunate legacy. For the first time in my life, I discovered that I was not made out to be a soldier. Of course I had never actually wanted to be a soldier, but now I had to face the fact that I was in the middle of a war zone and someone might expect me to fight for my life. Given the work I had chosen, I had realised that I might get very close to fighting, but only now did I take on board the fact that doctors could become targets and that bullets are non-discriminating. This experience gave me a chastening insight into my perception of myself as a doctor. I had been conditioned to believe (and accepted) that I had a privileged place in society, protected and somehow existing outwith the rules. I had brought this attitude with me, never considering that it might have been a fragile model, valid only in limited situations in the UK. Much later, I reflected on the similarity between this conviction and that of the LRA rebels, who believed that sacred oil, rubbed on before battle, would protect their bodies against bullets.

Now, it began to sink in that these rebels might not feel constrained by arcane international treaties, designed to protect people providing neutral, medical assistance. They had in all probability never heard of such a thing. If they wanted me dead, there was nothing I could do about it. To make things worse, I found that I was now very nervous of all sudden noises. It didn't help that some of the indigenous palm fronds occasionally rubbed together, emitting sound very much like gunfire. I slept fitfully, wakening to listen intently, trying to distinguish between all the extraneous sounds. Sometimes there would be gunshots; single shots, or bursts of automatic fire, although mostly these were in the distance. Don't be a wimp, I'd tell myself, but wimp I was, as I lay restlessly in the warm, frightening darkness, listening for any sound that might represent a threat.

A week later, Sandra and Nadine returned, relaxed and refreshed from their break and bringing a breath of the outside world, the one that didn't have men rushing around at night, firing guns. Their cheerful normality helped to persuade me that it was not impractical, this idea of a sleeping sickness hospital, out in the wilds of Uganda. Nadine had been working for MSF for three years and was looking forward to the end of her mission, since she felt that it was now time to go back into full-time nursing in France. In the meantime, she was amazingly strong and directed in what she was doing, focussing intensely on immediate problems concerning the running of the hospital. It would have been embarrassing to wilt in front of Nadine.

It was Sandra with whom I now spent most of my time, however, since I wanted to learn more about the diagnostic techniques. Her role was to persuade people to return for checkups, once their treatment was completed. She organised a team of assistants in the community, whose task was difficult, because patients who felt well, did not see the need to be tested. Sandra was tall, blond and slim and quite impervious to fear of rebels and what they might do to her. This fact hardened my determination to master my own fear. If she could cope, so must I.

Despite her ability to sleep at night, Sandra was less sanguine about crazy George. In fact, she was terrified of him and this fear helped to redress the balance between us. George was undoubtedly mentally ill, but in the Omugo community he was tolerated, without too much difficulty. He had uncut and unkempt curly hair and wandered around all day, carrying a small paper-plate, bearing one or two choice items. He was always completely naked, but no one seemed to mind except Sandra. With an almost maniacal laugh, George would appear at our office window and push something through the grill, as often as not, a turd. Once, I unintentionally incurred Sandra's wrath by inviting him into the office, a treat that he seemed to appreciate. He stood silently, without really looking at anything, but Sandra immediately shot into a back room, from the safety of which she threatened me with unspeakable atrocities, if I didn't remove him immediately.

As the weeks passed, I persuaded myself that I had overreacted to the night of trouble, then one of the local chiefs came to see us. He warned us of a rumour, that rebels would attack the village tonight, to kill the administrator. He had been the focus of the first attack.

"They will also be looking for food and supplies," he assured us cheerily. "This is the obvious place for them to come. I would take care!"

Then, just as cheerily, he left. We had to decide quickly, whether to stay, or retreat for the night. In Arua, we would be safe. In Omugo, we might not. We went round and round the problem, not sure what was the right thing to do.

"Surely, we shouldn't leave the hospital on the basis of a rumour," said Alain.

"I think it would be prudent to go to Arua. What will we lose if we leave for one night?" was Nadine's view. "At worst, they will only want the supplies. They're not likely to attack the locals, but the sight of foreigners might set things off. It would be best for everyone, if we were out of the way."

"I'm for staying," was Sandra's feeling. Nothing, it appeared, would ever threaten her equilibrium.

I was unsure, but finally voted to go to Arua. We would, after all, come back in the morning. What harm could it do? We packed a few things and left, spending a pleasant evening in the hotel, where I slept soundly, relieved to be free of the fears that had become my nightly companions. And we all told ourselves that we had done the right thing.

When we returned the next day and found that nothing had happened, we were embarrassed. Had our excuse that white faces might trigger some violence, just been a way of getting ourselves out of trouble? I felt really terrible, realising what we had done was to run away, leaving the local staff to cope alone. I had let down the patients and forgotten my responsibilities and was very embarrassed when I met the staff that morning. What made it worse, was that they were very polite and said nothing. I swore to myself that next time I would stay, whatever happened. Despite my resolve, the continuing rumour-mill re-awakened my anxieties and for the next few nights I lay restlessly in bed, listening intently for noises, especially anything that might be gunfire. Six months now seemed like an awfully long time to be in this place.

The days passed slowly and as the distant fighting did not seem to get any closer, memory dulled and fear became theoretical again, rather than nauseating, as it had been at the time of the murder. Despite my continued, nightly unease, I was able to concentrate on the routine work of the hospital during the day, for by now I was familiar with the disease and secure in my ability to treat the patients.

Sleeping sickness has two phases. In the first, the parasite is only in the blood, but in the second, it invades the brain. The first phase is treated by ten injections of a drug called Pentamidine. These are painful, especially for infants, but there is almost always a cure. In the second phase, another drug, Arsobal is needed, because Pentamidine cannot penetrate the brain. Arsobal must be injected slowly into a vein, over a few minutes. Nine injections are required, spread over twenty-three days. Two days of preparation are followed by three days of injections, six days of rest, three days of injections, another six days of rest and then a final three days of injections.

The pain of the injections is very upsetting for everyone concerned and when I think of the hospital, I still hear the sounds of the children screaming. Children learn very quickly what is happening, when a nurse appears with a syringe; and if they have fat arms and legs, it can take many attempts to get the needle properly inserted. The procedure is upsetting for the children, the nurses, the parents and British doctors with sensitive feelings. Sometimes, I had to move away out of range, for even though I knew it was necessary, hurting small children is difficult to endure. Occasionally, the chemical was injected into the wrong place, producing painful inflammation and large ulcers. Fortunately our nurses were very experienced and this was a rare event, so that overall, the treatment was very effective.

Much more serious than these painful injections, some patients had a violent reaction to the Arsobal. This proved to be fatal in more than 50% of the patients who experienced it. We could not predict who would react badly. Furthermore, once a reaction had begun, we had no real way of treating it. We explained the risks to everyone, so that patients knew that without treatment, they would die in several months (or maybe a year) but with it, they had a one in twenty chance of dying from side-effects of the drugs. This situation was also upsetting for the staff. Although they knew that they were doing the right thing, emotionally it felt as if they were killing patients. To make matters worse, adverse reactions were not necessarily immediate. A patient could develop the problem at any stage of the process. It was an awful game of Russian roulette.

Each morning, the nurses would prepare the trolley and begin their work, bringing health to the majority, but occasionally and inevitably, death to some. The adult patients lay anxiously, but quietly on their beds, their arms outstretched, waiting for the needle. For the lucky majority, at the end of three days' treatment, they had a break of six days to recover. Patients were at first much relieved to have survived and then increasingly apprehensive, as the time came to start the game again. Amazingly the wards were relatively cheerful places.

During one of my nights on call for the hospital, a young boy had violent convulsions and died within two hours. It was a harrowing experience, exacerbated by my own feelings of impotence. The next morning, while I was completing my ward round, I was surprised when one of the nurses made an unexpected observation.

"That boy was poisoned by another patient. It was in retaliation for a previous death, two weeks before, when his father poisoned a female patient. We all knew about it. It happens all the time," she said.

I could feel my eyebrows rising to my hairline as I absorbed this information, but I tried to keep a noncommittal expression on my face. This was clearly ridiculous, but what could I say? My informer took the story seriously and with my British sense of decorum, I didn't want to offend her. So I said nothing and moved on.

After the ward round, I made further enquiries in the nursing station.

"What is this story about poisoning?" I asked Harriet and Olema, smiling to show I knew it was all a joke.

"There are certain local people who know how to use plants and animals to make poisons. It is best not to interfere with them," Harriet told me earnestly.

"Do you believe that too?" I asked Olema.

For a minute he looked uncomfortable, but finally admitted that he too believed that it happened.

"That is why people are careful to cook their own food on the ward," he told me.

"There is a lot of rivalry. Normally, people live within their own clan and they feel safe. But here in the hospital, they are mixed together, in a way that doesn't usually happen. People who know how to poison your food, can do it here, without you knowing."

"That is ridiculous." I said. "You know the drugs sometimes have bad side effects. I'm sure the deaths are as a result of adverse reactions!"

But as I spoke, I saw that none of the local staff believed me. They clammed up and stopped meeting my gaze, and I realised that I would not be able to change their conviction. Later, I began to wonder. Was it ridiculous? Did some people use the hospital to settle old scores? Surely not! But how would I know? It wasn't as if we carried out complex post mortems. Perhaps there were poisoners at work in the wards! Again, I marvelled at how quickly my sense of certitude was vanishing, when confronted with a different culture and another set of values. Although I almost persuaded myself that the rumour was only primitive folklore, I did occasionally wonder what would happen, if I myself offended a poisoner.

The local dispensary in Omugo was now proving to be a source of problems for me. It had no equipment and was isolated from specialist treatment centres. Often, when Dominique asked for help, it was for difficult cases requiring particular medical expertise. Usually, if he could not help a patient, neither could I. Even in Arua, facilities were very limited. They had a surgical team, but the only X-ray machine had been out of order for two years.

One night, I was awakened by one of the nurses, with a request to attend the dispensary. I had found a rather swish, solar-powered, hand lamp, by which eerie blue light I now pulled on my clothes, telling myself that it was just like being on call, back home in the NHS. But when I opened the door, there were four people waiting.

"What's wrong?" I asked, for they all looked decidedly spooked.

"Be careful of the ants," one of my guards warned me.

This seemed rather odd, because ants are an everyday fact of life in Africa. You get used to shaking them out of your clothes, your shoes, your hair and even your food. Then I looked down and saw advancing towards me, a thick column of ants, processing in a black ribbon of movement about 25cm wide. Luckily, it passed my door, but less fortunately, it was heading into the darkness towards Nadine's tukul. We watched its advance for a few seconds in respectful silence, then one of my guards said he would alert Nadine, in case the ants decided to march through, rather than around her bedroom. The next day, I learned that the column had passed straight through the hospital, patients being woken by painful bites on any exposed area of skin. However, since this was a known local phenomenon, they calmly picked up their blankets and went to sleep outside on the ground, near the hospital and out of the way of the column.

While the ants were disrupting our hospital wards, I was facing a much more troubling situation at the dispensary. As I approached, I could see, by the light of their kerosene lamps, a confused crowd of people shouting and crying, as they milled around on the verandah. Then I saw two bodies on the ground, one a boy of about fifteen, the other, perhaps twenty-five, both clearly the bloody victims of gunshot.

As I tried to save the young boy, he died and one of our nurses burst into tears. It was her brother.

"What happened to them?" I asked, quite shocked by the unexpected brutality.

"Armed men burst into their house and accused them of spying for the authorities. They shot them both. Afterwards, they discovered they were in the wrong house, so they apologised and left."

I could hardly believe what I was hearing. I now focussed on the second patient, dealing with entry and exit wounds and attempting to assess his internal damage.

"We carried them here during the night. It took us eight hours. They had a bit of pain and bled a lot," a man told me.

Given their injuries, this was an understatement, if ever I heard one. By now the second victim was in slightly better shape. He had a bullet wound in his stomach and an exit wound in his back, near his spine. Since he had told one of the nurses that he could not move his legs, I think he understood that he was probably paralysed, but there seemed no point in labouring that fact further at the moment. I needed to get him well enough to move to a hospital, where he could receive the necessary surgical care.

By 3am, his condition had improved, so I decided he was fit to travel to Arua, where he would need surgery for probable bowel damage. Alain appeared and we discussed whether or not it was safe to send the man in a car at night, since the last thing we wanted was for him to experience any further trauma. Normally we didn't move after dark, since the rebels tended to travel at night, but even although I had no experience of gunshot wounds, I was sure that a six-hour delay until morning would prove fatal. If possible, he should go immediately.

Once I made up my mind that he had to travel, the question was, who would go with him? Olema was away and if I left, there would be no medical back up at the hospital and some of the patients were in need of constant attention, so I must stay. I knew that. Nadine then joined us and immediately decided that she would go with the patient. She calmly set about organising his transfer to the car, packing medical supplies for the trip. As I watched them disappear into the darkness, I was concerned. It had been my decision to transfer the patient. I lay awake all night, wondering how I would feel if rebels decided to attack the car and kill them all.

Fortunately, their journey was uneventful, except that they lost two hours trying to persuade someone to open the hospital gate and find them a surgeon. The hospital was not set up to cope with night-time emergencies! It must have been very distressing for the man to be bounced over these rocky roads and then to lie bleeding in the car, whatever Nadine was able to do for him.

Two days later, a funeral cortege passed through the village and when I saw our young nurse in the procession, I expressed my surprise that they had not buried her brother sooner (as is the norm in Africa).

"The funeral is for the other man," I was told. "He died in Arua."

These deaths reminded us all that gunmen were our close neighbours and this topic returned to the top of our agenda. Over time, I had learned more about the complex history of rebels in Uganda, where in some areas they constantly threatened the population. In the East, were the Karamajong, who were primarily armed cattle raiders. In the Northeast there was the Lord's Resistance Army (LRA) and in the West the Allied Democratic Forces (ADF). Finally, around Arua, was the West Nile Bank Front (WNBF). These last two were politically motivated, but neither was averse to massacring the population, without any obvious reason.

In our area, the situation was complicated by a civil war, raging just over the border in South Sudan. Here, the Sudan Peoples' Liberation Army (SPLA) had been fighting for some twenty years against the Khartoum government, who wished to impose their Islamic rule on the Christian south. Khartoum accused Uganda of supporting the SPLA and Uganda accused Khartoum of aiding some of the Ugandan rebel groups, against the Museveni regime. This whole, horrendous mess meant there was a constant movement of armed men and refugees, travelling back and forth, creating havoc over a wide area. It was estimated that there were around 100,000 Sudanese refugees and about 250,000 Ugandan displaced persons, but no one really knew the numbers. (Refugees have moved across an international boundary, displaced persons or internally displaced persons (IDPs) have moved within their country of origin.)

Such disruption was a severe handicap for our programme; since we needed a stable population and freedom of access to all the villages where sleeping sickness occurred. We realised that many of our patients must have been involved in the conflict. Fortunately, we did not know who had done what and to whom. The fact that we were seen to be helping anyone who asked, probably gave us a considerable degree of protection. But other agencies working with people in the refugee camps had been threatened and some of their staff had been killed. It seemed that our project was seen as medical, rather than political. I prayed that this view would continue.

CHAPTER SIX

Critical times in Omugo

The return of Nadine and Sandra had dramatically improved our social lives, since they were both such good fun. The local staff had their domestic responsibilities when they finished work, so we expats relied on each other's company. It was also a delight to work with them, Nadine calm and supportive, Sandra lively and mischievous. Because Harriet was so competent, Nadine spent a lot of her time teaching the other nurses and fulfilling her role as team leader, which helped the mission to function successfully. Nadine's only difficulty was that her English was not very good. This fact handicapped her in the formal weekly meetings in Arua and also in her relations with military and civil authorities. I offered to help with some of these functions, but she would not agree. She may have seen me as interfering, but I only wanted to meet other people and to speak English for a while. Omugo offered little in the way of stimulation during my time off and once used to the routine, I welcomed any diversion.

Yet Uganda still had much to teach me. I will never forget the day the water-fetcher came into the courtyard, just as I began to eat lunch. He hovered at the doorway, in a manner that suggested he wanted to say something. Since he could not speak English, we asked Regina to translate.

"Can you see his son? He says he has been ill for a day or two."

"Yes, I'll be there in fifteen minutes, when I finish my food. Say that I'll see him in the pharmacy."

He left and we continued eating. Then, within a few minutes, the man re-appeared. I stood up, irritated that here, as in England, everyone wanted an emergency consultation to suit his or her personal schedule. But I paused at the door when the man spoke and waited for Regina to translate.

"It's okay, you don't need to see his son now."

It must have been something very trivial indeed, I thought, to myself, if the emergency had already passed.

"The child died," Regina added, totally without expression.

The water-fetcher then turned and left, also with no show of emotion, leaving me feeling utterly wretched.

The whole team tried to console me.

"If he was so sick, you would not have been able to do anything for him anyway."

"Life is like that, in Africa."

"You couldn't have known."

"I would have done just the same. There was nothing to suggest it was an emergency."

"Regina didn't say it was an emergency."

"He must have been at death's door already."

They were very kind, but it didn't help me and it didn't help the water-fetcher, or his wife. If I had been there, perhaps they would not have lost their child. In fact, it seemed so wrong that I was the one getting support and although I knew that there was in all probability nothing I could have done, still I felt guilty. For all doctors, "if only", is a concept that we need to come to terms with, if we are to remain sane. Particularly, I now realised, when we practise our medicine in remote, less organised parts of the globe.

Of course, this was not the last of my encounters with infant mortality and the different perception of what is possible in Africa. All our attitudes are conditioned by experience, culture, and upbringing. In Britain, I had worked in a paediatric ward, where the death of a child was a rare and catastrophic event, not only for the parents, but also for the staff. Here in Uganda, it was everyday stuff, something which "cannot be altered and so must be borne". I once heard a European propose that "it hurts less, because it happens so often", an opinion, which elicited a variety of vigorous responses from his listeners, but offered no real clarification of the issue for me. How can we know what others feel? How can we judge how others grieve? In Victorian times, death was more of an everyday occurrence in Britain, but we have no reason to believe that those people became hardened to its consequences. Why should we believe that in Africa, people take a child's death in their stride?

This very rarity of child death in Europe, has made the topic almost taboo, re-enforcing its status. In Omugo, women on average had eight or nine pregnancies. Often they had one or two miscarriages and a stillbirth, while one in five of the live-born died before their fifth birthday. Part of the reason for this high death rate, was that poverty-stricken families could not afford adequate food or medical care, but mothers did not want contraception, because they wanted to ensure that they were looked after in their old age. This practice is a deep-rooted part of their culture and any change will most likely take years to accomplish, so local medical staff not only expected, but accepted, a large number of infant deaths. The government, even if it was willing to try to change such social behaviour, was currently fighting just to survive. High infant mortality seems set to exist for many years to come. But Europeans should avoid feeling superior, for attitudinal change in a society is extremely difficult to achieve. The "smoking is dangerous" message has been publicised for years, but the reduction in the number of smokers is small.

Alain meanwhile, was devoting time to planning his farewell party. He did not have enough work to keep him occupied, so he was pleased to be coming to the end of his contract. His plans included a menu based on goat meat and a local gin called Waragi and he intended to invite all the hospital staff, some nearby village headmen and a few of the District's administrative staff.

Following my ward round on the morning of the party, I returned to the compound in time to see two goats being slaughtered and hung for the festivities. It was the first time I had witnessed the killing of animals to eat and it sickened me to see them held down and their throats sawn through methodically. Since I had to be on duty the next morning, I decided to make an early night of it, but I heard that the party was a success. Many of the staff had danced till 5am and I marvelled at their stamina, when they all managed to appear for duty at the appointed time. Alain left that morning, sorry to say goodbye, but hoping that his next assignment would be more challenging. Although in theory there should be a hand-over period between old and new team members, in practice this opportunity is often missed and Alain's replacement was not due to arrive, until four days later.

I eagerly offered to meet the new log, because I had not visited Arua since my arrival and it would be a treat to drive into town. Benoit was in his late thirties, of medium build and fair complexion. He had been a farmer in Normandy for most of his life and this was his first experience abroad. He was very enthusiastic about his new role.

"It will take a week or two to get used to the place and to understand the work, but it's good fun," I told him, as we made our way to Omugo.

"What exactly will my work be?" he asked.

"It's probably better if you let Nadine explain the detail. She is in charge; she has more experience of MSF and she has spent much longer in Omugo."

"There's not really a problem with security, is there? In Paris they said it was calm and peaceful, but in Kampala, Evan told me that the village had been attacked three weeks ago."

Benoit now seemed very anxious. I wondered what Evan had told him and explained what had happened, as calmly as possible.

"It's been very quiet since then and anyway, the rebels are not interested in us."

I had already persuaded myself that the policeman's murder was an isolated event. In fact, as long as the troubles stayed out of earshot, I found that most of the time I could forget about them, or at least control my anxiety sufficiently, to carry on working.

Unfortunately, around this time, the security situation began to deteriorate again. During the night, we heard more and more gunshots and then one morning, just after dawn, we awoke to the sound of mortar shells and machine-gun fire, coming from the direction of the mountains. It lasted about an hour and then we heard no more. Could the rebels be on the march and coming our way? There was no way of telling. As much as anything, it was the lack of information that was worrying. I could only imagine what the rebels were up to and found such speculation unhealthy.

We all endeavoured to work as normal, but over the next two weeks there were more and more reports of confrontations between the army and the rebels, all around Omugo. Every day or two, we noticed increased levels of gunfire and military helicopters occasionally flew overhead, towards what we presumed was a battle. Once, when the mayhem seemed to be getting very close, I climbed on to the roof of the bank, to see what I could make out. I felt a little daft up there, staring into the forest, while everyone else was going about their daily business, especially since the battle was about five kilometres away and only the occasional puff of smoke betrayed the origin of the noise.

I wasn't the only one to be spooked. Poor Benoit found the strain wore on his nerves more than the rest of us. After a while, I realised that we had all been in difficult situations before, while Benoit had never even been abroad, far less to a dangerous place. He spoke incessantly about the rebels, grasping at every morsel of news, as it worked its way around the village and into the hospital. As with Alain, there was not enough work to occupy him, so he had too much free time to spend in the village, talking to people. Were we targets because of our radios, drugs, cars or money, he wondered. Would they attack us, after we had been to the bank?

Whereas the rest of us could persuade ourselves that things would soon return to "normal", for Benoit, this was "normal" and he couldn't imagine an alternative. Not that the rest of us were indifferent to the situation. We communicated our news by radio to Kampala each day, constantly looking for advice, anything that would make us feel more secure. No one in Omugo was relaxed.

"There was more shelling yesterday and today, on both occasions from the direction of Wati," Nadine told Evan, during the morning radio contact. "It seems to be getting worse."

"Were there many people injured? Should MSF go and have a look, to see what's happening? Perhaps you could drive out there and see if you can help," Evan suggested.

His viewpoint was somewhat different from ours, probably because he was in Kampala, where no one was shooting.

"You don't seem to understand," Nadine told him firmly, "The shooting and the mortars are not somewhere else, they're just up the road a bit from the hospital. I'm not going to drive blindly into a battle, to wave the MSF flag about. I've no idea who's doing what to whom and how they feel about us. We didn't come here to go into a battleground; we came here to run a sleeping sickness hospital. They know we are here. If they bring any wounded to us, we will do our best for them, but we're not going out there to look for them."

We agreed with her. Out there, seemed less and less attractive. Every day, more refugees from the fighting passed through our village, all frantically looking for a safe haven. None of them stopped in Omugo.

Despite Benoit's worries, he did have his responsibilities as a log, even if these were not terribly taxing. And we now found out that he had a hobby; like many French people, he was interested in cooking. He decided to construct a large brick oven in the courtyard, next to the kitchen, which he assured us would enable the cook to bake a whole new selection of recipes, enriching our lives beyond measure. The chimney was wobbly, the bricks were uneven and none of the walls was straight, so it became known affectionately as "Benoit's Folly". Although not a huge success, this edifice did provide a few alternative dishes and more importantly, a welcome distraction at a time of stress.

One morning, Benoit arrived back from his errands, with news of two hundred rebels in Utumbari (the next village). Allegedly, they were preparing to attack Omugo. Increasingly, Benoit's stories affected us all, so we waited nervously to see what would happen next, endlessly exchanging information and gossip. Nadine had attended the United Nations High Commission for Refugees (UNHCR) security meetings, but this had not produced any concrete advice or information. Anyway, to maintain its neutrality, MSF preferred to be independent, especially from the UN.

After another day of gunfire, I suggested that we hold a meeting, to discuss openly what we knew and what we thought we should do. Nadine agreed, although she clearly thought I was overreacting.
"I want you all to say what you think of the situation." she began, "Then we can decide if we need to do anything immediately."
Sandra was unconcerned.
"I don't see any problem. Nothing's changed, has it?"
She has her head in the sand, I thought. How can she be so calm? There are armed men coming to Omugo and she doesn't think there's anything to worry about!
Benoit was a mass of anxiety and contradiction.
"We should leave immediately and go to Arua. I don't think we are a target. We are helping the community, but they may want our money and our drugs. They could attack us at any moment."

I found these issues difficult. I had much less experience of this environment than the two girls, but I was sleeping very badly and every small noise wakened me. I would lie in the dark for hours, listening intently, despite the fact that there was often nothing at all to hear. More importantly, the troubles were beginning to change the nature of our work.

"I think we need to analyse our position," I said. "We are here to run a long term programme, one that requires us to keep in contact with the local population. We need to move about freely and keep track of all the patients we treat, but the sleeping sickness assistants have fewer safe areas to visit, so we're not fulfilling our screening and re-treatment responsibilities. If the patients are in fear of their lives, they certainly won't come to hospital for treatment. Yesterday, the people from Kubala ran through Omugo, with their mattresses and stoves on their heads, all trying to get away from the battle area. One day they go south, the next day they go north. Meanwhile, we have fewer and fewer patients and we can't follow up on the people we treat. I'm not sure what we are achieving any more and I'm worried about the situation deteriorating. How will we deal with patients who are half way through their treatment, if we have to evacuate in an emergency?"

By saying it out loud, I think I had finally worked out what I felt. The rebels' activities were destroying the programme, so we had to make a provisional plan for abandonment, one that would take care of people in the midst of a course of drugs.

"But this is only temporary. It will all blow over in a few days, you'll see," repeated Sandra predictably.

"I think we should continue for the moment and see what happens over the next few days," was Nadine's final decision. "We shouldn't rush to abandon the project. Things might change."

Benoit made a final effort.

"That's all very well, but what happens if we are attacked? It won't help anyone if we're dead."

"I have decided. We'll review the situation in a few days," snapped Nadine and got up to leave.

She was beginning to feel pressurised by us all and I didn't blame her. There was no easy answer, but at least we had the chance to say what we were thinking. I was willing to wait for a few more days, when we could review the situation. As I left, Benoit pulled me to one side.

"I know its crazy, but I can't stop thinking about the rebels. I can't control it," he told me.

"I know how you feel. I am not relaxed either, but if we panic, it doesn't help us to make good decisions."

I explained about the time that rumour had persuaded us to leave for a night. I knew from that experience, how easy it was to do the wrong thing. We had to take our time over this decision to be sure we acted wisely.

"You know, as a foreign medical unit, we are not particularly at risk," I tried to reassure him. "If there was a definite danger, we would do something immediately. Nothing has really happened yet."

"I know, I know that logically, but it doesn't help," he mumbled, going off to his room.

I felt sorry for Benoit. It wasn't his fault that he had jumped into the middle of a difficult situation, for which he was not prepared. Now, it became hard for all of us to concentrate on the programme, as each day brought more sounds of fighting. Benoit became increasingly anxious. If only he had more work to take up his time, I think that would have helped. The girls and I still had plenty to do with patients during the day. It was only at night that I lay there, thinking about the distant gunfire.

Then, on the 5th September Nadine said she wanted to speak with me.

"I have decided to send Benoit back home. He's not happy and his anxiety is transmitting itself to us all. It's better that he goes home now. It's arranged."

I was surprised and wondered why she had not discussed it with me, even though I knew that staffing was not really part of my remit. Nadine was in charge and it was her job to make difficult decisions. Not only did she take her responsibilities seriously, she appeared quite sure of herself, without the need to talk with me. Benoit would leave on the following Monday, giving him a week to sort out his work. I decided not to say anything that might be construed as negative and made supportive sounds.

But Nadine had another decision to impart.

"You know, this is my third mission with MSF and I have had to evacuate from each one. I'm fed up with it and I'm going to stop. We can't do our job in conditions like this. These programmes need stability to function."

I agreed with her in principle, but still I wondered if we were over-reacting. After all, the whole point of MSF, was to work in difficult areas. Surely, that was what it was set up to do. But how could a long-term, public health programme be expected to work, if you couldn't see it through to the end? The problem continued to gnaw at my mind, with no real conclusion.

At least Benoit seemed relieved by Nadine's decision and he began to make preparations to complete his current tasks and go home. Nadine went to Arua the next day on routine business, but she reported more trouble on her return.

"At Owafa, we ran into a battle that seemed to be on both sides of the road. Bullets were falling near us and people were running in and out of the forest. It was not obvious what was happening, so we decided we might as well come on here, as go back."

This was bad news. The situation was undoubtedly getting worse and sure enough, the next day brought the gunfire nearer, so we organised another meeting. Now, it was impossible to ignore the fighting, or pretend that it might not affect us. Furthermore, we had to be sure of our supply-line to Arua. If our escape route was cut, our alternatives were unattractive. There were rebels to the north and the south, land mines on the roads to the northeast and no available boat, to take us down the Nile.

"There is no point in staying here to be killed. We should leave immediately," was Benoit's comment.

"Don't be stupid. No-one is going to be killed," Nadine told him. "The rebels only want to de-stabilise the government. They're not interested in a sleeping sickness hospital and foreign aid workers."

"What about the twelve Oxfam staff who were killed in the refugee settlement, just six weeks ago?" retorted Benoit.

"That was different. Oxfam is helping the refugees to stay in Uganda, whereas we treat hardly any refugees, because they have no cases of sleeping sickness."

"These rebels are just young thugs. I don't think they follow your sophisticated logic. Ideology is not their strong point," Benoit replied. "And what about the two young men they shot near here recently?" he added loudly.

Nadine asked my opinion.

"I think there are three factors to consider," I said. "Firstly, I am now really nervous all the time. Secondly, it is very difficult to run a public health programme when entire villages are running around like headless chickens. It makes the job quite impossible. But thirdly, and on the opposite side, I do not want to leave patients in the middle of their treatment. If someone should have a reaction after we left, I would feel terrible, even though in reality I could do little for them. If we could just get on with our work, it would make such a difference. But we can't work in the present circumstances. It's too dangerous."

Nadine remained silent, so I continued.

"I propose that we stop all treatment, gradually discharging people over the next six days, so that the hospital is empty before we leave. We should plan to return in one month and restart the treatments then, providing the situation has improved. That way, the current group of patients will not suffer and there is a chance of retrieving everything, if things go quiet."

Nadine finally agreed, saying that she would notify Evan of our decision. Except for Sandra, we all felt a great sense of relief, as this decision allowed us to escape, while assuaging our feelings of guilt. Benoit asked if he could stay to close the programme, as we would all be leaving, but Nadine had decided. Benoit would leave early, as arranged. He was upset, but in her defence, Nadine was under a lot of pressure. Making the decision to "evacuate" a programme, is a great responsibility. She felt badly about it, but didn't have the time to worry about his feelings. So although I felt sympathy for Benoit, I said nothing on his behalf, deciding that it was important to support Nadine. I would try to talk to Benoit in private.

Despite our mixed feelings, there was a silly, end of term cheerfulness, as we went back to work. It was probably an expression of relief. We had not realised that we had been under quite so much pressure. Now, whatever we felt about the work, we were all glad to be leaving Omugo, relieved to escape from the tension and pleased that we could withdraw in an organised fashion. Yet, as darkness approached each night, I felt the tension mounting. Each day I went round the wards, explaining to patients our plan for the end of their treatment. Some were undergoing their third, or even fourth treatment and their outlook was grim, whether they continued or not. One boy was just waking up from a coma and I hoped that what we had done, would see him through until we could restart his treatment. Running down the hospital made us all feel guilty. We were doing what we thought was best, but was it? No one could give us any answers.

Nadine went to Arua to inform the authorities of our decision. When she met the military, they reacted aggressively, suggesting that we were cowards for leaving. However, she then learned that the Red Cross office in Arua had been attacked and burgled by armed men. Even more significantly, the Oxfam team, who worked about fifteen kilometres from us, had evacuated to Arua three weeks earlier. We felt a bit better knowing others had taken the same decision, but each of us remained silently guilty, avoiding talking about feelings. Really, there wasn't anything to say. To make things worse, there were no further battles for a day or two, so we began to doubt our decision. Finally, all the packing was completed, and our hospital materials were placed in a steel container, which was welded shut and left in the compound. We guessed that the rebels would not have the time, or capacity, to break it open.

The last night was quiet and in the morning, we made preparations for an afternoon departure. Around 11am, there was loud and continuous gunfire from Kubala, just up the road. A man came in to see us, reporting that twenty rebels had been looting the market and they were now coming this way, shooting randomly. We advanced our plans hurriedly and set off with unseemly haste in less than forty minutes, constantly looking back, over our shoulders. The journey back to Arua was uneventful, if tense and I spent most of the time in morose introspection. Was I a coward, retreating again, or had I simply made a rational decision? Round and round it went in my head. Whose interest was I serving: mine, the patients' or those of MSF? The programme would almost certainly never resume if the hospital was attacked and we were killed. This way, it had a chance to reopen. But what did the patients and the local staff think?

During my time as a GP, there had often been important decisions to make, but these had been based on specific information, experience, or shared opinion. More importantly, there had been on hand professional guidelines and expert second opinions. Here, I felt as if I was on quicksand. For the first time, I was not sure where the right course lay. Perhaps, there was no right course?

We spent the night in the Afro Triangle, a small hotel in Arua and the next morning, we were booked on the plane to Kampala. We parked our vehicles with Mr Choudray, a prominent Asian businessman. Somewhat surprisingly, he had been a good friend of Idi Amin, the despot famed for expelling all Ugandan Asians and appropriating their assets. While waiting for our delayed flight, I met a BBC journalist, who asked what was happening. Although I gave her a résumé of our experiences, I asked her not to implicate MSF in any story, since I had been told to be cautious in my dealings with the press. Significantly, we also met some Jesuit nuns who had been working for many years to the south of us, in the Rhino Camp refugee settlement. Several of the Sudanese people there had been hacked to death with machetes. The nuns were leaving and had no plans to return.

The guesthouse in Kampala was just as grim and unwelcoming as before, doing nothing to alleviate our communal gloom, although it did help when we met up with other aid workers from Action Contre la Faim, at a local restaurant. We three now felt uncomfortable in our own company and welcomed the opportunity to forget our problems in the presence of strangers. The next day, we heard via the radio, that rebels had entered Omugo. They had broken into the bank, ransacked the pharmacy and stolen some drugs. A shopkeeper who had watched them, received a beating for his temerity, but no one else had been hurt. This news did little to resolve our difficulties, however, and the atmosphere in Kampala was terrible. We avoided talking to one another and it didn't help that Evan was preoccupied by a staff strike, in Adjumani, the second sleeping sickness programme. Sandra and Nadine began to express the feeling that the Kampala team had not given us sufficient support. I felt that we required a debriefing, to try to exorcise some of our demons.

This meeting was a disaster. We mulled over the facts of what had happened, but no one expressed any emotion. I decided to try to start the ball rolling, since I was sure that we were all feeling the same sort of things, even if we expressed it differently.

"I feel badly about leaving the patients without support, even though logically, I think we did the right thing."

Silence.

"I feel I might have acted differently, if I'd had more experience."

Silence.

I knew that it would be better if we worked out our feelings of guilt and fear together, but I couldn't persuade the others to talk. Perhaps they didn't feel as I did? I'll never know, for Nadine and Sandra left Kampala and flew home to France and we never met again.

I hope and imagine that they assimilated the experience and managed to adjust. Possibly I was the only one who found the aftermath so stressful. In retrospect, what helped me most of all, was the fact that I still had four months of an MSF mission to serve and after a few days, I began to think about my future. There had been a suggestion that I might transfer to Afghanistan, but the Taliban had recently captured the capital, Kabul and all projects in that country were now on hold.

"What have you in mind for me?" I asked Evan, after a few more days of rest. "Can you find something for me in Uganda?"

"I think you should now go back to Arua. I'd like to find out what happened to the material we left in Omugo and about the attack on the bank. MSF has a lot invested in the sleeping sickness programme and we have to try to carry on, somehow. We have a big grant from the European Development Fund (EDF) who now expect results, unless security issues make it impossible for us to continue."

"Okay. I'm happy to go back and make some enquiries," I told him. "I'll leave on Monday."

"Our other partners in the EDF project are trying to work to the north of us, in Yumbe and Koboko and the Save the Children project has been on standby for the last ten months. You should talk to Dr Bua, who is their representative in Arua," said Evan. "He may have more information."

So I flew back to Arua on the 10th October and booked into the Afro Triangle hotel, at six dollars per night! There was no running water and no electricity, just a bed and a tiny table. It was less comfortable than Omugo had been, but fine for a few days and it had the distinct advantage that no one was shooting nearby. Washing was arranged by carrying a twenty-litre jerry can of water into my room and sloshing myself with a cup and basin, in a designated corner. In the morning, the water was a little cold, but by the evening it had heated up and was quite pleasant.

The hotel staff were young, friendly and incompetent, but that didn't matter too much, except that on the first morning it took them about forty minutes, to boil water for my tea. From then on, I walked one hundred metres to the bus and taxi-park, where the "restaurants" were already in full swing, serving early travellers. The speciality was tea, made with very strong ginger and accompanied by fried savoury flour balls called mandazi, a cross between a doughnut and a croissant. These establishments were set up each morning and removed every night. If I was up early enough, I would watch the women passing my hotel, each carrying her "restaurant" on her head: a table, two chairs, some food, plus a brazier of burning charcoal. At the taxi-park, they asked for help with their dangerous load and then they were set up and functioning. The whole process took two minutes flat. It was a most remarkable performance.

A more disturbing aspect of my morning view from the hotel, was the number of passers-by who had suffered from polio. One in particular both impressed and distressed me. A man of about thirty, he "walked" by putting sandals on his hands and his knees, moving with his withered, lower legs cocked up in the air behind him. Another had a pelvis so wasted, that he could walk on his hands, swinging his legs and bottom beneath him. He had huge powerful shoulders and made good speed. I wondered if I could persuade MSF to establish an orthopaedic surgery programme here. There is so much to be done, so much illness and disability everywhere.

My first official task in Arua, was to see the District Medical Officer, Dr Imoko. I had met this very polite and extremely competent man once before. Like all members of the Dinka tribe, he was very tall. His speech was slow and considered and he had an occasional broad smile that lit up his face and inspired instant confidence. I decided that he must have made some enemies in the Government, as he obviously had the capacity to progress well beyond Arua. We discussed the security position and since he was not very optimistic about the next six months, he suggested that we set up our treatment programme in Arua hospital. The superintendent had done his PhD on sleeping sickness and Dr Imoko was sure he would be sympathetic. He was also convinced that the patients would travel to Arua, if they knew that MSF was still running the programme.

And so it turned out. The superintendent allowed us to use one of his wards and we contacted our staff, who quickly reappeared. The first few days we had five patients, two weeks later we had twenty-five and soon we were back to our habitual forty. Now I reduced the number of nurses, as we always had far more than was required in Omugo. Setting up a new programme is always a difficult task and I was involved in less and less clinical work, as I endeavoured to establish this new base with good medical standards. At the start, the most pressing issue was to recover the drugs we had left in Omugo. So a lorry was hired and I was able to transfer our medical supplies to a room lent by Dr Bua, the doctor in charge for Save the Children UK. He had been waiting for ten months to start his own community-based programme of vaccination, in the North. Unfortunately, there was a wasp's nest in this room, so that every time I moved stock, it became a hazardous affair, as I react badly to wasp stings. I found the best plan (when the wasps became agitated) was to stand quite still until they settled. The rebels had not stolen very much when they raided our pharmacy in Omugo, and I was able to order missing items from Kampala. It was satisfying for me to re-establish the programme with so little delay. I was finding my new role interesting.

In addition to my medical commitment, I had now started to attend the UNHCR security meetings. These were a good point of contact and I was amazed to discover that a large group of Europeans and several hundred local staff were involved in looking after the many refugee settlements. They represented a wide range of organisations, mostly funded and controlled by the UN and like us, they were practically all on standby to return to their posts. Only an Italian surgeon and his wife were still working in Yumbe, a dangerous area near the Sudanese border.

The UNHCR had declared the Arua district, as a "level 4 security zone", meaning that only essential work was permitted, such as supplying food and medicines to the camps. No families remained in the area and everyone kept a bag packed, in case of emergency evacuation. The situation was complicated by events in neighbouring Zaire, only ten kilometres away from Arua, where Laurent Kabilas' troops had moved north, en route for Kisangani. Eight thousand soldiers were now stationed in Aru, a small town just over the border and although it made no sense that they would come into Uganda, uncertainty raised the general tension. This information, together with the fact that we had restarted our programme in Arua, persuaded me that we had done the right thing in leaving Omugo.

Access to a new network of people was stimulating and I found that the best source of news was the evening beer session, at the White Rhino Hotel. From around 6pm, expatriates would gather to chat and swap any new information that had come in from their projects. The NGOs covered all the important areas, including their access roads and despite the programmes being on hold, there was usually someone who sent in news. One unusual source of information was Andrew, a post-graduate anthropology student from Oxford University, who was completing his PhD. He had spent a year reading extensively about the area and had now come to live in a local village, to learn the language and complete his fieldwork. His topical thesis was, "The Origins of Violence in the West Nile"! Although Andrew spent most of his days sitting in the Continental Hotel drinking coffee or beer, he was living in another hotel, home to most of the military personnel seconded to this area to combat the rebels. His contacts made him such an amazing source of information, that even the army asked him for advice. We spent hours chatting and swapping books and I heard that his chosen village was subject to frequent attacks, the houses burned and the people beaten, or killed. I suspect that Andrew never got round to living there.

Another of the interesting people I met in the White Rhino Hotel, was Anthea, an English nurse who had worked for Oxfam in the Rhino Camp settlement. She had been kidnapped by a group of rebels and used as a hostage, to enable them to cross the Nile to safety. Furthermore, twelve of her colleagues had recently been killed in an ambush. Not surprisingly, she was visibly disturbed by these events. Having now been on standby for five months, Anthea was waiting to go home, unhappy about resigning, but knowing that for her there was no possibility of going back.

From these various sources, I was able to keep a record of events in the district: the looting, the burning of houses, the military battles, the abductions and the killings. As my record grew, I could not believe that we would quickly be returning to Omugo.

CHAPTER 7

Land mines are inevitable

The sleeping sickness programme was now established in Arua and I was pleased to be joined by Yan, the new log for the mission. Since he had a strong administrative background, we agreed to share logistic duties and our first task was to find accommodation. So Yan looked around for a few days, before deciding to rent a house on the outskirts of town. Then we made a quick trip back to Omugo, to recover some furniture and other materials, so that we could move in. For me, the best part was that we had our own generator and water supply, which seemed like heaven, after six weeks of the "cup and basin" washing routine. The house was comfortable, with a small garden and idyllic roof terrace. However, when we put it to the test, we discovered this location was too hot until twilight, when swarms of mosquitoes then made it intolerable!

The land below the house sloped down to a small stream which served as the local water supply, washhouse and bathing area for anyone who could not afford piped water, in essence most of our neighbours. On the opposite side of the stream, lay another of Arua's suburbs and a different route into town, but when I walked there in the evenings I felt awkward, since there were no clearly defined paths and I seemed obliged to walk through private gardens. There was no alternative to this act of trespass, which would have been less embarrassing, if the houses had not been so close together. Often, I found myself passing within a few feet of a front door. I asked Harriet how to resolve this problem and she explained that as long as you called out, "hello" to the household, it was okay to cross someone's land.

In this suburb, straw-roofed, mud tukuls were dotted haphazardly all over the place. Each was surrounded by an area of bare earth, kept tidy and swept daily by the young woman of the house, her broom leaving distinctive swirl patterns in the red-brown dirt. I was told that it was necessary to keep these areas clear, to deter snakes. Without being instructed, our guardians swept our ground and kept the grass short for the same reason. Despite this attention, a snake was killed every few weeks in the compound and there would be great discussion about just how venomous it had been. I was fairly sure that a lot of this chat was exaggerated gossip, until Harriet told me that she had once been bitten by a snake and had almost died. Suddenly, it seemed judicious to walk with a little more attention, particularly in gloomy, overgrown areas and at dusk.

The number of patients in the hospital had risen to a satisfactory level, but I noticed that in the main, we were treating people who had been discharged before our evacuation of Omugo. Since I anticipated that we would be based in Arua for a while, I wanted to encourage a "business as usual" approach. The illness would not be taking a holiday, simply because we had moved from our original location. I then realised that lack of transport was an impediment to persuading new patients to come from Omugo, so I decided to organise a twice-weekly, patient bus service, at irregular times, so that the rebels would not get to know our schedule and be tempted to attack. It might be difficult, but if the sleeping sickness assistants (who were still living in Omugo) were willing to co-operate, I was confident it would work. At that time we had two pick-up trucks, which were certainly not suitable for transporting patients, so I requested two ambulances from Kampala, in exchange for one of our pick-ups. With two vehicles, we could run a reliable service.

Needless to say, we received only one ambulance in return for our pick-up, but I decided to launch the service anyway. Before each trip, I contacted the security chief in Arua, to check whether he thought there were rebels in the area. This man was always charming and helpful, sometimes even giving us a warning to wait. I was impressed with his directness and confidence, if somewhat surprised, when eight months later he was arrested for being a rebel sympathiser! The army found a large stock of ammunition, rifles and land mines in his house. It was only then that we understood the basis of both his confidence and accuracy concerning local security information, but I was glad that he had been on our side and keen that we should continue our programme.

Just as we seemed to be making a little progress, security conditions deteriorated in the north. Messages started to arrive from Koboko, a town close to both the Sudanese and Zaire borders, saying that there were now many more refugees arriving every day. To make matters worse, the increase in rebel activity meant that all aid organisations in the area were leaving, just when they were most needed. Many cases of diarrhoea were reported and as this was an area known to be at risk from both dysentery and cholera, an increase in refugees could be disastrous. Evan decided to come to Arua, so that we could go on a short, fact-finding visit together. Although in agreement with him, I did feel a little anxious, since there had been several land mines reported on the road north and we had been told that all the local bridges had recently been badly damaged by rebels. I prepared carefully for this expedition, packing a variety of drugs and other materials that might be useful as donations to health units. We were always wary not to impinge on the "territory" of other aid organisations, but if they were pulling out, we presumed there was less call for diplomacy.

On the day of our departure, I phoned the Red Cross Federation base in Koboko, to check on the current security situation. Asa, my usual contact, was not there, so unfortunately I had to speak with someone I didn't know.

"Is there any problem about staying the night in Koboko? We are planning a visit to assess the current health needs."

"No problem," said my unknown informer.

"You're quite sure the road is okay," I pressed.

"As far as we know, there are no problems. We had a car go down to Arua about thirty minutes ago and have heard nothing negative since then."

So it seemed that the route was fine. But to be sure, just before we left we obeyed standard procedure and called at the taxi-park, to see if the drivers there had any further news. The taxi drivers assured us that cars had passed through Arua several times that day and no one had reported anything amiss, so it was in a positive mood that we finally set off at about 10am with Ben, our driver. We crossed the first bridge without any problems, but the second was badly damaged, so we got out to give Ben some guidance. There were only narrow wheel tracks remaining for him to drive on, leaving no room for mistakes. Then, after the third bridge, I saw four neat holes in the ground, two on either side of the road, about a wheel track's distance apart. I glanced at Ben, to confirm what I was thinking.

"Land mines?" I tried to make it sound like a normal, everyday enquiry.

"Yes" he replied, "but don't worry. The local people have already spotted them and they will have informed the army. If we see any broken branches placed on the road, it is probably the same thing. I know what to look for."

I was glad that he felt relaxed, but that didn't stop me from feeling somewhat apprehensive. We stopped to discuss the situation for a bit, but then decided to continue, since we were only six kilometres from Koboko. There was other traffic on the road, so the locals could not have been unduly worried, but it was fair to say that we were no longer relaxed.

Fifteen minutes later, we arrived safely at Koboko. First, I decided to visit Asa, to check that all was well. It was difficult to persuade the guard to let us into the Red Cross compound and when we were finally allowed past the gate, we found the place deserted, except for the administrator. He explained that Koboko had been shelled by rebels from an emplacement inside Zaire, both this morning and the previous night. All the Red Cross staff had been evacuated and because of the danger, he could not let us stay in the compound without authorisation. He suggested that we try the hotel in town! By now I was feeling decidedly annoyed about the message that I had received from my mysterious, early morning informant.

I was exasperated by the administrator's unhelpful attitude and it was now too late to return to Arua that night. Anyway, the whole point of the trip had been to find out about this area, so we would remain, although we still had to find somewhere to sleep. Then I remembered that the Red Cross was represented in Koboko, both by its Federation and by its International Committee and I knew one of the ICRC delegates. So we set off in the direction of their compound, one that they had inherited from MSF. We found Jean and Sven, now living there alone and they seemed pleased to have visitors. Jean showed us to our tukuls and explained where everything was.

"If there is any more shelling, go straight to one of the bunkers over there in the corner. You won't be alone, as we'll be there before you. We've had plenty of practice." He smiled ruefully. "They're not very comfortable, but neither is a mortar shell landing on your tukul. They're aiming at the army camp just behind the compound, by the way. So far, they've been quite inaccurate, but you never know, we might just get unlucky."

On balance, it wasn't the most positive welcome I had ever received, but that was hardly Jean's fault. We survived the night and over lunch the next day, we asked Jean about the local health situation.

"Have you heard anything about an outbreak of diarrhoea, or any new refugee activity?" I began.

"We're trying to assess what, if anything, we might need to do here," Evan added. We were careful not to sound as if we were muscling in on the area.

"ICRC are handling the food distribution for refugees, so I have some information about that, but I don't know much about the health issues. There's a lot of refugee movement just now, because the rebels keep threatening the camps. Everyone seems to run back and forth over the same bit of land, desperately trying to escape harassment and at the moment, one of our camps is completely empty. Overall, numbers are increasing. We never know where we are from one week to the next, so it's difficult to assess the actual need," Jean told us.

Evan and I decided to go into town ourselves. We visited the public dispensary, which reported that it had no particular problems at the moment; no more diarrhoea than normal and no deaths from sickness. That at least, was comforting. But as we talked, there was a distant whump and the nurse said

"Another land mine; if they are still alive, they will be here in an hour or two."

We moved on to the church dispensary, run by a nun called Sister Betty. It was about three kilometres out of town, in the direction of the refugee camps. She confirmed that there had been about thirty cases of children with diarrhoea, but no deaths as yet. We left her some supplies and wished her well. Ten days before our visit, a gunman had come into the ward and shot four of her patients. Since there was no apparent reason for the attack, she had assumed it was an attempt to close the clinic, by dissuading refugees. She could not now get anyone to work for her, so she continued bravely, alone.

When we returned to the compound, Jean informed us that Red Cross trucks, used to deliver water to the refugee camps, had been targeted that afternoon. Now, he had no option, but to suspend the work for a day or two, because his drivers were too afraid to make the journey. Despite all this bad news, we had a pleasant evening, eating outside and enjoying each other's company. True, most of the conversation was about the refugees and about Uganda's problematic relationship with South Sudan, but at least we were able to discuss these issues in peace. As we went off to bed, Jean reminded us cheerily about the bunkers. Luckily, that night there was no shelling and as I drifted off to sleep, I could hear Jean playing some appropriately mournful jazz on his saxophone.

The next morning after breakfast, we thanked our hosts for their hospitality and set off for Arua, taking Jean's advice to have a word with the military security chief, before we left town.

"Is it safe to travel to Arua today?" I asked.

"No problem," he assured me most positively, "the road was checked this morning."

"What about mines?" I was not quite so trusting this time.

"Ah" he said, waving his arms expansively "land mines are inevitable; we can't do anything about them. If you drive on our roads, you will encounter mines."

It is an uncomfortable feeling, sitting in the front passenger seat of a pick-up truck, knowing that if you were to hit a land mine, it would probably be the front nearside wheel that would sustain the blast. The explosion would then come up through the floor and hit you in the backside. Most of the mines used in Uganda at this time were of the antipersonnel variety, which damaged vehicles, but left you with a good chance of surviving the blast. The greater danger came from the resulting traffic accident. Slow and careful driving was in order, we stressed to Ben, who seemed amused by our anxiety. Extreme care however, also made the journey seem endless.

Following our routine report to Paris, Evan was reprimanded for not taking the security situation more seriously. We were told that we should have confirmed the reliability of our information! Six weeks later, I made a similar trip with an MSF "security expert" and I was gratified to note that he had no more success than we did, when using MSF designated guidelines. On the positive side, these excursions gave us a first-hand view of the problems, enabling us to gauge risk factors more realistically and helping us to make informed decisions, both about the refugees and our future programmes in the area.

After this trip, which I found quite stressful at times, I was surprised to find that I felt elated. It seemed stupid, but I was oddly pleased with myself and looked forward to further adventures with an element of risk. Life seemed more real, more relevant, when you were facing up to danger. In retrospect, I realised that we had achieved almost nothing, but it all seemed strangely worthwhile, once we were back at base. Now, I began to recognise the "cowboy" element that I had noted in other MSF people and was surprised to find it in myself. Previously, I had considered myself to be healthily risk averse.

MSF recognises this tendency and has developed quite strict rules of conduct, to try to avoid disasters amongst the more "gung-ho" of its workers. The organisation knows there is a fine line between having sufficient guts to be at the sharp end and having the wit not to take unnecessary risks, once you are there. Mind you, as with any set of rules, they can have ridiculous implications. Some time later, when I was working in Haiti, my girlfriend drove me to the beach, because MSF did not allow me to drive on certain roads.

During the evacuation of Omugo, we had felt that more logistical help would have been useful. Of course there had been a problem in justifying this to Kampala, as it had been Nadine herself who had sent Benoit off for, "an early bath". In Arua, however, we now had the opposite problem, a plague of logistic officers. In addition to Yan, four different logs visited in succession, each with his own agenda, his own correct way of doing things and his own strong personality. The radio antenna was put up and taken down, three times in two weeks, even though it had worked before any of them arrived. Irritatingly, we found that each enthusiast felt obliged to correct the imagined errors of his predecessor.

Not that Yan was complaining, because he said that each new person had something to teach him and he had enough common sense to ignore anything that he didn't like. But for me, there was a problem with this raft of technical help — I spent three weeks walking to and from the hospital, since there never seemed to be a car available. It wasn't that I minded the exercise, but for some journeys, I really needed a car. All our vehicles were required by the logs, for vital new activities. Finally, I cracked.

"I need a car for the hospital, today if it's not too much trouble". Blank stares and indignant resentment, were the immediate response. For the hospital!

"We need to set things up correctly. Security is important, you know.

It takes time to do everything properly. You can't rush these things." I contained my irritation, only slightly.

"Look, we've been three weeks without a backup car and now I have no car at all. I've got to have transport for the hospital."

"You only had to ask," said Fredo.

I went away, thinking I had made my point. Yet, nothing changed; it was as if the hospital had become a mere distraction to the logistical work.

Then, six weeks after my visit to Koboko, a new security adviser called Pascal arrived in Kampala. Evan intimated that Pascal wanted to visit Arua, to evaluate MSF strategy regarding the growing refugee problem.

"He will want to visit both Koboko and Yumbe, so you must go too, as he can't evaluate medical needs."

Despite the short rush of adrenaline after my last trip, I was not entirely thrilled with this idea. There had been several vehicle attacks recently and I knew that land mines were still found regularly. On the other hand, the sleeping sickness programme was running well at the moment and did not require my constant attention. So I warned Ben that we would be returning to Koboko and made sure that I had plenty of extra supplies to take with us.

Pascal duly arrived and immediately swung into action, repositioning the radio antenna and explaining that we should always use two vehicles together.

"It's for security," he said. "If one hit a mine, the other would be just behind, ready to help," he explained. "The presence of two vehicles will dissuade the rebels," he assured me.

This policy had been picked up from the International Red Cross, but I didn't think it was very practical in our situation, as we only had two vehicles, one of which was always required for the sleeping sickness programme. I mentioned to Pascal that for six weeks, there had only been one vehicle and that in poor condition.

"If we constantly commandeer the "ambulance", we won't have a sleeping sickness programme," I explained.

So we set off on our trip to Koboko with just one pick-up, checking ahead about the security situation. I also contacted Jean by radio, to ask if we could avail ourselves of his hospitality.

"Delighted to see you," he crackled. "We don't get much company up here now, not since all the other organisations left."

That sounds most encouraging, I thought; but if he was still there, the situation couldn't be too bad, I told myself. There was still only one possible road, so we retraced the same route of broken and barely passable bridges. I was surprised, when our trip was interrupted at almost exactly the same spot as before, at the third bridge. As we crested the hill, we saw in the distance a column of marching, uniformed men. Ben confirmed that they were soldiers, not rebels, so we decided to continue, although more slowly than before.

Then Pascal spoke.

"They seem to have stopped in the middle of the road. I think there's something happening ahead."

We caught up with them and a soldier motioned to us to get out of the car, asking if one of us was a doctor. I got out the emergency kit and followed him up the road, to where a man was lying face up, with two small bullet wounds in his chest. He was dead, from a sniper attack that had happened just a few minutes before our arrival.

I was in the middle of explaining that there was nothing I could do, when I noticed that most of the soldiers were now crouched down defensively in the ditches that ran on either side of the road. We were still standing out in the open, alone and exposed. I quickly decided that it was a rather poor idea to offer myself up quite so blatantly as the next rebel target, so Pascal and I speedily scrambled down to join the soldiers in the ditch. From this position, we discussed what we should do next, now that we knew for certain that there were snipers along the route. It didn't take us long to decide to go back where we had come from.

However, as we were turning our pick-up, a young soldier jumped in with us, motioning violently with his rifle at Ben, while speaking vehemently in a local language. The boy was clearly insisting that we turn round again and head with him, to Koboko. Through Ben, we argued for what seemed like an eternity, the MSF vehicle straddled across the road, in no position to go either forward, or back. Since the soldier was carrying a rifle, we wanted him out of the car as quickly as possible. One of the guiding principles of MSF is "no guns in the vehicles". I reflected however, that it was rather a pity that they didn't also give advice, about what to say when a gun is pointed directly up your nose by a young, excitable soldier. In my opinion, it certainly gave one of the protagonists an unfair bargaining position. Finally, a senior soldier approached, with the information that the gunmen had fled back in the direction of Maracha and that the road ahead would now be safer. Reluctantly, but with no alternative, we drove on to Koboko behind the military vehicles, having at least managed to decant our armed friend.

Despite our safe arrival in Koboko, there was a legacy from this incident. We now felt vulnerable to attack, an uncomfortable feeling that remained with us, long after we had parted company with the soldiers. The rest of the day was spent repeating all the visits of six weeks before. I was relieved to find that Sister Betty was still there, having experienced no repetition of her earlier troubles. We left her more medical supplies and wished her well. Having finished in Koboko, we drove on to Yumbe, a forty-five minute journey that was considered to be more dangerous, since it was a quieter route, crossed regularly by rebels. On arrival, we went straight to see the Italian doctors, Consuela and Antonio, finding them apprehensive, since their hospital had been attacked the day before. Fortunately, the army had arrived in time to repel the rebels and no one had been hurt. The staff felt that the motivation for the attack was that the hospital helped both refugees and government soldiers. With soldiers as patrons, there could be no doubt that this place would remain a prime rebel target.

We asked what they knew of the local refugee problem, but they were not able to give us much information. In fact, they were so busy in surgery, they rarely left the hospital. Then I asked if they had seen any cases of sleeping sickness. Consuela thought there were always a few around, although she was not really sure. The hospital only had a small stock of expired Pentamidine and no Arsobal at all, so the staff were not motivated to look for cases. I had a quick glance at the ward and spoke with the sister in charge, who told me they had one confirmed patient at that time, although there had been others recently. She explained that since the previous aid organisation left, people had lost their confidence in sleeping sickness treatment.

I offered to send them some drugs and began to consider how we could treat more sleeping sickness patients in this area. First of all, we needed to know how many patients there might be every month, so that we could assess if it was worthwhile to establish a base. I asked Consuela to find the previous year's figures for me, even though I knew she already had enough on her plate. Soon after my return, the information arrived in Arua. We sent some drugs, but unfortunately it was to be five more years before security conditions allowed MSF to establish a sleeping sickness programme in that particular area.

We set off once more and found the "new" Sudanese refugees, camped just outside Yumbe, on the road to Omugo, possibly as many as 7000 people. We stopped to talk and found to our surprise that quite a few spoke good English. They had been driven out of the settlement camps of Rhino, Bidi-Bidi and Ikafe, having been attacked several times by different rebel groups. At first they were threatened and told that if they did not go back to Sudan, the rebels would return and burn their houses. They tried sitting it out, but the rebels did return and as promised, burned many homes. Their parting words had been, "Next time, if you are still here, we will kill you".

Not surprisingly, the refugees believed them and accordingly fled, but not back to Sudan. Feeling protected by an army presence, they had now been outside Yumbe for about seven days, but they were running out of food. There were only two water taps, no toilets and no shelters. It was a recipe for disaster.

We chatted about the problem and Pascal said,
"No one is doing anything here, so we must help. There is a UNHCR presence so we must contact them first".
"Why do we need to talk to UNHCR?" I asked.
"Because they have an agreement with the government and they are mandated to help refugees and displaced people. We can't just decide to jump in, without contacting them. One of the things that goes wrong in emergencies, is that people start doing things, without co-ordination. It can be worse than doing nothing."
I felt that since no one seemed to be doing anything, co-ordination was not an issue.

We found the UNHCR representative and asked him what was happening.
"These people have already been chased from two of our sites," he told us. "But we cannot respond to their needs, if they keep moving. Each time, it means new tents, toilets and distribution services, not to mention rehabilitating buildings like dispensaries. We can't do that every couple of weeks."

"But you can see their point of view. They can't stay around waiting to be killed," I pointed out.

"True, but it's completely unmanageable if they keep moving. There is also the problem that any new camp established here, would upset the population of Yumbe. There would be conflict, since there is a shortage of land and not enough water. These refugees must go back to their original settlements. It's the only way we can help them. I will ask if the army could provide more men to protect them."

It was an impasse. The refugees were justifiably afraid. They had a choice between returning to the camps and possibly being attacked, or staying where they were, with no food, shelter or water, not to mention the possibility of trouble with the local people. And there was another issue. There was nothing to stop the rebels from coming here to attack them, for there was only a limited army presence in Yumbe. In fact, it seemed that there was no real guarantee of safety for them, anywhere in Uganda.

Faced with such a complex problem I felt a bit lost and suggested to Pascal that we should contact Paris and Kampala, when we got back, to see if they had any idea about what we should do.

"I think there is nothing that we can do for the moment," Pascal said. "We should talk to the authorities in Arua while we keep an eye on the situation here, to see how it develops. It's unlikely that they will send more soldiers to protect Sudanese refugees, since they don't seem to have enough to protect Ugandans. But we can try to persuade them." I was quite depressed by the feeling of impotence, in the face of so much complex need. We drove back to Arua via Omugo, completing a circular route, all the while keeping our eyes skinned for anything unusual. It was a considerable relief to approach familiar territory, butOmugo itself looked sad and deserted, bringing back memories of the way it had been abandoned.

We arrived in Arua just before sunset and as the evening wore on, I began to think of the many questions that I had failed to ask, both in Koboko and in Yumbe. Fear, especially the threat of land mines and snipers, had hampered my ability to think clearly. My respect for Sister Betty and the Italian couple increased considerably. They were functioning every day, in an unrelenting climate of uncertainty and fear.

Pascal returned to Kampala to make his report, but the trip left me with a terrible feeling of frustration. We had seen people in need of protection, yet we had done nothing to help them. "Keeping an eye on the situation," appeared to mean ignoring immediate need, while waiting to see if things got worse. I know that you must view things from a wider perspective, that you must have proper assessment and analysis, but I had not realised that doing nothing would be so difficult, when in the midst of such obvious distress.

During much of this time, Evan was occupied by events in Kasese, a small but important town in the West of Uganda near the Zaire border. Here, the ADF rebels had attacked various villages, including Kasese itself and the resulting population displacement, had led MSF to become involved in opening yet another Ugandan mission. I realised that there were too many things going on at once and we were limited by resources. We did not have any spare staff in Uganda and vehicles that could have been used in Arua, now had to be sent to Kasese.

There was of course, work to be done in Arua. We had been there for two months, and the sleeping sickness programme was established and known in the local community. Thanks to the transport scheme, those who lived in sleeping sickness areas were able to get to us, once they knew they were ill. We still felt that insufficient numbers of early cases were attending for screening, so as an interim measure, we decided to introduce a testing laboratory at Owafa, halfway between Omugo and Arua. Almost immediately, this brought in a steady stream of new patients.

The sleeping sickness assistants were by now working in many of the communities around Omugo, conscientiously cycling forty kilometres to Arua for a weekly meeting. It was during one of these, that they tried to persuade me that it was safe to go back to Omugo, which they were sure was the best place to base the programme. They had a point, since sleeping sickness cases did not develop in Arua, despite there being an abundance of tsetse flies, in and around the town. The first cases of the disease appeared just beyond Owafa and although the demarcation line was quite distinct, we had no idea why it should be so localised. There was clearly a great deal still to learn about this condition.

Although I was sympathetic to the sleeping sickness assistants' point of view, we could not chop and change the base every few weeks, since this involved so much effort. Despite the fact that Omugo seemed calm at the moment, we had to be sure that peace would last. My recent trip to Koboko had reminded me what it was like working in a remote area, under threat of rebel activity and Koboko was only fifteen kilometres from Omugo! I informed the assistants that we would be staying in Arua, until conditions in Omugo became less volatile. The meeting broke up early, to give the assistants enough time for their three-hour cycle trip back to Omugo, before nightfall. After they left, I wondered if I had made the right decision. Was I being sensible, or over cautious?

Back in the ward, I bumped into Harriet. She was coming off duty, so I suggested that we go for a late lunch together, at the Continental Hotel. I needed to talk with someone about the programme and in the months since I had come to Uganda, I had grown to value Harriet's friendship. I knew she understood why I hesitated to return to Omugo and we discussed all the current issues.

She went on to tell me a bit about her life in Uganda. It was not often that we had the opportunity to chat about anything other than medical matters, so I took the chance to ask her, what she saw as her future.

"My ambition is to finish my training. I have only done the first level, which makes me an enrolled nurse. I need to do another one and a half years, to become registered."

"Will that be possible; do you have enough money?" I knew that all the nurses found money to be a problem.

"No, not at the moment. For now, I spend most of my money on my daughter's education."

"I didn't know you had a daughter," I said, surprised that she had not mentioned this before.

Harriet was someone I thought I knew quite well and I had certainly told her about Michael. She smiled broadly.

"She is ten. She goes to the convent school, here in Arua. Normally I see her about every two months."

Harriet was twenty-six, so that made her sixteen when she had her daughter.

"Where is your husband? Does he help?"

The words were out, before I could stifle them. Idiot! I knew Harriet had no partner.

"He disappeared as soon as he discovered that I was pregnant," she replied, quite undisturbed by my faux pas, although by the look on her face, the father of her child was not a topic that she wished to dwell upon. Under the circumstances, I could understand and changed the subject.

"Did you grow up in Arua?"

"Yes, I also went to school at the convent. It was a difficult time then, because of Idi Amin and the war."

"Were things difficult here in Arua? I thought Amin's regime mainly affected Kampala."

Even now, I had no real idea about what he had done to this part of the country. People seldom mentioned him and given the current strife, it had seemed politic not to harp back to past difficulties. The present was quite bad enough.

"The civil war made life bad, all over our country. One day, when I was thirteen years old, a group of gunmen walked into our school and opened fire on us all. Seventy children were killed. I was lucky."

Her voice was calm, but her eyes shone. I was overcome by the consummate horror of what she had said and found it difficult to know what to say next, so we went on to talk of more mundane things, safe things, trivial things to do with the hospital.

While we were still talking, Ben came running up the road. He was looking uncommonly agitated. I called and waved for him to join us and he rushed over, beginning to speak rapidly to Harriet. It had to be bad news. I could see that from Harriet's face as she listened and I became quite anxious to find out what was wrong. Then she started to fire questions at Ben, but still no one spoke to me.

"What is the problem?" I asked, leaning between them in an effort to stop their discussion. Harriet turned to look at me.

"The rebels have kidnapped Yan."

With Harriet translating, Ben quickly told me the whole story. Yan had gone out with the ambulance that morning, to pick up personnel files, left behind in Omugo. The trip was uneventful, until the vehicle slowed to cross a bridge near Omugo where they were confronted by four armed men. They were forced to stop and when Ben pulled up they were ordered out of the car and everyone except Yan had to take off their clothes and lie on the ground. The four men gathered up all the clothing and pushed Yan back into the ambulance, driving off with him at high speed. Ben was left to hitch-hike back to Omugo, in his underpants. This had occurred at 11.30am, just when the sleeping sickness assistants had been trying to persuade me that it was safe to return to Omugo. But the comfort of knowing that I had undoubtedly made a right decision, paled when I thought of Yan and his unknown fate. What had the rebels done with him?

"I must tell the Security Chief and the UN people what has happened. Harriet, you tell the others at the hospital."

Without any further discussion, I sprinted up the road towards the Communication Centre at the UN compound. I spoke first to the UN chief, Mr Tamba-Kumba and he radioed the Security Chief directly, so that a message about Yan was immediately transmitted to all police and army units. Then I contacted Evan in Kampala by satellite phone and explained the position. After that, there was nothing I could do, but wait. I sat on the wall at the UNHCR compound, anxious to stay near the Communication Centre. It was a dreadful time, for all I could do was imagine the awful, gory things that the rebels were doing to Yan, as I sat there in safety.

Mr Tamba-Kumba appeared and stood around irresolutely.

"This is serious," he said.

I suppose he too was under pressure, but I felt that he ought to be able to think of something more constructive to do. Then Christopher, the German second-in-command emerged and he too sat on the wall.

"We saw a group of rebels near Omugo last week," Christopher told me, "but when we drove past, they did nothing."

I looked at him, astonished.

"Didn't you think that information would have been quite useful to us? We're sending the ambulance back and forward to Omugo all the time now. Why didn't you say something?"

Christopher looked embarrassed, mumbled something, got up and went inside again. Soon, Mr Tamba-Kumba joined him. Now, I sat alone on the wall and worried.

What if Yan didn't come back? Maybe he would be found dead and dreadfully mutilated. What a terrible thing for his family! Perhaps he would be ransomed. What if we never heard? What if he simply disappeared without trace?

It was very hot sitting on the wall, but I didn't want to be inside the

UNHCR office. Anyway, I preferred to worry on my own. As time passed, I began to consider my decision to start a patient-transfer service to Omugo. Perhaps it been an unnecessary risk. The more time that passed, the more I found it impossible to think sensibly. I wondered if MSF had already contacted Yan's family in Paris. How were they feeling? Then I wondered how my own family would feel, if such a thing were to happen to me. I sat on the wall, disagreeable conjectures circling aimlessly in my head. There was nothing to do, but wait. By 5.15, I had persuaded myself to accept the worst, when Mr Tamba-Kumba emerged.

"There is a message that Yan has walked into Maracha hospital and he is okay," he told me.

I didn't know what to say. I simply nodded and set off back to the house, stopping at the hospital to convey the news to the staff, feeling strangely flat and greatly relieved. Then I drank some beer and ate something and felt a little better, especially when I managed to reach Maracha on the radio. Reception was very poor, but Yan sounded surprisingly normal, saying he would try to get back the next day, if the road was clear. Maracha was on the road to Koboko, where there had been land mines in recent weeks, so he would have to be careful. In fact, only recently, Maracha hospital itself had been attacked by rebels. The expatriate staff had managed to escape out of the back door, but they had been forced to walk almost all the way to Arua, before getting a lift from a passing car. The NGO doctor, Walter, told me, "I had to walk the ten miles in flip-flops. I will never forget to have good shoes by me in future, whatever I'm doing."

I knew that since this attack, a military detachment had been based at the hospital, so Yan would be safe. I just hoped that he was not in too much of a state of shock. In fact, we were all relieved that he seemed his usual self, when he returned the next morning.

"It was frightening at first," he explained, as we all gathered round, "but once we were away from the area, they talked to me in French. They had come from Zaire and said they were taking me back there. The driver was truly amazing, travelling at 110 km per hour, over the narrowest of tracks. The worst part was, when we drove through villages, since they put me in the front seat, between the driver and another armed man. Their guns were constantly pointed out the windows, so I knew that if the military saw the car, I would be killed.

Then we crossed the border, where they stopped and told me to get out and they took all my money (unfortunately, Yan had been carrying 1,500 USD for salaries), but then they gave me five dollars back, said "have a nice walk," and they disappeared. I met a small boy and said "Arua?" to him. He pointed down the road and said "Maracha", so voila, here I am."

He was amazingly calm, much more so than I was.

"How far did you have to walk?" I asked.

"I don't know exactly, as they stole my watch too, but I guess it was about three hours to Maracha."

As if that was all there was to it, he went off to his room, to change. Shortly after, he started work as usual. I had no experience of helping people after this kind of trauma, but knew that I should not pressurise him. If he felt comfortable beginning to work again immediately, it was probably good to let him.

I waited for the moment, when Yan would want to talk about his experiences, but over the next two weeks, despite leading questions from me, he added little to his story. He became increasingly isolated and stopped going to the White Rhino Hotel in the evenings. More and more time was spent in the radio room, talking to people in Kampala and to his contacts in the other projects. His relatively poor English and my French, made in-depth communication difficult, but I was frustrated that I was not able to help him more. Yan remained withdrawn until he left, two months later.

Here I felt was another volunteer, subjected to a stressful experience, without access to appropriate support. Because of the type of work they do and the situations in which they operate, aid workers may face land mines and gunfire, endure kidnap and rape, or witness untold misery and horror. The potential for mental trauma is significant and some attempt has been made recently to provide counselling, when people return from missions, but this is poorly publicised and many who have had such experiences, are unwilling to ask for help. It is regrettable however, if staff feel they have done something wrong, or that they have failed, when they have simply become victims.

I too was coming to the end of my contract and since I had the option of prolonging the mission, it was time to decide if I wanted to leave

Uganda. I liked the country and the sleeping sickness programme was interesting, but I knew that there were not enough patients to provide full-time work for me in Arua. I was under-utilised and I was fed up with the political situation interfering with what we were doing, although at least I had made it to the end of my assignment. Rebel activity was escalating once more and I began to wonder if this was how full-scale civil wars began.

Eventually, I decided to return home to France, to consider what it was I wanted to do next, for no doubt MSF had many other interesting missions to offer. Uganda had enhanced my confidence about coping in dangerous locations and I had learned a great deal about a new disease. Aid work was still fascinating.

My final task in Arua, was to organise a major conference on sleeping sickness. The purpose was to train as many health workers as possible to recognise the disease, so that more patients would be referred to the hospital for earlier treatment. A secondary objective was to increase general awareness of the programme, so more people would be encouraged to come to Arua, to take part in the screening programme. We were, in essence, advertising.

In England, I had organised a few conferences, so I imagined that this would be a rather similar experience. I made some preliminary enquiries about how things worked in Uganda and discussed the project with Dr Imoko, the District Medical Officer. He contacted every district in Arua, urging each to send a representative. The conference would be open to all health staff, as well as any local authority personnel involved in health planning. In England, where there are many conferences, I had the experience of sending mailshots to seven hundred doctors and having fifteen turn up, even with a meal and drug company freebies as incentives. Here, I hoped I might do better.

Once I realised that conferences in Arua were not an everyday occurrence, I did some positive thinking. planning for fifty delegates and hoping that the novelty might attract even more. Next, I had to find a venue. The only suitable place was the church hall, which I duly booked, trying to imagine how just a handful of bodies would look, gathered in its generous space. To be on the safe side, I decided to cater for one hundred and since the Sisters were doing the catering, they could distribute any excess food to the needy, so that there would be no waste.

The message was to be fairly simple. I wanted to convey to as many people as possible, the basic facts about sleeping sickness and what people should do if they thought they had contracted the disease. I asked Evan and our new Ugandan laboratory technician, to present some of the basic medical information, as simply as possible. Dominique, the epidemiologist from Kampala, agreed to present the scientific details. The last speaker would be Dr Mbulamberi, the national director of the Ugandan Sleeping Sickness Programme and a widely acclaimed expert.

I set off to the church on the day of the conference, slightly nervous and hoping for a good turn out. The MSF speakers struggled through their stuff, in the awkward manner of those unused to public speaking. Dr Mbulamberi was a star, speaking clearly and without notes, a true orator, in total command of his topic. He managed to get the message across in an interesting and stimulating way and more importantly, encouraged everyone to try harder to identify cases in their areas. It was inspiring to listen to him and when I heard the many, well thought out questions from the audience, I knew that it had been a success.

However, instead of the thirty people that I had expected, or the one hundred I had catered for, there were two hundred and forty-five hungry people in the lunch queue. The Sisters did a sterling job, finding more cassava and rice from somewhere and allocating half rations to anyone who was under 1.9 metres tall. These ladies were tougher than the "Penguin" in the "Blues Brothers" film, so no one dared to argue. Without them, my conference might have ended on a sour note.

To cap it all, no one had told me that Ugandan employees received a four dollar a day conference fee, which is distributed at the event! I also discovered, that since four dollars represents a significant sum of money to the average Ugandan health worker, no one was going to leave until they had been paid. It took quite a bit of borrowing and rummaging around, to come up with the thousand dollars we required to get rid of the delegates.

Just before I left Uganda, I heard over the radio that Evan was preparing to finish his own mission, in two months time. Since I was happy to return to Africa, I began to think about the possibility of applying for his post, as Head of Mission for Uganda, or perhaps that of Medical Co-ordinator. The timing would be perfect, as this would also allow me two months at home, enough to see my family and go skiing with Michael. I supposed that my French might possibly be a problem, but it was improving.

As the time came to leave Arua, life became increasingly hectic. At the last minute I found myself faced with a long list of tasks: reports, filing and instructions to pass on. My main objective was that the sleeping sickness programme should continue seamlessly, so I ensured that I had everything prepared for the short hand-over period. John, my replacement, was from New Zealand where he had been a GP for eight years. This was his first mission with MSF and he made a very good first impression. He was short, stocky and confident. What's more, he turned out to be as capable as he looked, with the added bonus of a good sense of humour.

The transfer went smoothly. I outlined my two primary objectives, which were, increasing the number of patients treated and moving the programme back to Omugo, once conditions permitted. I introduced John to the team and explained how I had tried to operate with them. With a new leader every six months, it must be quite difficult for local staff to cope with differences in management style, not to mention contrasting temperaments. Although regular change does have the advantage that incompetent people move on, continuity is important and on balance, short-term staff contracts, cannot really be a good idea for long-term projects.

I hoped that my "Adams family" were not secretly glad to see me go, for we had been through a great deal together and adversity builds solid bonds. I said my goodbyes to them with real feeling. Harriet, Olema, Nunu, Ben and all the rest, had done so much to make the project work and seemed pleased to hear that I was trying to return to Uganda after my leave. Perhaps we would meet again. I hoped so, but as yet, there had been no reply from Paris about my offer to replace Evan. On the way home, I spent just one day in Kampala, because I had already written my end of mission report. I talked to Evan about the project and wished him well, not knowing if we too would ever meet again.

I reflected that there is something strange about this type of work. You get to know people intimately over a short period of time, only to have them disappear from your life, usually forever.

CHAPTER EIGHT

On the move

I was delighted when Paris agreed that I could return to Uganda, as Medical Co-ordinator, based in Kampala. This time, I might be able to influence the direction of the programmes. In the meantime, I ate my fill of French food, drank a lot of wine and caught up with my family, friends and neighbours. The two months passed incredibly quickly and then it was the end of February and time to leave.

On arrival in Kampala, I was informed that due to increasing security problems and the opening of another mission in Kitgum (in the North, close to the borders with Sudan and Kenya), Paris had appointed a Head of Mission, Yves, to deal with non-medical issues. At first I was a little disappointed, feeling that I could have handled the combined post in the same way as Evan. Yet Paris often appointed a Head of Mission, in addition to the Medical Co-ordinator, if the workload was deemed to be heavy. Evan also explained, "Paris communicates better with a true Francophone. It reduces misunderstandings".

In time, I began to see that Paris did have a point. Continued political unrest had resulted in ever increasing demands being made on MSF in Uganda (a country the size of the UK, with a much less sophisticated communications system), so it would be an advantage to have two people to share the workload. Anyway, although my French had improved, there were still gaps and I would never fully understand the Gallic nature.

Evan's wife was expecting twins so she had returned to Paris some weeks before, leaving him alone to cope with his three-year old son. Understandably, he was pre-occupied and unable to do more than give me brief updates about all the programmes, together with a list of the activities that I was expected to undertake. In Paris, nothing specific had been said about the terms of reference of the Medical Co-ordinator's position, so I decided that I must just learn for myself. At the start I was arrogant enough to think that I would pick it up easily, but I later recognised that this was a poor start, giving me a biased view of the job. Initially, I tended to act as a joint Head of Mission and Medical Co-ordinator, instead of concentrating on one or other, as was appropriate. My innate desire to see more widely meant that I sometimes neglected the purely medical.

In retrospect, it was also a mistake to move in with Evan, taking over his house when he left, as this meant that I was isolated from the other team members. True, I had daily contact with Dominique, but he restricted himself to vehicle supervision. So, already separated from the group by age, language and culture, this physical separation was not a good idea. The Kampala co-ordination team included Yves, Jean Luc, the log and Caroline, our administrator. Although these three could get by in English, they spoke French to each other, which suited me well, as one of my objectives was to improve my fluency. However, as the sole, native English speaker, I was the natural choice for dealing both with the authorities and with the European Development Fund, our major donor. This was an element of the work that I expected to find interesting.

In addition to the co-ordination work in Kampala, there were three projects to manage in Uganda: the two sleeping sickness projects at Omugo/Arua and Ajumani and an IDP (Internally Displaced Persons) camp at Kitgum. The Kasese situation had recently become more controlled, enabling our staff to withdraw.

My first priority was to familiarise myself with all of these projects and their staff and as I had previously worked in the sleeping sickness programme, I decided first to visit Kitgum. The situation here had been created by a rebel group, called the Lord's Resistance Army (LRA). This particularly aggressive group had bases in South Sudan, to which they regularly retreated for rest and training, before returning to Uganda. Their origins lay in an earlier group, whose leader Alice Likwema had led an army to the outskirts of Kampala in 1987, before being defeated by President Museveni. Her nephew then assumed leadership and began to terrorise the local population. Although they had a fanatical, religious focus, their objectives did not seem clear. They made unilateral edicts, such as forbidding the people to travel or work on Fridays and Sundays. (I am told that Friday is the second holiest day in the Christian calendar). The punishment for walking on the roads on these two holy days was the amputation of either a hand or foot and anyone contravening one of the many other bizarre rules risked mutilation, by having ears, lips, or nose cut off.

One of the most horrifying aspects of LRA behaviour is their method of recruitment. They attack villages and kidnap all the children aged between seven and eighteen years, taking them to a training camp in South Sudan. There, they are subjected to torture and indoctrination, taught to use firearms and sometimes even driven to kill another child. When these children have been sufficiently intimidated, they are taken back to their own villages and forced to kill members of their family, or other villagers. Then they are told and believe, that there is no going back, since they are now outcasts both from family and clan, the bedrock of African society. It should be remembered, that the LRA commanders themselves are only about eighteen years old and have experienced the same training.

Amnesty International recently estimated that over ten years perhaps as many as thirteen thousand children had been abducted and treated in this way by the LRA. Other rebel groups use the same methods to obtain new recruits all over Africa. Rehabilitation programmes have been established with psychologists and counsellors, to help the few who manage to escape, but it is difficult to see what to do when the rebel leaders themselves are as much victims as aggressors.

The LRA had operated around Kitgum for ten years, but recently and inexplicably they had massacred one hundred people, just north of the town. The terrified local population had fled, either into Kitgum, or to one of the nearby villages with a military presence. About seventy thousand IDPs were involved, located in six different sites. These people were subsistence farmers, separated from their only source of food and quite unable to look after themselves. The villages which had been inundated were now two, three, or even ten times larger than before, resulting in shortages of shelter, food and water.

MSF had offered to help the IDPs, who had located in the town of Kitgum itself. This mass of humanity had appeared without warning, five thousand individuals taking over the school, the church and even the streets. Although the local council was moving them to a specific site called Gang Dyang, some two kilometres from town, they had no money to do anything other than to allocate the land (500m by 300m). MSF arrived and found the people had no shelter, no water supply and no toilets. Conditions were both unpleasant and unsafe. To provide shelter, the team quickly installed three hundred tents (enough for 3000 people), encouraging the rest of the population to build themselves huts from local materials.

The water problem was harder to solve, given that northern Uganda is quite arid, so our temporary solution was water-trucking, using a five thousand litre cistern mounted on the back of a lorry. In a hot country, the standard requirement in a refugee camp is twenty litres per person, per day, two litres of which is for drinking. (For reference, a toilet uses about 10 litres for a single flush.) Gang Dyang's daily target was one hundred thousand litres, well beyond the capacity of either the lorry, or the local water source. Delivery was initially closer to two litres, per person, per day. Eventually, another source was identified, one and a half kilometres away and a pipe was laid into the camp, increasing the supply to five litres, per person, per day. People use water to drink, to cook, to wash themselves and to clean their clothes. Five litres was only acceptable as an emergency measure. It left the IDPs at risk of epidemics.

At Kitgum, MSF had provided a team of four. Jean-Loup the doctor, was young and conscientious. Annie, the nurse, was bohemian in character, with dyed, spiky, red hair. She was experienced, with a near total disregard for her own safety. Emile, another nurse, was outrageously camp and very amusing, while Laurent, an archetypal, macho logistician, completed the group. Tall, thin, "Neanderthal looking", he spoke very little, but with good humour, accepted that he was regularly the foil for Emile's jokes. This amazing bunch danced, sang and worked unrelentingly, through difficult times.

By the time I arrived, there was considerable pressure on this team to extend its activity into the other camps, although these were of a completely different character to Gang Dyang. Some were simply loose agglomerations of new huts, located near barracks and extending into existing villages, making it almost impossible to differentiate between old and new inhabitants and raising the issue of who should receive the aid. We did agree to do more, but only gradually, since our resources were limited. Progressively, we increased our area of responsibility, so that team members were making regular visits to three of the other five camps.

Security was extremely important here. Every morning, before setting out, the team checked with the military chief that things were quiet in the area of their proposed visit. This restriction became increasingly frustrating, as often he did not turn up until well after nine o'clock, so that it could be after 11am before they arrived at the camp, reducing their working days considerably. We could never take a chance and leave without checking and there were times when the team couldn't move at all, so an entire day's work was lost. One morning, Annie did go without checking, only to be stuck in Padibe Camp, because a party of rebels had attacked a village between her and the base in Kitgum. Fortunately, on this occasion there was no real problem and she was able to return when the soldiers gave the all clear, but she was firmly warned to take more care in future.

One of my first questions, when I visited these new sites, was to ask why we were providing drugs and paying dispensary staff, who were government employees. Furthermore, where were the rest of them? After all, these IDPs were Ugandan citizens. Until recently, they had been looked after by the medical system of Kitgum District and had only moved about twenty kilometres.

"Why has the District Medical Officer (DMO) not moved his staff to the new sites, so that they can carry on as before? " I asked.

This seemed to be the most logical way to increase medical assistance to all the camps. Jean-Loup explained the problem.

"We've pushed for that since the beginning, but the DMO is totally unsupportive and says it's impossible to move his staff, although he won't explain why. We think it's because he's an absolute arsehole. The workers say their salaries haven't been paid for months and they're not interested in working for nothing any longer. They have opened private clinics in their houses and work from there."

It was not a new story, but that made it none the less infuriating.

"So we are intervening in a chronic situation, that is in part due to a lack of government funding?"

I wanted to be sure, before going off to battle with the authorities.

"Not completely," Jean-Loup explained. "The authorities in Kampala say that the money has been sent here, but it doesn't seem to have been paid to the workers."

"So where is it?" I asked, fairly sure of the answer.

"In someone's pocket, or at best, used for some other purpose."

I knew that this sort of thing was not uncommon in Uganda, especially in the North. Sometimes it was understandable that the authorities allocated scarce funds elsewhere, confident that an NGO would step in. The worry was, "elsewhere" could mean anything!

"What about the drug supply? From the quantities I saw in the inventories, it looks as if we are supplying almost everything," I said.

"That is more complicated," said Jean-Loup. "But I have found out how the system is supposed to work. Danida, the Danish NGO, gives free drugs to every dispensary in the country. They calculate the quantities to send, on the basis of the register of medical consultations for the previous three-month period. This is fine in principle, but if there is a sudden increase in consultations, there are not enough drugs for new patients, who may have walked miles to be seen. Naturally, they don't come back a second time and consequently the number of new patients falls. Here, the population has changed so dramatically, that the system has totally collapsed and there are no drugs at all."

"I see," I said.

And I could see. A system designed for a stable environment, had failed completely, because it could not respond to rapid population shifts. Bureaucracy was denying patients access to drugs that were available, somewhere else in the country. This was the responsibility of the DMO, so it seemed that I would have to get involved.

"Can you get the figures for each dispensary? I will visit Danida in Entebbe and discuss the problem with them," I said. "They might be persuaded to reconsider their system."

"It could take a week, but I will send the figures down to Kampala as soon as I can."

Jean-Loup seemed pleased that there was some hope of resolving one of his problems.

The subject of Danida reminded me that there would be other groups working in this area and I asked Jean-Loup for details.

"The World Food Programme (WFP) is here, but it's short of supplies. Anyway, their priority at the moment is Ethiopia." (There was another huge famine predicted for Ethiopia) "They say they can supply some food, but they have no manpower to organise distribution," added Laurent. "Food is a huge problem here."

I began to wonder if there was anything in the Kitgum area that was not "a huge problem".

"It doesn't help that the guy in charge of WFP is a really pretentious Frenchman, with a hyphenated name," Jean-Loup finished.

Hum, shades of the revolution, I thought. I had already learned that France has a social hierarchy, rivalling that of Britain.

"In theory, Oxfam is installing water supplies, but it's been six weeks now and nothing has happened," interjected Laurent.

"Do we have a contact for Oxfam here?" I asked hopefully.

It would help if I didn't have to traipse around the country, searching for the people who might have answers to these questions.

"There is an Oxfam rep. He's very pleasant, but we think there's a problem in Kampala, where his boss is based. They don't seem to be able to get things moving, so he's been waiting for two generators and pumps for four weeks. Meanwhile, we are still trucking water to Gang Dyang."

"We should try to avoid becoming involved in the food distribution," I suggested. "It's time consuming and very political. Anyway, it's not what we're really about. We've plenty of other problems to deal with. Maybe Action Contre la Faim could help?"

"In theory, yes, but they're already running two feeding centres and they've only two expatriates and no expert nutritionist," Jean-Loup explained.

I spent the next two days visiting the other sites and contacting as many different agencies as possible, both to introduce myself and to assimilate information. It was clear that the old and new populations were difficult to differentiate, particularly in sites where newcomers had built houses amongst those of existing villagers. The number of incomers was almost impossible to assess, a fact that is essential for any IDP planning, since accurate numbers are necessary to determine requirements for food, water and medical supplies. In theory, the local chiefs had population figures for their villages and kept a record of arrivals and deaths, but here, the combination of inadequate food delivery and losses to the local market had put pressure on the chiefs to inflate numbers.

Although I had been in Kitgum for only four days, it was my job to give direction to the team, linking this to what Paris would want. It was a complex task, with some difficult decisions to be made. First, I decided to call a meeting, to confirm that I had collected accurate information. Also, I wanted to find out what the team felt.

"What do you think we should be doing? There's been four months of intervention, so you must have an idea about what is needed?"

The team left Jean-Loup to reply.

"Our problem is, that we can't be everywhere at the same time. The original project was to work in Gang Dyang, but now there is Palabek as well and it's been suggested we look in on Palabek Kal, because it's on the same road. I have been asked to give supplies to Lokung as well. We are over-stretched. It's not at all possible for four of us to maintain a presence in six camps."

"Would it work if you each looked after one camp?" I suggested.

"No, the work is too specific. I need to be full-time in Gang Dyang, for both the nursing and the feeding centre. There are three hundred children attending each day and it's increasing all the time. We can't abandon it." Emile spoke out, quite definitely. "And Laurent needs to be here too, for the logistics."

"At the moment, I'm here almost all day, overseeing the building of latrines and houses, because more and more people keep arriving," agreed Laurent.

"What about you, Annie?" I asked.

"I am up to my ears in Palabek. We have now started a vaccination programme and we are weighing the children at the same time, to get an idea of their nutritional state. I'm sure they are going to need a feeding centre there soon," she replied.

"I don't see how four of us can possibly look after seventy thousand IDPs, in six different sites," said Jean-Loup.

Neither did I, but I tried to summarise what they had told me, to be sure that I understood.

"Right, so you have too much to do. But I am fairly sure that Paris will not send more people at the moment, because of the uncertainty and the security problems. We need to identify the needs and then draw up a list of essentials. The standard priorities are: water, shelter, security, food, measles vaccination, latrines, health services, a disease surveillance system, co-ordination and liaison with the authorities. You must suggest specific plans for what can be reasonably achieved. These will allow you to work logically; they are also essential for your successors, who will be overwhelmed if you don't make the issues absolutely clear." (For this team was about to be gradually replaced by a new set of volunteers.)

"In the meantime, we must encourage the DMO to take back some of his responsibilities," I continued. "Try to make him act, but we must also carry on doing as much as we can. If we stop, the population will have no access to health care at all."

They looked at one another and then nodded.

"We've got to do our best to maintain existing health structures, or they could disappear completely. The dispensaries must be made to work, somehow. I will see if there is anything to be done in Kampala, at the Ministry of Health, to improve the flow of money for salaries and drugs."

"It's hard to see people with nothing", said Jean-Loup "There are so many problems. The DMO doesn't seem to care and we can't handle this level of demand. It's upsetting. Sometimes we get so angry."

I knew what he meant, but if they could rationalise what they were doing and make the problem manageable, they would be able to cope. I promised to do what I could and told them I would return soon, to see how things were progressing.

Back in Kampala, I went immediately to see the Minister of Health, but he was not very helpful. President Museveni had recently introduced a policy of decentralisation to district level, so the answers lay back with the unhelpful DMO. There was also a complete freeze on the hiring of new staff for all government sectors, including that of health. These two strategies had been a condition imposed by the World Bank, for the renewal of loans, so the Minister was restricted on all sides. Gently, I tried to suggest that the DMO was not doing as much as he might, but I had to be careful to avoid suggesting wrongdoing. We had no proof of corruption, only an awareness of the non-payment of salaries. Unfortunately, my plea had no effect and no action was taken to restore staff to the dispensaries.

Ten days later, replacements arrived for Laurent and Emile at Kitgum. Both Véronique, the nurse, and Jerome, the log, were on their first missions; these newcomers were most definitely being thrown in at the deep end. So I spent half a day with them, explaining the position of MSF in Uganda and introducing them to the principles of the project. They would be working with the existing team for about a week and I planned to visit them some time in the near future.

Before that, I had to consider my other responsibilities, the sleeping sickness projects. This work had started in 1983 in Moyo, a town north of Adjumani, near the border with South Sudan. At that time, MSF had been rehabilitating dispensaries in and around Moyo, when one of the medical staff noticed large numbers of sleeping sickness victims. So was born the programme, which still exists today in its three phases. The first treats patients, who come because they are ill, or who wish to be tested. The second involves going out into the district, to screen the whole population and discover early cases. The third phase is the introduction of a surveillance system, to guard against re-infection. Since eradication is impossible, we aimed for an incidence of fewer than one in two hundred. If that is achieved, normal health services should be able to treat the remaining cases and MSF intervention would no longer be needed. Since 1983, ten thousand people had been treated.

Although I had worked on part of the sleeping sickness project, when in Omugo, I had been totally focussed on my own responsibilities, paying scant attention to the situation elsewhere. Now, I discovered that in Moyo, the programme was in its third phase and we simply sent supplies there once a month. In Adjumani, we were in the second phase, trying to introduce a third phase, surveillance system. Full responsibility would then return to the DMO and the Ugandan Sleeping Sickness Control Programme, based in the town of Jinja, on Lake Victoria. In theory, the Ugandan Sleeping Sickness Committee had been in control of the programme all along, but a lack of resources had limited their contribution. MSF had been involved in Adjumani for over fifteen years and had rather taken over the whole thing. It appeared that there had been a failure to work closely enough with the authorities, so now, during the handover period, there was some tension. Whatever the original plan, with an endless turn over of MSF staff on short-term contracts, it was not really surprising that this had occurred. My role was to try to resolve this problem.

The flight to Adjumani goes via Arua, where we picked up two passengers, before taking off again for the thirty-minute flight over the Nile. The final descent is spectacular, with a narrow landing strip that seems from the air to be no more than two metres wide. Fortunately, the pilot knew what he was doing and we landed safely. For him, it was a daily event; for me, having been an amateur pilot, it was both impressive and alarming.

The programme at Adjumani was very similar to the one I had been involved with, at Omugo. It was run by Odile, a French doctor, who organised her work well. She lived on her own, although there were about twenty other Europeans in the town, working for various NGOs. It was a strange little community, boasting one bar (with a satellite TV), frequented nightly by most of the expatriates, but Odile seemed happy enough, in this company of mainly macho men. Yves said that they did not get on very well, so he would leave the running of her programme entirely to me. One of their issues of dispute was the fact that she was alone, which is against MSF policy. Although Odile was adamant that she wanted no help, she then demanded that a log be sent at the drop of a hat when she required any small item to be repaired.

In Kampala, our main concern for Adjumani was security, because the rebels had recently attacked the UN compound, firing indiscriminately into the living quarters. Miraculously, no one had been seriously injured, but all the expatriates were immediately evacuated by air and did not return, until the army had secured the area. Things had calmed down, but as in Kitgum, there were always rumours and alleged sightings of different rebel groups in the bush. It took a rather unusual personality to work in such a situation.

I found Odile to be competent, if a little recalcitrant. I agreed with her that there was no need for a full time log, although I also tried to explain that she might sometimes have to wait a bit for things to be done. As for the security problem, one of Odile's solutions was to have two evil dogs running loose in the compound at night. These beasts had already bitten several other visitors, so at night when I was staying with her and nature called, I went just outside the tukul door to relieve myself. I don't trust dogs. As a GP, I was bitten several times by animals whose owners claimed, "They won't hurt a fly".

Another reason for my visit to Adjumani, was to evaluate the sleeping sickness activity in Moyo, where the hospital had been operating autonomously for three years, except for the monthly drug delivery. We had rather ignored Moyo, so I wanted to make an assessment, to ensure that all was well. The drive from Adjumani takes about one hour, plus time for the ferry crossing at Loropi. The ferry itself was a large barge, with a powerful diesel outboard motor, carrying up to four cars, or one big lorry on each journey. As we crossed, I leaned over the side and watched a never-ending stream of blue, water hyacinth floating past. Although extremely attractive, this plant is a menace for wild life and for the waterway itself. At the source of the Nile, in Jinja, there is a major hydroelectric dam, producing most of Uganda's electricity and these hyacinth regularly block the turbine inlets.

Despite the fact that there were rumoured to be crocodiles, children were washing and playing in the water. On the far bank, the land rose up into low mountains that continued on into Sudan, and as we drove up the hill, we stopped to look back at the spectacular view. The Nile wound away to the north-east and tree-covered savannah rolled off to the south, finally becoming lost in the haze.

The situation at Moyo was acceptable. MSF funded two laboratory technicians, who supervised the continued screening of patients. Any with positive tests were sent on to the wards. The treatment of these patients was less well supervised than I would have liked, but the staff had other patients and priorities, unlike the MSF hospitals at Adjumani and Omugo, where we were treating only the one condition. The main problem was numbers. There were fewer and fewer patients, indicating the possible need for a surveillance system. If the reduction in cases was genuine we would be content, but if we were simply not finding the cases we needed to do something about it.

In countries like Uganda, a surveillance system must be affordable, as well as effective. Our current sleeping sickness assistants were both competent and effective, but as additions to the normal health system, they were too expensive for Uganda to maintain. We had to find a way of resolving this problem in the longer term, if the disease was to be kept under control when we left. Evan and Dominique (the epidemiologist) had produced a draft plan for a surveillance phase, which proposed a continued system of sleeping sickness assistants, though much reduced in number. They would be based in the existing dispensaries, taking small blood samples from "suspects" and sending these to the laboratory for testing. Results would be sent back within two weeks and if necessary, these patients would be treated. But I had been told that there was resistance to this scheme, because it involved a separate group of staff.

Consequently, when Odile and I arranged to meet the local DMO to discuss this issue, I was prepared for a battle. Dr Ben, the DMO was also Hospital Superintendent and Sleeping Sickness Supervisor, a busy man indeed. I was aware that he had earlier reported his dissatisfaction with some of MSF's work and Odile had already sent him a draft of our proposal, requesting feedback.

After Odile's introductions and some polite remarks, I came straight to the point.

"We have come to talk about the proposed surveillance system for sleeping sickness. Could you give me your first impressions?"

"I don't have any money to pay for sleeping sickness assistants and I don't know why you persist in pushing this scheme at me," he replied bluntly.

I was not too surprised at this, since Odile had warned me. But now, he continued.

"We have more than one problem here in Uganda, but MSF continues to focus on its own agenda."

"I'm not sure that I understand. Could you explain a bit more?" I asked, just a little bemused.

Surely, no one could deny that MSF had made great strides in treating sleeping sickness.

"In Adjumani, we usually have about thirty cases of sleeping sickness under treatment, but we have thousands of cases of malaria and pneumonia, not to mention surgical emergencies and all the other pathologies, for which the government sends me barely enough money to pay dispensary salaries. To help the majority of the population, I need drugs, cash and building materials, not more sleeping sickness assistants."

He was very articulate and very annoyed and I guessed that for him, this was an ongoing battle with MSF.

"I'm not in a position to change our programme at the moment. Paris would never agree to it. They would say that such massive spending on infrastructure is a government responsibility and Uganda should approach the major donors, such as the World Bank, or USAID. MSF is a small humanitarian aid organisation, attempting to support specific programmes and deal with emergencies."

Dr Ben had the air of a tired teacher, explaining something for the umpteenth time, to a difficult pupil.

"The World Bank won't give us any more money, unless the economy follows their rules and we spend less on our army. Tell me, how can we run our country without an army, when there are at least three major rebel groups trying to bring down the government? Without our army, there would be chaos!"

Of course, he was right, but the wider issues of Ugandan health care were far beyond my remit. At the moment, I could only deal with the need to implement the final stage of the sleeping sickness programme. How could I persuade this man to help me? Then I remembered. I was supposed to be here to help him. I had accepted the MSF agenda and fallen into the aid workers' trap of thinking that my role was to tell people what they required, even experienced professionals, like Dr Ben. No wonder he was annoyed.

"I'm sorry. I can only concentrate on the programme as it exists now. What do you think we should do?" I asked him.

"I would scrap the elaborate plan that you are proposing and integrate the sleeping sickness programme into our existing system. Treat sleeping sickness as any other disease, with no special staff. That would limit the expense and make it affordable for Uganda." Warming to his subject, he continued, "In the medium term, we can't afford Arsobal and Pentamidine. A donor will always have to provide that, but it would be a small sum, such as is spent in Moyo. There would be no more powerful cars, no big radios and no expensive salaries."

Dr Ben had unwittingly identified one of his problems with MSF, the perceived high standard of living of its workers. But this was no time to get into a debate about aid agencies and their staff. Although my salary was by no means impressive, I had arrived in a big car with a driver and our programme had three vehicles. The DMO had to make do with public transport. It seemed wise to guide the conversation back to the main issue.

"Dr Ben, if we abandon sleeping sickness assistants entirely, all their experience and knowledge will be lost to Uganda and the disease will return in epidemic proportions, as it was fifteen years ago. If we have no experts in the field, the disease will be ignored and superseded by all these other medical problems you have identified."

I thought for a moment.

"Would it be possible to integrate the assistants into the dispensary system and train them to be normal health workers, as well as sleeping sickness specialists. You would have to ensure that you identified someone as the sleeping sickness specialist in each location and allocated them specific time for that role, so that their job was not overwhelmed by day-to-day issues."

Now it was Dr Ben's time to consider. After a long silence, he spoke.

"That is a possibility. I have, in theory, room to hire more nurses, despite the government freeze. I will think about it."

This seemed a good place to end our first meeting. I told him that I would communicate with Paris, to sound out expert opinion in the medical department. Perhaps we could meet again soon, to establish a strategy. There had been two years of conflict with MSF, but I felt we had the start of a working relationship and the beginnings of a plan. This was progress! Pleased, I returned to Kampala

One of my more routine duties back in the capital was to complete exemption documentation for a new car. As an NGO, in theory we paid no import tax, which at this time in Uganda was 90% of the car's value. Our vehicle had cost £10,000, so this was an important issue. I began the process rather casually, thinking that as an educated English speaker, I would have no problems. Thus began a long journey, one that appeared to lead me round every government office in the country. It was to be eleven months before I completed the last stage of the process. By this time, the documents would have passed through fourteen different offices in Kampala and Entebbe, not to mention many personal meetings and endless paperwork.

After my first flurry of visits around the country, daily life in Kampala settled into a relatively ordinary routine, although there were constant reminders that this was Uganda and there was a "civil war" in progress. Newspapers regularly reported unusual events, like the day six fishermen died in Lake Victoria, when their boat was capsized by hippopotami. With depressing regularity, children fell into cesspits and drowned. In rebel areas, where most of our people were based, there were endless reports of shootings and killing. Sometimes there were grenade attacks right in the centre of Kampala, causing a bit of damage, injury or death, but in the main life in the capital was like the work of an anaesthetist: long periods of routine, followed by short, desperate bursts of panic.

It was disappointing to hear from Paris that my proposal concerning the sleeping sickness surveillance system had been rejected. The medical department had asked Epicentre (a sister organisation) to oversee the original surveillance system and they were not keen to see their contribution ignored. It did not seem to matter that it was extremely difficult to implement on the ground, or that it was pointless to insist on a system which would collapse as soon as we left. Surely it was better to compromise now and build something that would continue, ensuring that recent achievements would not be swept aside. Thus began a long battle to persuade Paris to change its mind.

I was now more than ready for a visit to Arua, to see how things were progressing. Since the road was currently supposed to be safe and one of our vehicles was being sent north after a major service, I decided to join the driver on this trip, to see a bit more of the country. It was a fourteen-hour drive, so we set off at 4am, making good progress and stopping at midday, to give our driver a rest. Soon after lunch, we passed a burned-out bus at the edge of the road.

"The bus was attacked last year and nineteen people were killed," the driver told me. "There are still rebels around here."

So much for "safe" roads.

We had a second stop, at the Murchison Falls, a well-known tourist attraction, where the White Nile flows from Lake Victoria and passes through a spectacular, narrow gorge, tumbling one hundred feet, into the river below. It was well worth the detour, though the area was infested with tsetse flies and I was bitten several times. Luckily, there is no sleeping sickness in that part of the country, so I only had painful bites to worry about. Although the journey was enjoyable, after fourteen hours in the pickup, I resolved not to repeat the experience.

Returning to Arua made a pleasant change, for here there were old friends and a familiar situation, a contrast to the seemingly endless stream of new and difficult problems elsewhere. In fact, it almost felt like coming home! John had erected tents in the hospital grounds, enabling him to carry out extensive screening of the people from Owafa, increasing the number of patients up to sixty. He was keen to move the programme back to Omugo, but security there was not yet good enough.

Arua had developed a great deal in the short time since I had left; the market was much busier and there were two new restaurants and even a night-club! Unfortunately, this change resulted from the civil wars in neighbouring Zaire and South Sudan, which made Uganda seem safer by comparison. Thanks to the conflict in these countries, the only useful regional currency was the Ugandan shilling and this fact, together with increased traffic from Nairobi, via Kampala, had caused Arua to flourish. My visit went smoothly and although I enjoyed spending time with old friends, the distinct lack of problems gave me no reason to stay. There were problems enough waiting in Kampala.

CHAPTER NINE

Injustice everywhere

At Gang Dyang, food distribution was causing difficulties, so I made a return visit. Jean-Loup met me at the airstrip and we went straight to the camp, where we found about fifty residents assembled outside the dispensary tent. A young man was speaking.

"There is no food left. The last delivery was two weeks ago and that was only enough for three days."

Hervé, the World Food Programme (WFP) representative, was trying to explain his organisation's problem.

"We are not in a position to provide all your needs. Our next supply is delayed because of transportation difficulties, but your fields have food in them and there are stores in your villages. You must try to help yourselves. At best we can only supply one thousand kilocalories per person, per day. That's about half the amount you need."

"And there's another problem," the young man said. "The food you send doesn't reach everybody. You should give it directly to each family."

Apparently, the food was distributed from a WFP lorry to the six headmen, who had the responsibility of sharing it between all the families in the camp.

"The headmen always take more food than they should," the young man complained.

"They sell it on the market in Kitgum," someone else shouted.

"I can't be responsible for distribution. That's up to the headmen," repeated Hervé. "I don't have the staff to hand out supplies to individuals. If there's a problem with your people, you must deal with it yourselves. We can only bring the supplies. With the resources we have, that's difficult enough."

We got nowhere and the meeting broke up without a constructive conclusion. Afterwards, although I tried to talk to Hervé, he left immediately in the UN aeroplane. In the meantime, I gathered as much information as I could from Jean-Loup and said that I would talk to

Hervé, back in Kampala. If that didn't work, I would speak to Mike (the WFP boss) to see if he could think of anything. But neither of us was optimistic about the outcome. The WFP was really short of staff in Uganda, so it was necessary for the local people to organise distribution themselves. However, with a background of subterfuge and corruption, we all knew that this was never likely to be done fairly.

Another of my tasks as Medical Co-ordinator, was to remain vigilant about Uganda's other needs. Famine conditions had been reported, both in the East, near Mbale and in the West, at Kasese. As a result, the WFP people planned to visit Mbale and since they had no medical staff of their own at that time, I offered to join them, to provide medical input. We spent two days travelling around, but found no sign of food shortages. On the other hand, I was able to discuss the deteriorating situation in Kitgum with Mike, the WFP boss.

"There are about twelve thousand people in the camp and they are only receiving half rations," I told him. "If this goes on, we'll face increased sickness, especially amongst the children. Is there anything you can do about increasing the quantities, even a little?"

"We only have about two thousand tonnes left in stock for the whole country," Mike told me. "There's another eleven thousand tonnes in Dar es Salaam, but the rail link is poor at the moment. Anyway, it looks as if most of that will be sent to South Sudan."

"So what does that mean for Uganda?"

"World-wide, we have barely received 50% of what we need this year and we can only distribute what we are given. The Americans may release more stocks, but that won't be appropriate for here. As you know, Ugandans don't like American grain. It doesn't help that in Uganda, much of what we distribute reappears on the black market within days. It's been a bad year so far and I don't feel too optimistic about the next few months," he concluded.

It seemed as if the situation in the camps was going to get worse, so that, like Mr Micawber, I could only hope that something would turn up. After Mbale, I moved on to check on the reported famine in the west of the country. The ICRC base in Kasese said that there were one hundred thousand IDPs in the area. These people had fled from the Allied Democratic Forces (ADF), who had taken possession of the Ruwenzori mountains, evicting the peasant farmers from their land in the foothills, to give themselves freedom of movement. Three thousand men were attacking both government and civilian targets. The rebels had gained a substantial larder of food, while the communities who owned the land now had nothing.

During two busy days in the Kasese area, I visited twelve different "camps" that were clustered around small towns. The majority of people were accommodated in hastily constructed huts, the exception being at Kilembe Mine, where a once thriving and profitable cobalt-mining operation (now non-productive) had five hundred empty mineworkers' houses. Now, these were home to eight thousand IDPs! I found this mine and its village, at the end of a long, winding road, with tightly spaced buildings on either side of the mountain stream that tumbled down into Kasese.

In contrast to Kitgum, the authorities here were offering some help to the IDPs. They could use the dispensaries and, if they had no money, treatment was free. In the various dispensaries and camps, I looked at the children and asked health workers if they had noticed an increase in malnutrition, but there was no evidence of an acute problem, as yet. I booked into the Marguerita Hotel for the night, enjoying its comparative luxury, from the days when the Ruwenzori Mountains were open to walkers and mountaineers. Local people said that there were no current security problems in the area, but early in the morning I heard machine-gun fire from the hillside opposite my window. It was some distance away, but I was warned by the hotel staff not to go up the valley to Kilembe at night.

The mountain people, who had been forced to descend onto the savannah by the rebels, were now suffering badly from malaria; they had no immunity, because there were no malarial mosquitoes at the higher altitudes. Since the number of new cases had depleted local stocks of the drug chloroquine, I arranged to send additional supplies.

At the various sites, I talked to displaced people, who told me that many of them were staying with family or friends and thus they had no problem with shelter. Food supplies, were adequate for the moment, because some of the fields on lower mountain slopes were accessible during the day. However, the rebels had begun to bury land mines, so no one knew what would happen next. There was no evidence of acute malnutrition, but I made a note to return in three months, to check if there was any deterioration in the situation.

On my return to Kampala, I spoke to the food expert from Oxfam and learned of her concern that there would be long-term nutritional problems, rather than acute famine. This issue was clearly outside MSF competence, so I explained that there was nothing we could do.

Caroline, our administrator, now raised another issue.

"We had a visit from a man called Roger, who said he was a lab technician in Moyo. He has been studying in Kampala and wanted to collect money for his expenses. MSF has been sponsoring him for eighteen months. Do you know anything about it?"

"I know we have several students, but I haven't had time to discover much about it yet. I'll get back to you with the details."

I remembered I had seen something in one of Evan's files, making reference to a training programme, so I began to shuffle through the papers and eventually found the details she required. MSF was sponsoring six people: two laboratory technicians, two nurses, and two medical assistants, who were studying in a town called Gulu, in the North, between Kitgum and Adjumani. Although training is not part of the core business of MSF, it is obviously an important element when you are trying to improve a country's health care.

I decided to visit Gulu, taking advantage of the opportunity to find out about the health problems in the area. This was a delicate situation, since MSF Holland, our sister organisation, had a local project and there is an unwritten rule in MSF not to poach on one another's patches. When I learned that MSF Holland was also planning to visit Gulu to evaluate the refugee situation, I offered to write a medical report for them, since they currently had no doctor.

This involvement in sensitive protocol prompted me to ask Yves if he knew how the problem of the MSF sections had originated. He explained that the organisation was formed in 1971, when a group of French doctors working for the Red Cross, became frustrated by the imposition of the Red Cross code of silence, demanded of all its employees. This requirement is soundly based, on the principle of absolute neutrality, which allows the Red Cross to work effectively on both sides of any conflict. However, these French doctors saw and experienced atrocities in Biafra, which convinced them that speaking out was sometimes more important than remaining silent, even if it meant expulsion from the country. Silence, they felt, could be equated with collusion, so they formed their own organisation, which became Médecins Sans Frontières. Today, it comprises 19 sections, working in the most needy countries in the world.

Only five major sections, those of France, Belgium, Holland, Spain and Switzerland, are "operational" and only these have the authority to initiate projects. The other fourteen sections link to one of the five, raising money, recruiting staff and increasing awareness of the organisation within these countries. There is also an international committee, but it has no real power. The result is five organisations with the same name, but often with different objectives and working practices. There is even competition, which must be confusing for countries where MSF is working. And then there is the language issue. MSF Holland uses English, MSF Spain uses Spanish and MSF Belgium mainly uses French, but sometimes English. Even within this arrangement there are anomalies, since United States volunteers often speak Spanish as their second language, but their section is linked to MSF France!

I was grateful that I had managed so easily to organise the trip to Gulu, with Iris, the MSF Holland administrator. After the five-hour journey, we installed ourselves in the now empty MSF Holland house and that afternoon began the rounds of the camps that Iris wanted to see. The next day, I visited the hospital at Lochor (just outside Gulu). This institution had been founded forty years earlier, by an Italian doctor and his wife and became the most prestigious hospital in the country. Wealthy Ugandans went there for treatment, in preference to Makarere University Hospital in Kampala. Some years later it would suffer a devastating outbreak of Ebola virus and, sadly, the hospital superintendent I met would become one of the 160 victims.

The founder of Lochor was now elderly and his wife had recently died of AIDS, caught while operating on a contaminated patient. Uganda, like most African countries, has a major AIDS problem, but due in large measure to the support of President Musaveni, it has begun to control the epidemic.

Iris dropped me off at the hospital and went off to continue her work at the camps. I spent some time with the head of nursing and with the Italian doctor, who ran the laboratory. For the return journey, I joined a queue for one of the Toyota, twelve-seater mini buses. Half a dozen of us boarded and then we waited…and waited, for it seemed that the driver had no intention of setting off without a full load. Eventually, more people got on board and then even more. By the time we left, we were twenty-eight souls, fortunately two or three being small children. I was glad that in such intense heat, it was only five kilometres back to town. My second port of call was to the Medical Assistant Training School in the middle of Gulu, where I met its Head, somewhat surprisingly named Cliff Richards. Of the two MSF students, one had absconded and the other was doing reasonably well.

The following day, Iris and I visited the two IDP camps, but neither of us felt that conditions warranted intervention from MSF. All the people I talked to insisted they did not want to go home. These camps had been in existence for three years and, although not perfect, they had most of the basics. There were perhaps two hundred and fifty thousand displaced people, forced there by the UPDF (the Ugandan army), in order to clear the countryside of individuals who could be considered dangerous to the regime. Anyone remaining in the newly created buffer-zone was shot. The tactic was called, "forced re-groupment" and MSF had originally decided not to intervene in the camps, as this would represent tacit approval for the coerced movement of a civil population–a definite abuse of their human rights. It is of course debatable whether this MSF decision was appropriate, since the population suffered badly from lack of support during the first few months. On the other hand, to send aid might have encouraged the government to do more of this type of thing. But whatever the human rights position, for the ordinary Ugandan it was a no win situation.

On returning to Kampala, I had a meeting with John, who proposed moving the sleeping sickness hospital back to Omugo, since there had been a long, quiet spell. We discussed the idea at length, sounding out various sources of opinion and then we requested permission from Paris, who gave the green light. Dr Imoko was particularly happy with the news, as he liked to have MSF based in Omugo, to support the dispensary. The staff were delighted, as it was more expensive for them to live in Arua. For the MSF team, it was more isolated, but the needs of the programme were our priority. We agreed a schedule and I left John to arrange the details.

It seemed ridiculous, that once back in my office, I was again involved in the wearisome pursuit of tax exemption for our car. While waiting in a variety of offices, I began to wonder why we were so insistent on demanding tax exemption in the first place. Seen from the MSF point of view, we were there to help the population of Uganda to have better health. However, the government also needed as much money as it could get, to improve roads, schools, manufacturing and agriculture, so perhaps, as a humanitarian gesture, we should pay taxes? Then I wondered what the people, who donated money would think was right. Whatever the answer, it was much too late to withdraw this application, so I ploughed on, curious to see if I would succeed before leaving the country.

Despite the fact that Yves and I had shared responsibilities, we rarely met, since he had a diurnal rhythm, completely at odds with my own. I rose at 6am and worked until 3pm, going to bed quite early. Yves got up at midday and worked till 10pm. He spent his evenings playing pool in Al's bar, a famous dive in Kabalagala, the local "hot spot", simply enjoying the contact and company. Our differing habits meant that we tended to work in isolation from one another and although I suggested regular weekly meetings, Yves seemed to have an aversion to such formal arrangements.

Then, one morning I read in the paper that ADF rebels had attacked the area around Bundibugyo, a town at the northern end of the Ruwenzori Mountains. After a day, the army had repulsed the rebels, but the surrounding population had flooded into the town for safety. It was reported that people were everywhere, swamping the local facilities. Since this seemed to be relevant to MSF, I left the paper on Yves' desk, with the article circled and a note saying, "Should we respond?" I didn't see Yves that day, but the next morning, he was in the office at 11am, saying that he would make an exploratory visit.

"Ten years ago, one of my first missions was in Fort Portal, so I know the area quite well," he said. "I spoke to the Red Cross yesterday and they have heard rumours that fifteen thousand people have moved into Bundibugyo. It normally has a population of just two thousand, so the result is chaos."

This situation could easily develop into another Kitgum and reliable information was urgently required.

"Do you want me to come too?" I asked.

"Not at the moment. We won't get access to Bundibugyo, until the military secures the road, so it's just a case of sounding out local opinion. I can do that on my own. When we have access, we can go together. Then you can tell me what you want to do, from a medical standpoint."

He set off the next day, spending three days in Fort Portal talking to the authorities, local taxi drivers and anyone else with information. Then he sent a message, saying that the military was being attacked each time they tried to go round the mountain road. For the moment, there was nothing we could do, but wait.

Of course, everything happens at once. The next morning we had a radio contact at 7.30am, saying that the Kitgum team had spent the night barricaded in the pharmacy (the only room with no windows). There had been a pitched battle near their house and they were all very shaken, asking to be evacuated immediately. I hired one of the MAF planes and they were back in Kampala by 2pm.

Jean-Loup, who had felt the burden of responsibility, was visibly upset. Not surprisingly, Annie seemed fairly unconcerned, although Véronique had a few tears. Jerome said nothing, but it had clearly been a traumatic night. The next day I arranged a meeting, but they said very little and I don't think it helped. Later, I spoke to Jean-Loup by himself, when he was able to talk a little more freely.

"I feel badly about leaving in such a hurry. I panicked," he said. "None of the other NGOs left, only us."

"What do the rest of them think?" I asked.

"I think they just agreed with me to make me feel better, to justify my decision," he said glumly.

We talked a little more and I tried to find something positive to say.

"Your first responsibility was for the safety of the team and you assured that. If anyone had been injured or killed, it would have been the end of the project. MSF would have withdrawn completely and the IDPs would have suffered. Remember, if things had gone the other way, you would be in no doubt that you had made the right decision. We just have to make judgments at the time and live with the consequences."

Unfortunately, Jean-Loup then overheard a radio conversation with Paris, where it was suggested that the group had indeed panicked. It was near the end of his mission, so he decided to leave immediately, rather than return to Kitgum. I was disappointed that he could not be persuaded to carry on for the remaining weeks, but I later heard that he completed a successful one-year mission in Kyrgyzstan. It was none the less a painful episode and for my part I wondered if I should have re-acted more slowly, to give the team time to re-consider their decision to pull out. Of course, they might then have resented not getting help quickly, at a time when they were truly in fear of their lives. If anything serious had happened, I would have had much more to worry about than a few bruised feelings. Many critical decisions have to be made without perfect information and circumstances that involve armed conflict always demand great caution.

Once we established that it was now safe for MSF to return, the Kitgum project carried on with a new nurse (Maria) and a new doctor (Helma). Maria, an Australian, with experience in humanitarian aid, replaced Jean-Loup as project leader. It was her first time in charge and she was very nervous, though extremely enthusiastic. Helma was German and at first seemed somewhat out of place in this situation. About fifty years old, she was very glamorously dressed, arriving with two huge suitcases full of food and clothes. This contrasted rather with the usual style of most of our workers, who came in tee shirts and shorts, their few belongings stuffed into a rucksack.

Helma had both medical and management experience, so she had automatically assumed that she would be in charge and was astonished to find that a nurse would be entrusted with such responsibility. MSF ignores all the normal rules of medical status that most of us have been brought up to expect and project leadership is based on relevant experience, rather than technical knowledge. The organisation has developed an individual code of behaviour and rules to meet the very individual demands that are made on it.

"Dealing with security is an important issue and that skill has to be learned in the field," I explained to Helma, in an effort to soothe ruffled feelings and ensure that she had a viable working relationship with Maria.

"Who will be in charge of the medical side?" she asked, a little warily.

"You will make all the technical decisions and recommend how the dispensaries function, but Maria has seen more of the way things work in the Third World and she has nursing knowledge, which you do not," I told her. "Medical work here will be very different to what you have known. It's vital that the person in charge is familiar with running a medical facility, in this environment. You will discover that you have a lot to learn," I assured her.

"It seems a bit odd to me, but I can give it a try," she said.

I felt there was a chance the relationship might work. It was up to the pair of them to co-operate. Before Maria went to Kitgum, I had a final chat with her, to show that she had my support. She admitted that she was still nervous and wondered how she would manage, "in charge" of a team that included a doctor.

"In Australia, it's always the other way round," she said.

"I know, but MSF recognises that nurses may have more management experience and anyway, no one is allowed to be in charge on their first mission. Helma will take a little time to adjust, but I'm sure she will do her best."

Yves now came back from Fort Portal, suggesting that we maintain a presence there, so that we would know when conditions allowed us to get into Bundibugyo. He had already identified a group of IDPs who required assistance. These people had walked over the mountains to Fort Portal and were overloading one of its dispensaries. If Annie and I visited, we could make contact with the medical authorities and let them know who we were, as well as making a donation of basic medicines to this dispensary. So three days later, Annie and I set off. We booked into a small hotel on the edge of Fort Portal, run by an eccentric English couple, who were trying to establish "women's lib groups" in the town. The hotel was a way of earning enough money to survive, while pursuing this goal. From our point of view, it was less expensive than the two bigger hotels, with the prize-winning advantage of functioning, hot showers.

When I had been at the southern end of the Ruwenzori Mountains in Kasese, I had not appreciated their size. The range is about eighty kilometres long and ten kilometres wide and the highest peak is snow covered for almost the whole year. Such steep, rugged countryside was an ideal place for the ADF rebels to hide and even with American training, the Ugandan army had not managed to dislodge the rebels from this natural fortress. Now they roamed around the high ground at will, sometimes descending to attack villages, sometimes retreating into Zaire. Unfortunately, they had learned from the Lords Resistance Army and were abducting children and adolescents to train as new recruits. It was generally assumed that foreign money was sustaining the ADF, probably from Sudan and perhaps Zaire, since they seemed to have no shortage of ammunition and land mines. Now, in June 1997, they had become strong enough to attack Bundibugyo.

In Fort Portal, I met two members of the MSF Holland team, Jules and Dirk. They were also evaluating the situation, so we agreed to share information and perhaps plan a joint intervention. They currently had four expatriate staff in Kampala, plus a great deal of logistic material, but no projects. If they did not identify something worthwhile soon, their headquarters would close the mission. But when I returned to Kampala, Yves was upset by this news, feeling that Fort Portal was our patch and that MSF Holland did not have the right to intervene, unless we gave them permission. He had several long conversations with the Desk in Paris and they encouraged this competitive stance. I felt embarrassed by their attitude and tried to push for a co-operative, rather than a combative position. At my behest, the Heads of Mission held a meeting, but it was unproductive, becoming a childish game of one-upmanship. I was irritated by this behaviour, seeing no point in fighting for ownership, when there was so much obvious need.

Annie then sent a message, saying that a military helicopter would be taking the WFP staff to Bundibugyo, to assess the requirement for food aid. I planned to go with them, intending to hitch a lift, but at the last minute, Dominique told me that the car was being serviced and it wouldn't be ready in time. Since I couldn't go, the WFP took instead a nurse from MSF Holland, increasing Yves' distress even further.

But the news about the refugees was confirmed and we began to plan a project, to begin as soon as we could get staff into Bundibugyo. I suggested hiring a helicopter jointly with MSF Holland, but neither headquarters would agree! So Annie stayed on in Fort Portal, sending regular radio reports about security conditions, on the only road into Bundibugyo. We waited, knowing that all the time the situation of the IDPs would be deteriorating.

Meanwhile at Kitgum, the Gang Dyang camp was growing all the time and increasing numbers of malnourished children had forced us to open up a feeding centre for the under fives. In any population, when there is insufficient food, it is the young children who suffer most. Children need food to sustain growth and if they cease to gain weight over a period of months, they stop growing, a condition called stunting.

Severe cases are obvious, but the less severe require an objective measure. MSF derives the relationship between height and weight and those who are less than 80% of "normal," are sent to a feeding centre, where they are given three meals a day. This way, we can be sure that the children get the food. An alternative approach is to give each child a parcel of food to take away, but this inevitably gets shared out amongst family members.

Feeding centres are usually tents, quickly constructed, where each week children are registered, weighed, measured and given a medical examination, if there is any doubt about their health. The kitchen is wondrous to behold, with a wood fire, heating great cauldrons of beans and maize flour pasta, with added oil. If some children are seriously malnourished, a separate unit can be set up, for intensive treatment and intravenous fluid therapy. These feeding centres are normally very cheerful places.

The dispensary in Gang Dyang Camp had initially been asked to cope with about thirty consultations per day, which had seemed quite achievable. Now, the number had risen to seventy, so that we had to employ a second nurse. The DMO had still not found any staff who would be willing to help. MSF was clearly being left to cope with this camp on its own, however many representations we made to the local authorities. It was outrageous, but we were caught between political manoeuvring and the needs of individuals.

On one of my regular visits to Kitgum, Maria wanted to talk about numbers. She invited Jerome to join us and he explained the problem.

"It's quite chaotic," he told me. "There are new arrivals every day and we have no place for them to go. There are not enough tents. Each morning, we find more huts, in between those that already existed. It's so overcrowded, that we are having difficulty getting in with the lorry, for food and water distribution. The toilets are full and we are digging two hundred more. Even that's not nearly enough."

The situation was worse than I thought.

"When did this start?" I asked.

"It's been getting worse, ever since we arrived," Maria told me. "The change-over meant that we did not spot the problem as early as we might. Now, the situation is becoming critical."

"Exactly how many people are there?" I asked glumly.

"We think twelve thousand, but our registration system is breaking down, so we're not even sure about that," Jerome said.

"You have to get the authorities to find more land, or we will have sanitation and water problems," I said to Maria. "The last thing we need is an outbreak of cholera."

"Can I also talk about the other camps, while you're here?" asked Maria. "Although we are providing health-care support in Gang Dyang and Palabek, the other four camps have nothing at all. And there's a problem with the water supply at Palabek Kal. For three weeks, Oxfam haven't managed to mend the water pumps. Palabek Kal is on the same road, so we stop there sometimes. The DMO has done nothing and the people there are desperate. Action Contra la Faim said they would help in one of the camps, but that still leaves three others. You must try to get some response from the DMO."

"What did he say to you, when you saw him?"

"I told him that he should allocate new land for Gang Dyang and I suggested that he move some health staff into the other camps. As usual, he said it was impossible. I think he is holding out, in the hope that we feel obliged to do something ourselves. Then, he will have less responsibility and can use his money elsewhere."

In a short time, I could feel that Maria had developed a decided antipathy towards this man. This team was encountering problems that he should have cleared up for its predecessors. I offered to go with her to see him and she seemed relieved.

"How are you getting on with Helma?"

"She isn't easy, but after a couple of clashes, we're able to function."

"I'll help, if you like," I said, "but it really boils down to good relations between you two. As the project leader you have my full support, but it's usually best to avoid too much confrontation, though there are times when you must assert yourself."

I knew that Maria hated confrontation and this was a veiled way of suggesting that it might be best if she took a strong stand. With the right handling, I thought that Helma could be a very positive force. In fact, apart from personality clashes with Maria (and the rest of the team), Helma had by this time shown herself to be extremely capable of both organising and at times bullying local staff into action.

I suggested that Helma should organise the dispensaries in the other three camps. At the same time, Maria should tell the DMO that we would start things off, but he would have to take over. I knew that this was giving in to his pressure, but it seemed crazy to do nothing, when people were suffering from easily treatable conditions. Maria was both pleased to accept my suggestions and satisfied that we had agreed a plan for the next two months. Helma also expressed delight in having a defined task to attack and she set to with enthusiasm.

When I returned to Kampala, I arranged a meeting with Oxfam, to discuss the broken water pump at Palabek camp. Since the population now had, on average, only two litres of water per day for each person, there was a massive increase in diarrhoeal disease. I prepared a simple graphical display of consultations in the dispensary, which showed that the outbreak had started just after the water pump failure. When we showed this data to Oxfam they responded immediately, repairing the pump within three days. Kitgum now seemed to be under short-term control, but I did wonder where things were going in the longer term.

John meanwhile, had arranged to move the Sleeping Sickness programme back to Omugo. The timing was good, as it coincided with the arrival of his replacement, Susan, from California. It was her first mission and she had requested a project with a large number of expatriates, in a safe area, speaking either English, or Spanish. In best MSF tradition she was sent to Omugo, a small mission, in a dangerous area, with only herself and a French-speaking log for company. She accepted the situation pluckily, but was dismayed when the log turned out to be a 23 year old French lad who commented, "If you don't smoke, don't drink and don't like men, what are we going to do here for six months?"

He solved his problem by planting cannabis in the garden and soon we had to step in and pack him off, back to France. His replacement was a jovial, 45 year old Quebecois called Robert, who admittedly liked a beer but was otherwise, Susan reported, "adorable".

Fortuitously, Susan's arrival meant that we had the opportunity to use John's support in Bundibugyo, if he could be persuaded to stay on for another six weeks. He was a tough, resourceful character and our new project cried out for someone of his calibre. Yves had gone off to join Annie in Fort Portal, as soon as she reported that a few private cars had travelled safely into Bundibugyo. Later, Yves reported that he had been very nervous, when they had made the journey together, but Annie had remained remarkably unconcerned. We pondered over her bravery and our faint-heartedness.

After two-days assessment of the situation, Yves reported back.

"It's just like Kitgum was during the first few weeks. The people are sleeping everywhere. We must do something immediately."

He estimated that there were ten thousand IDPs in Bundibugyo itself, but in total there were possibly seventy thousand, scattered for some miles along the access road. If we did nothing, an outbreak of illness was inevitable.

Paris agreed that a project should be established and confirmed that a team would arrive within a few weeks. Since we had already been watching the problem for several weeks, this was not classed as an emergency, so we were encouraged to make the best use of existing resources. Of course, MSF is capable of responding internationally, within twenty-four hours, but it is often possible to reassign local staff and equipment, to satisfy an immediate need. Unfortunately, by doing so, ongoing projects are sometimes compromised.

We were fortunate that John had agreed to extend his contract. Annie meanwhile returned to Kampala, to prepare her end of mission report, before going home to France. It would certainly be difficult to replace such enthusiasm and blind courage. John set off for Fort Portal, accompanied by Jean-Luc, the log from Kampala, and I agreed to visit a few days later, both to become familiar with the site and to help John plan the medical component of the work.

In the meantime, I made a trip to Omugo, so see how Susan was managing. One of her first tasks had been to establish mobile teams to screen the population. This active phase of the programme required free access around the country, so we had equipped a vehicle with testing equipment, dispatching it to one village at a time. Any patients found to be positive were transported back to the Omugo laboratory for full testing and necessary treatment. To obtain 100% screening, the sleeping sickness assistants had to alert villages about their forthcoming visits and persuade everyone, including busy farmers, to stop work to be tested. We estimated that it would take about ten months to screen the one hundred thousand people in Terego County, if we had one vehicle working full time. I knew, however, that rebel activity had always precluded such continuity in the past.

Regrettably, we now had a more serious problem to deal with in Omugo. When we had previously evacuated the hospital, I had noticed a high percentage of re-treatment patients on the ward, people whose check-ups had revealed that the parasite was still in their spinal fluid. At first, I thought this was due to the interruption in treatment, but the percentage remained persistently high, at around 20% or 25%. Another suggestion was that these people had simply become re-infected. Dominique, (our epidemiologist) had become interested and was reviewing the records of all patients treated over the previous ten years. Fortunately, he was already using computerised patient records for existing research projects.

To my dismay, he came to the conclusion that we had evidence of resistance to Arsobal, which was the only effective drug we possessed for second stage patients. It was indeed a terrifying thought. If this resistance became widespread, there would be no treatment for the condition and it would once more become the plague that it had been, at the beginning of the 20th century. Initially, I could not believe that it was resistance, suggesting that Arua might just be an anomaly. However, over the following weeks Dominique built up what seemed to be a cast iron case. In Adjumani, we had only 3% re-treatment and in Omugo, from the very beginning, there had been an 18% treatment failure. I became convinced that we were seeing the emergence of a resistant strain and had to consider what to do next.

This awareness changed our attitude to people who were returning for re-treatment. Susan had the unenviable task, of deciding what to say.

"You have a resistant strain and there is nothing more that we can do. Go home and die," seemed harsh. But should we instead keep silent and re-treat people, knowing it was probably useless? We realised that the much lower incidence of reaction to Arsobal in Arua could be another indicator of an ineffective drug, but it was no consolation to think that if patients were resistant, at least the treatment could not kill them. Now, their future seemed even more desperate. After some discussion, we decided to treat people three times and then stop. In effect, this was putting off the horrible job of telling patients there was nothing we could do for them, but it gave us some comfort to have a protocol. For Susan, it made her job terrible. She was a very caring doctor and found her new task extremely stressful.

Since the treatment for second phase patients was of doubtful benefit, we decided that the whole population should be screened quickly, so that we could identify more first stage patients who could be treated with Pentamidine. For some unknown reason, this screening did not work as planned and we continued to encounter a large number of second stage cases. It was all extremely frustrating, but I had to return to Kampala, leaving Susan to battle on alone. Despite my commitment to the programme, this was not my only responsibility.

Once I had checked on the progress of our other projects, I met with Dominique, to see if he had any new ideas about Arsobal resistance.

"I have been talking to Karim in Paris," he told me. "He has consulted the WHO sleeping sickness experts in Geneva."

"What do they think?"

"So far, they have found no similar situations in other countries. It would have been nice to have a comparison. We need to find both an immediate solution for Omugo and a longer term solution, since resistance will surely spread."

I too had been considering the problem and a course of action.

"It is my opinion that we have to do three things. First, we should try to prove that we have genuine resistance to Arsobal and not another factor. Then we must get hold of some DFMO, the research drug, to see if it helps our patients. And finally, we must present the problem to the International Sleeping Sickness Conference at Maputo."

Dominique said that he would approach the Sleeping Sickness Institute in Jinja, since they might have the capacity to culture the parasites and test their response to Arsobal. He had heard that a Ugandan expert, Dr Enyaru, was doing research there and he might be able to help.

"I could visit him," I suggested.

"Okay. I will get in touch with Pierre Catand in Geneva, to ask if he has any DFMO left in stock," said Dominique. "But we must present the problem to the Conference, whatever the state of our analyses."

So two days later I set off for Jinja, to discuss the problem with Dr Enyaru and ask if he could conduct a trial culture in rats. He offered to try, warning me that the success percentage was unlikely to be high.

While in Jinja, I also visited Dr Maiso, who had been writing a thesis on the subject of DFMO, the new drug that we were hoping to use. I asked him if he knew of a source.

"There were about a dozen bottles left in stock from the trial, but I think the WHO has a reserve stock of five thousand bottles, either in New York, or in Geneva."

This was excellent news.

Then I remembered to enquire if he had a contact in the WHO. He found the details and I sent an e-mail immediately, to ask if they could supply us with some vials, while Dominique supported my request with details of his resistance study. All I could do now was to wait with crossed fingers. Knowing what I did about the effects of this disease on the Ugandan people, the thought of resistance spreading was devastating.

CHAPTER TEN

A lost world

A few days later, I set out to visit John at Bundibugyo. From Fort Portal the drive around the northern end of the Ruwenzori Mountains is spectacular, with a 300-metre difference in altitude between the Ugandan plateau and the rain forest of Zaire. Near Bundibugyo, the land falls away towards the Semliki National Park, whose dense vegetation conceals both a large number of wild animals and a reclusive group of pygmies. As the IDPs began to encroach on their land, these people judiciously retreated, so that their lives were relatively unchanged by the upheaval.

After two and a half uncomfortable hours on the single-track road, we passed a few simple huts and occasional people. Then military posts appeared, every two kilometres or so, each boasting a complement of teenage boys. These were either lounging around in camouflage uniforms or sleeping in the shade, with their Kalashnikovs strewn carelessly by their sides. Some had built tiny shelters from banana fronds, some were drinking tea, but all looked extremely bored.

The town had been established on the only flat piece of land for miles around, with barely room for a thin ribbon of houses on either side of the road. It was not hard to find John and Jean-Luc, as the MSF cars were parked outside their small hotel, where they were having lunch. This establishment had ten rooms, each about three metres square, with a single shower located at one end of the central courtyard. The toilet was perched precariously on the very edge of a steep slope, which then allowed gravity to take its course.

"I see you had an easy trip—no bullet holes in your car," joked John. Then, after a Coke and more banter, he outlined some difficulties. This was where we discovered that he wasn't joking. In fact, he had nothing in the least encouraging to say about the place.

"It's the armpit of the world. Even before the attack, nothing worked and no one wanted to come here. According to the last census, twenty years ago, the regional population was about one hundred and forty thousand and now half of them are displaced. So more than seventy thousand people are settled along the roadside, from here to The Hot Springs. There are six groups, but it's more a general condensation of people, rather than separate camps."

"What are the authorities like?" I asked.

"Most have left and are afraid to come back. The DMO was suspended from his post on suspicion of fraud two years ago. He volunteered to return, in an effort to regain his credibility, but he spends most of his time in Fort Portal. Luckily, the administrator is competent, so we try to work with him. The hospital had two doctors before this trouble, but one went back to Fort Portal after the attack and the other is an alcoholic, who also has AIDS."

Clearly, John was warming to his theme.

"So far, we have achieved almost nothing. There are three distinct groups of IDPs in town: one in the old coffee factory, one in the church grounds and another on the football pitch. There's absolutely no organisation for any of them."

"How many people are there in Bundibugyo itself?"

"About ten thousand, but it's hard to be sure. People are streaming in and out, all the time."

"Have you managed to formulate any plans?"

Jean Luc took over.

"Up till now, all our efforts have been to provide clean water. The camp in the church grounds is the only one with a tap, so we try to encourage people to move up there. But the IDPs here say that's not safe, since it's too far from town. They're worried that the rebels will return, even with soldiers around. Meanwhile the IDPs on the football pitch have to walk seven hundred metres to get water from the river, where there's absolutely no control. Some use it as a toilet and others wash themselves and their clothes, alongside people collecting water for drinking. It must be contaminated. There's no system of upstream drinking water collection."

"Can you give me a quick tour?" I asked.

I wanted to see this debacle for myself, before deciding what to do.

We visited each of the three sites and I quickly saw why the MSF staff were disheartened. The settlement was even smaller than I had first thought, with the market and hospital as the main landmarks and the old coffee factory, which was right in the middle of town. This area was absolutely full of people, sleeping on mattresses, simple straw mats, or directly on the ground. Here, the sanitation was appalling and the overcrowding was both ridiculous and unnecessary. There was a notable lack of rubbish, however, and in aid organisations we recognise this as an indisputable sign of genuine poverty. We went on to visit the other sites, finding some people established in Red Cross tents, others squatting in existing buildings and yet more in makeshift huts. Finally, we returned to the hotel to discuss a strategy for this huge, disorganised mess.

"I think we must revert to the standard checklist for refugees, to give ourselves a reliable framework," I suggested. "Water, which you have started, Food, Shelter, Measles Vaccination, Health Care, Latrines, Surveillance, Camp Organisation, Security and Liaison with other involved parties, including the authorities. Since there is virtually nothing here, we must go back to basics. Are there any other NGOs working here?"

"There's a local branch of the Red Cross, but they have no money at the moment. The ICRC came two days ago from Kasese and dumped a load of tents, but they couldn't control their distribution, so they are now all over the place. The ICRC are too short-staffed to have a presence here. It was just fortunate that they had some spare tents."

"Anyone else?"

"There was a German NGO, but the doctor and his wife were abducted for a few hours, just before the rebel attack, so their headquarters sent instructions that, for the moment, they should leave. It's a shame. They've had a good programme for years, both here and in Fort Portal. It is rumoured that they will come back next month."

I felt that Jean-Luc was glad to have found something positive to say. Then he thought of something else.

"There's a missionary called Rick Gray living in Nyahuka, the next village along from here. He's been there for eight years and we've contacted him once or twice on his HF radio, although we can't get to him, since the bridge was blown up. He says there are lots of IDPs with him and they need help badly in their dispensary."

I thought for a moment. We were facing a huge task. Then, I jotted down a few things on a bit of paper, to help me think.

"Right, normally the first priority is to set up measles vaccination, but here, I think we need more information. You can't do much on your own, so you need some partners. Try to identify people to liaise with in each camp. They can collect information and do some of the work—the headmen will know who are the best people. Tell them we must have an accurate assessment of numbers, to plan toilets, shelter, water and health care. That phase may take up to two weeks, but once we have data, we can move on quickly. More importantly, we'll be sure we're doing the right thing. The authorities should be able to tell you which health structures are still functioning. They won't all have disappeared. Try to avoid paying people, as that creates problems later on. Use existing networks, where you can find them."

I was sure that the situation was sufficiently like Kitgum to use the same formula.

"Is there any news from Paris about a team to take over from us?" asked Jean-Luc.

He was, par excellence, the man for emergencies, bored unless he was at the sharp end of projects. After two weeks here with no progress, he was keen to move on. I was able to reassure him.

"We sent a message to Paris that they should send four people: a doctor, a log, and two nurses. Do you think that's right?"

"Yes, it will certainly take more than two people to get this place moving," John agreed. "And initially, I think they should all be male. Three nights ago, several young soldiers were drinking here and at about 2am, they started firing in the air and being abusive. We believe they raped three of the women workers in the hotel. I don't think it's secure enough here, for women to be sent."

"Have you identified a house to rent?" I asked Jean-Luc.

"There's one about half way to the camp, at the church, but people say it would be too exposed if the rebels returned, so I'm still looking."

As I left the following morning, I did not envy them their task. This strange and beautiful spot was very isolated and with any further outbreak of rebel activity, it would be difficult to manage. We desperately needed a solid team to be sent from Paris, people who could cope with such a challenge, but I knew that as usual it was in the lap of the gods. MSF policy is to attract people who are highly motivated by the humanitarian ideal. They pay very little, because they want to avoid professional humanitarian workers, people who are just there for the money. I understand why they value the enthusiasm of a constant flow of new recruits, but some situations do require experienced people, who can cope with specialised demands. Faced by great and complex need in an unfamiliar environment, foreign aid workers have the capacity to do serious harm, as well as tremendous good, particularly when they have both resources and expertise that local authorities may lack.

Back in the relative calm of Kampala, I prioritised the writing of my monthly medical report for Paris, which included our plans for Bundibugyo. To an outsider, this might seem a trivial, bureaucratic activity, but continuity in MSF comes from The Desk. There are six Desks in Paris, each in charge of seven or eight countries and it is vital that Heads of Mission make regular, detailed reports.

I also had a meeting with Karim, from the MSF medical department in Paris. He had come out to discuss the sleeping sickness programmes. We talked about the problem of Arsobal resistance in some detail, Karim suggesting that with Dominique, I should prepare a report for the Maputo conference. The three of us would attend and MSF would also sponsor a representative from the sleeping sickness unit in Jinja, either Dr Maiso or Dr Mbulamberi.

"I think it would be a good idea for Susan to go too," I suggested. "She has first hand information, but more importantly, she's very passionate about the problem and will have quite an impact on the guys from WHO."

Karim was at first dubious, but he finally agreed.

More importantly, he brought a little DFMO, enough for twenty-five patients. The WHO stock would be released soon and MSF would buy as much as possible, but the total world stock would only treat three hundred and fifty patients.

"There is no long-term answer, unless someone can be persuaded to start producing DFMO again," he told me.

"Why wouldn't they?" I asked, unable to believe that such an obvious solution might be ignored.

"It's very expensive to make and even if it was produced, who could afford it in the places it's needed?" he asked bluntly. "People in Africa just don't have that sort of money and sleeping sickness is an African problem."

"How much is "very expensive"?"

"A company in Texas quoted two hundred and fifty thousand dollars, to make a batch of five thousand vials, enough to treat three hundred and fifty patients. That comes to seven hundred dollars, per person." So now I could understand the problem. Uganda spends fourteen dollars, per person, per year on healthcare. The cost of DFMO was therefore unthinkable for this country.

Despite this gloomy picture, we had a little of the drug to use now, so I went immediately to Omugo to discuss the issue with Susan.

"Have you thought about how to use the DFMO?" I asked, as soon as we could sit down and talk.

"We will start right away. I've read the protocol," she told me.

"Have you considered whether we should be using the seven day, or the fourteen day treatment?" I asked. "Dr Maiso's trial is not finished, but the results seem to suggest that seven days could be as effective as fourteen. And if we opt for seven days, we can treat twice as many patients," I added.

"Yes, but it also says the failure rate might be higher," she retorted.

"How many resistant patients do we have?"

"At present we have sixty, but Dominique's figures suggest 18% of all the cases will be resistant. That means about twelve new cases per month, plus the sixty that we already know about," she replied.

"We have enough DFMO for twenty-five people, if you want to use the fourteen day treatment."

Susan started.

"I hadn't realised we had so little. We need much more. How do we choose?"

"Well, we could decide to treat people under a certain age, or working men, or women who have to care for a family. Whatever we decide, all the DFMO will be gone in three weeks. We can only treat twenty-five people, or at most fifty, if we use the seven day regime."

"That's awful. We can't choose patients like that," said Susan and she burst into tears. The strain of treating the resistant cases every day, knowing what she was doing was unlikely to help them, had taken a big emotional toll. When she recovered, she said, "MSF must buy up all the existing stocks, to give more people a chance."

"I agree, but that will not solve the problem of the next week or two and it won't solve the problem for the years to come. Big stocks of DFMO don't exist, so let's just concentrate on the immediate issue. I could write a protocol about whom we should treat," I suggested. "Then it wouldn't be your responsibility."

"You have no right to do that," she almost shouted, "You can't expect me to follow your arbitrary directions!"

"It's difficult and unpleasant, but we have to be logical and I'm trying to help you find a way to decide. I'm trying to share responsibility," I told her.

I was upset too. I had worked with some of these patients and knew what she was feeling, but we had to arrive at some sort of decision. We made no further progress that day, but the following morning we began treating Alexi, a fourteen year old boy in a coma. This was his fourth treatment, but he began to wake up after only two days. It was a marvellous feeling, especially for me, since I had already treated him twice, both in Omugo and Arua.

It was saving this patient that led Susan to come up with a workable solution, that of treating the most advanced cases. Since the disease progressed only slowly, other patients were not in danger of dying immediately and we could hope for a further supply after the Maputo meeting. It was at best a delaying tactic, but we saw no more attractive option. The main problem would be telling some patients that they must either wait, or try Arsobal again. Whatever system we used there would be problems, but I left, confident that the programme was in good hands.

With the opening of the mission at Bundibugyo, we now had four projects on the go, plus the Kampala base. This gave me plenty of work, mostly very interesting, sometimes demanding. Just visiting each site every month, involved flying off for two or three days every week. Although this schedule suited me very well, I had gradually discovered that our administrators in Kampala were finding the organisation of our finances increasingly difficult to manage. We had one lot of funding from MSF itself (called own funds), an allocation from the European Development Fund (EDF) for the Sleeping Sickness programme, another sum from the European Commission Humanitarian Aid Office (ECHO) and finally, a donation from the United States, designated for Bundibugyo. So, in addition to other responsibilities, the administrator had to manage four separate sets of accounts and reporting. This, I was to discover, was not an easy task.

When I arrived in Kampala, Isabel had been in charge. Caroline, her replacement, found EU funding very difficult, so I offered to attend some of the meetings with her, in an effort to clarify how we should construct reports and request advances. But I found the explanations no easier to comprehend. In fact, I was not even sure that the man in charge fully understood the procedures himself. Caroline then admitted to being pregnant, which meant she had to resign and return to France, because of problems with insurance and liability. Cecile, the new administrator, inherited the mess. I arrived in the office one morning, four weeks later, to find her sitting at her desk, shaking her head and saying over and over again,

"I can't do it. I simply can't do it."

Cecile left.

Yves bore the brunt of these difficulties, since I was now so regularly in the field, supporting the technical elements of each programme. I felt guilty that he had to cope with the issue alone, for although he was calm and methodical, he was also more of a logistician than an administrator. For him this type of activity was both difficult and time consuming. In retrospect, I'm not persuaded that anyone should be expected to cope with the obscurity of EU funding. It seems that either you have to be a trained expert, or be willing to devote most of your life to puzzling it all out. Laure, our next administrator, coped a lot better, at least with the stress. As with Caroline, I introduced her to EDF administration as best I could, accompanying her to several meetings with the head of the project in Kampala. This Scandinavian doctor was disarmingly vague about accountancy rules and procedures however, so Laure, like her predecessors, was none the wiser.

The EDF proposal had been written four years earlier, by a researcher from The Liverpool School of Hygiene and Tropical Medicine. The programme involved training health workers, rehabilitating buildings, providing appropriate equipment and introducing various health projects, of which the MSF mission was only one part. Altogether, this involved about sixty structures, including dispensaries, hospitals, administrative offices and teaching facilities. Our Sleeping Sickness component had been appended, almost as an afterthought and hardly related to the rest of the programme, so it was little wonder that it was difficult to accommodate. During one presentation to the management committee, I was impressed by the fact that the other organisations emphasised leaving something in place; structures that would continue to function after the end of the project. MSF's plans for the future seemed less concrete. However, these other organisations had been on standby for twelve of the eighteen months of the programme, because of perceived danger in the area. Although MSF had evacuated Omugo twice, we were still treating patients and moving our project forward.

It was after this meeting, that I began to consider the differences between emergency and development aid, an important issue in the humanitarian aid world. For me, as for others, the distinction is not always clear. Should we focus on trying to save lives immediately, or should we concentrate on longer-term structures and programmes, an investment that may eventually save more lives?

It is an accepted belief in European medicine, that prevention is more cost effective than treatment. Thus, vaccination, health screening and education, are seen as top priorities. Such schemes benefit the entire population and can save huge numbers of lives. In places like Africa, they may greatly reduce the need for regular emergency aid.

In Uganda, it seemed unbalanced that sleeping sickness was allocated four million dollars, while the entire West Nile District received only six million dollars, for everything else! When I calculated the figures for the sleeping sickness programme, it came to five hundred dollars for each patient treated. In the first eighteen months, we had treated and saved twelve hundred people, more if you considered that those not infected would not spread the disease to anyone else. But had this European programme been assessed as the best use of such a large sum of money for Ugandan health care? And if so, by whom? I continued to puzzle about this problem of long term help for countries like Uganda, never finding an answer, but convinced that something, somewhere was wrong.

Towards the end of my time in Uganda, I had a meeting in Entebbe with Dr Mbulamberi, the director of the Ugandan Sleeping Sickness Programme.
"The Sleeping Sickness Department is being amalgamated with the Malaria Service. I am now going to be the head of both," he informed me straight away.
"What does that mean for MSF and the programme?"
"You must understand, malaria is the major pre-occupation for us. We estimate that one hundred thousand people a year die from it, many of them children. The Minister has decided that malaria must have a higher

priority, particularly in view of the worsening problem of resistance to choloroquine," he replied.

"How will that affect Omugo and Adjumani?" I asked, suspecting that I already knew the answer.

"No more sleeping sickness assistants can be hired and those that do exist, will be phased out quickly."

Dr Mbulamberi looked unhappy.

"That will demolish our plans for an epidemiological surveillance system," I said. Unless MSF pays for staff, the situation will just deteriorate again."

"I'm afraid so. I have had the same problem in the southeast of the country for the last eight years. There is no donor funding and we are losing ground. Sleeping sickness is just too expensive for Uganda to treat."

"I don't know what Paris will decide to do with the programme, in light of this information," I told him. "But I suppose that if the epidemic reappears in the future, there will be another intervention."

It was a depressing conversation, although in a way, inevitable. Yet, during the fifteen years of the programme in Moyo, Adjumani and Omugo, over ten thousand people had been treated. It seemed wasteful to allow the disease to creep back, to ruin people's lives. But MSF was running a highly expensive, if useful programme, along side a national system, which was chronically short of money and consistently under-performing. I left the meeting with a lot of sympathy for Dr Mbulamberi's position.

But this was not the time to deliberate the wider questions concerning humanitarian aid work. Unrest in Zaire was escalating and its repercussions were affecting Uganda. Kabila's forces had marched north to Kisangani, where there had been fierce fighting and terrible atrocities, so MSF Holland had evacuated its base there and most of the volunteers had passed through Kampala, en route for Nairobi and home. My contact with Iris kept me abreast of this activity and she told me that one hundred and thirty expatriates had passed through the house in one month. Some of the volunteers had to stay with me, as the MSF Holland guesthouse was full. My visitors had a strange, tired and distant look, as a result of things they had seen. Most definitely, they did not want to talk.

Despite the MSF Holland evacuation, MSF France wanted to establish a project in the northeast of Zaire, because that country was now totally chaotic and its health structures had either been destroyed or had stopped functioning. On a visit to Arua, I met three priests from a group called the 'White Fathers', who had been working in a small village in Zaire for forty years. An armed gang had recently broken into their house and shot three of their staff in front of them. The three priests then walked forty kilometres overnight into Uganda and were now recovering in the diocese of Arua. They said that the country had become completely lawless.

Zaire is a vast country, with almost no road system, so the best access for MSF was from Uganda. For several months, Yves had been trying to establish an aid programme in Beni, a small mining town on the other side of the Ruwenzori Mountains. Although access to Zaire was difficult, he made contact with a mining company agent, hitching a lift in their aeroplane. During his four-hour stay, he managed to meet both a military commander and a hospital administrator, who advised him that MSF would be most welcome. The population was desperate for help, particularly medical aid. However, on his return to Entebbe airport, Yves was arrested as a spy, because he had a French passport. His poor English only increased the authorities' suspicions. He was held for thirty-six hours, before customs accepted proof of his residence in Uganda. MSF's credibility smoothed his release, but it was a warning to us all to be more careful in future. After this, Paris decided that access to Zaire would be via Goma.

Then Yves made a rare visit to Kitgum and on his return, astonished us with his views about the evolution of the project.
"Gang Dyang camp has grown to nearly twenty thousand people and the work is overwhelming the team," he reported. "Kitgum is thriving in an extraordinary way. Roads have been repaired, houses built, cars are everywhere and commerce is thriving. Some people are doing very well out of the situation, though not necessarily the IDPs. Aid money is clearly slipping into the local community. The situation is no longer threatening, so if we weren't there, the people would return to their homes. Free health care, a clean water supply and food distribution are all encouraging them to stay. People are moving into the camp, because life there is now better than it is outside!"

This was a staggering thought. Our IDP camp had become a magnet for people who had nothing, just because we gave them a little!

"Are you suggesting we are to blame?" asked Laure. "Surely we didn't cause the problem?"

"I don't mean we caused the problem," Yves explained, "but our aid is making the problem worse. We are the biggest external presence, so we have a responsibility to sort it. WFP is contributing too, with their food distribution."

"The authorities did suggest that we close Gang Dyang, but I thought they were just being callous. For once, perhaps they were right," I had to admit.

"If what Yves says is correct, we should close it down," Laure agreed.

"I went into the market," Yves continued. "WFP food is being sold in large quantities. The number of children in the feeding centre is still high, but I'm not sure they all meet the criteria. Local staff find it impossible to refuse their friends and family, so equipment such as jerrycans and hoes also find their way onto the market."

"I can easily check the figures for the feeding centre, to see if you are right," I said. "I suppose I should talk to Maria, to find out what she thinks."

"We must consider closing the project."

Yves had made up his mind.

"It was an emergency response and should only have been required for a few months, six at most. We have been there for eight months."

Obviously, this had to be discussed with the team immediately and as soon as I arrived in Kitgum, I asked Maria to call a meeting. When I presented Yves' conclusions, they were dismayed and visibly upset.

"The dispensaries are still chaotic, hygiene is poor, and there aren't enough toilets," Maria said bluntly. "Vaccination rates are low and there were some cases of measles last week. How can you think of closing us down now?"

That started them all off and for a while they were quite vociferous. Then they began to consider the logic of what had been proposed, although they were adamant that the problem might refer only to Gang Dyang and not to the other five camps.

"You make us feel we've been wasting our time. Surely that's what it will be, if we just pack up and go now," said Véronique. The team had not considered the situation as a short-term, emergency response, simply embracing an existing problem, without considering its evolution. But why should they? Their role had been to set up a response to a bad situation. No one had asked them to look at the wider picture.

I realised that we should have introduced the idea of closure, before we even started to work. I too was learning. All such projects need a defined end point as one of the mission's terms of reference. Part of the problem was my own lack of experience. Perversely, some years later, during a massive malaria epidemic in Burundi, I tried to implement a policy of preparing for closure as soon as we began. To my surprise, the idea produced endless problems and was equally unpopular with the staff. Neither way seemed guaranteed to work.

Now, I had to identify what was appropriate for this situation and, importantly, I had to make the staff feel that they were part of the decision-making process. If they did not, they might leave, thinking that their efforts had been wasted.

"You need to analyse the situation," I told them. "What are we trying to achieve? Are we trying to provide an NHS for the Kitgum area? What standards are correct for these people, in Uganda, at this time? Remember, MSF money is limited. Is this still an emergency? Try to step back a bit," I told them.

The more we verbalised the problem, the more I was sure we needed to act now. Eventually, the team agreed to draw up a plan of action, with clearly defined objectives and a definite time frame. They were distressed by what had been said and I was sorry that they had taken the debate so much to heart. I agreed to return in two weeks time, to discuss their plan.

Two days later it was time to leave Kampala for the Conference in Maputo. I flew there with Dominique and Dr Maiso, and Susan joined us later. Karim had already flown out from Paris and I was a little surprised, when he asked me to make the presentation of our sleeping sickness programme and the results for Omugo and Adjumani, since I had assumed that he would be doing this. The presentation was in French, but I muddled through and was most relieved when the time came for me to sit down. We then replied to the questions from the floor and Dominique presented a preliminary summary of his analysis. Although not conclusive, his data showed very strong evidence for an 18% resistance to Arsobal.

Afterwards, we met the WHO experts, who had already been briefed by Susan.

"Have you got any supplies of DFMO?" I asked, at the end of our discussion.

"Yes. We have five thousand vials stored in Geneva."

"Can we buy them?" I asked immediately.

"We must check with Paris before we can negotiate that," Karim prudently interjected, since I hadn't asked the price.

"Yes, but if we have the money, can we have the vials?"

I was less interested in cost.

"Perhaps not all of it. I could initially let you have two thousand vials for Omugo. We hold the only stock in the world and as you know, there are several countries with sleeping sickness programmes."

The thought of two thousand vials was encouraging, even although these would treat only one hundred patients.

This contact with the WHO was to have important implications for MSF in the future. The cost of producing DFMO constrains the price, making it too expensive for Third World countries to purchase. It is not used for any condition, other than sleeping sickness and could never be an economic proposition. Although the WHO now owned the patent, someone would have to subsidise its manufacture.

The drugs issue with the highest profile is the treatment of AIDS, the scourge of Africa. AIDS treatment was originally very expensive, because manufacturers needed to recover their investment. Continued high prices, however, precluded Third World access. Gradually, as awareness and indignation increased in equal proportion, a project developed to address this situation, based in Paris and Brussels and supported by a range of groups, including MSF. The project has recently had considerable success in the fight to reduce the price of AIDS drugs. Only time will tell if this will work for the world's poorest people.

On balance, the outcome of our trip to the Maputo Conference was satisfactory, for us. The possibility of buying some DFMO existed and the problem of resistance to Arsobal had been highlighted.

Since John and Jean-Luc had now left Bundibugyo, it was time for me to meet the replacement team, to find out how they were managing. To the end, John had remained pessimistic about our ability to work with the authorities and I wondered if the new people were having any more luck. There was a German doctor (Hans), a Swiss log (Victor), a French nurse (Paul), and a French Canadian nurse (Denis), who was also the Programme Leader. Except for Hans, they had all worked for MSF before. Denis was forty-five, thin and short, with an Australian bush hat, worn over a long pony-tail. He was a good organiser, an experienced boss and diplomatic in his relations with other people. Each morning, during his radio contact with Kampala, he would serenade our administrator with a few bars of a song from the sixties, much in keeping with his image as an ageing hippie. I sometimes wondered what anyone "listening in" would make of this decidedly non-regulation serenade, but if it helped internal communication, I didn't care in the least.

The new team told me that the most urgent challenge for the camp at Bundibugyo was still hygiene. Most of these IDPs had lived all their lives deep in the forest, in small, dispersed groups. High rainfall had ensured them plentiful supplies of food and water and although isolation had denied them access to health care, this same isolation had protected them from disease. Now, they were crowded together in Bundibugyo, where all their previous habits put them at risk. Before, they had always used the river, or the jungle, as a toilet, but in a crowded environment this habit threatened to spread diarrhoeal diseases, such as cholera and dysentery. Living space was also at a premium. All these factors increased the risk of an epidemic.

Yet they could not understand our obsession with hygiene, toilets and the precise spacing of buildings, as we tried to avoid the spread of both fires and disease. It was this lack of understanding that made our task laborious. Each time we organised an area, new arrivals built between existing huts. It was very frustrating for us and created tension between the existing community and the newcomers.

After six weeks in Bundibugyo, the military had repaired the damaged bridge and secured the road to Nyahuka, the next village along the road. Our team assessed this situation and found conditions as bad as in Bundibugyo, with one positive difference; here the social fabric was better preserved and the authorities more helpful. The market place was packed with IDPs, Rick Gray estimating that they numbered seventeen thousand, so there was a definite risk of disease. Rick, an American from the Mid-west, was about thirty-five years old and worked for an evangelical organisation called World Harvest Vision. He had been in Nyahuka for eight years.

When I visited, I asked him how long he planned to stay.

"A while yet," came the laconic reply. "I'm just getting to know the people. Still got a ways to go though."

Denis had already assessed the priorities in Nyahuka. Although there were dispensary staff, they had no drugs. There was also a shortage of water. Victor planned to run river water into a reservoir at a strategic point and then down a two-kilometre pipeline into the village, although as yet this was not possible, because the military had not gained control of the hillside. Food was less of an issue, since this was a very fertile area and the people could live off the land. The main problem was fifty tons of rice, sent by a well-meaning Italian organisation. Rick had to store it, because the local people did not like the stuff. So it stayed in the warehouse, piled high and spilling out of holes in the walls, gradually being eaten by an ever-increasing rat community. Only in acute famine, will people eat any type of food that is offered to them.

After a few days in Rick's guesthouse, the team found a base in Nyahuka, a hotel built some years earlier by a local entrepreneur and whimsically known as, "The Holiday Inn". This effectively created two teams, Paul and Victor working on the water and dispensary in Nyahuka, while Denis and Hans stayed in Bundibugyo. It was a huge workload for four, so we sent a message to Paris, asking them to increase the team to six members. Paris decided that it should remain at four for the moment, until we were more confident of the stability of the region.

I returned to Kampala, satisfied that the work was progressing well in Nyahuka, only to receive an emergency radio message from Paul.

"The rebels are attacking the army post, near the dispensary. They are shooting it out now."

We heard gunfire in the background, as he transmitted his message. "Where are you? What's happening?" questioned Jean-Luc.

"I'm underneath the Land Cruiser and I'm not moving, so don't ask," said Paul.

He sounded frightened, as well he might. It was unpleasant for us too, listening to a battle, from four hundred kilometres away, unable to do anything to help. Of course it was much worse for Paul, only four hundred metres from the fighting. By ill fortune he was on his own, because Victor had gone back to Bundibugyo to collect materials.

We hovered distractedly round the radio in Kampala, talking about hiring a helicopter, but knowing that this would take three or four hours, even if one was available. Eventually the shooting diminished and after another hour, Paul saw the military moving about freely, so he cautiously emerged from under the vehicle. Immediately, the commander approached, asking him to help with the wounded.

The army had been taken by surprise, because the ADF rebels had attacked from an unexpected direction, climbing down into a ravine, crossing the river and climbing back up into the village. They had then opened fire on the military tents, but unfortunately IDPs were camped in the crossfire; there were twenty-one dead. Paul tried to patch up the wounded as best he could, sending them fifteen kilometres to Bundibugyo hospital, where Hans (a surgeon) was able to save some of them, though not all.

The team was ordered back to Fort Portal to await developments, while Paul returned to Kampala. He was very shaken and quiet. I tried to get him to talk about the experience, but despite my best efforts he remained closed.

"So, what would you like to do?" I finally asked him.

"I will stay here for another couple of days, then go back," he replied. This he did, but seven days later Denis called to say Paul wanted to leave. He returned to Kampala and flew back to France. I hated it when missions ended like this. It was no one's fault, but it was difficult to convey that to the individuals concerned. And I never forgot how I felt when I left Omugo.

In October, it was time for me to contemplate the end of my own mission, for I was due to leave in December. It is always difficult to find people to start missions over Christmas, so when my son said he would be busy until the middle of January, I offered to stay on a little longer. Meanwhile, I began to examine each of our projects, drawing up rough objectives for the remaining months. I was vaguely amused to realise, that at last I felt in charge of what was happening. By the time I left, I might just have the hang of it!

Adjumani was progressing reasonably well. Odile had continued to work with Dr Ben, integrating the programme with existing services.

Sleeping sickness assistants would be trained as auxiliary nurses and would continue their surveillance of the disease, without additional cost to the system, although Dr Ben could only integrate ten, of our twenty workers. Odile would be replaced by a final MSF doctor and staff would travel from Omugo to check on progress every month, delivering drugs and supplies and collecting data.

In Kitgum, Maria and her team were working hard. The most pressing need was to close the Gang Dyang camp and here the authorities agreed, since it had become a nightmare of rivalry and tension. There were nearly thirty thousand people registered, although it was clear that nothing like that number actually lived there. We suspected that many of the people, who were turning up for food distribution and health care, were inhabitants of Kitgum town itself. We could not prove anything, but it appeared that camp headmen were selling camp "registrations" as a concession and growing rich on the business.

Although it was a painful process, the team was united and supported each other through the last two difficult months. We left it to the authorities to announce the closure. The people were to disperse to villages with army detachments, where they would be closer to their fields and could harvest and cultivate when things were quiet. They were assured that the army would remain to protect them.

Then, one week after the announcement, camp representatives visited Maria.

"How will we get back to our homes?"

Maria was astounded. "The same way you got here eleven months ago," she replied somewhat tersely, "on foot."

"That is impossible. Now we have too many things to carry: basins, tents, jerrycans, blankets and all the other stuff."

These were our basins, our tents, our jerrycans and our blankets. It seemed absurd and outrageous to go along with their demands, but to get things moving quickly, we organised transport for the women and children, along with all the goods. Oxfam and the Red Cross allowed their lorries to be used for this purpose.

The team then returned to Kampala to write their reports, before setting off, either on holiday, or back to France. Prior to their leaving, I arranged a meeting with Maria, to evaluate what had been achieved during the twelve months in Kitgum.

"The most important thing was for the people to see that someone cared," Maria began. "When they fled from the LRA rebels, the authorities were either disinterested, or unable to help. They felt abandoned."

"What about health care improvements?"

"We managed to stimulate the DMO into finding staff eventually, but in the end we had to pay wages for more than half of them. Though I do think we may have prevented outbreaks of measles and dysentery."

"What do you think will happen now?" I continued.

"Some of the health staff will stop work, because they won't be paid. The situation could go back to where it was, before we intervened. But in Palabek Kal and Lokung, the service will carry on. The two head nurses there are highly motivated and will do their best for the villages," said Maria.

"The vaccination figures were quite good at the end too," I suggested.

"Yes. I hope that carries on, but I'm not optimistic, without a change of DMO."

Then Maria laughed.

"And we certainly encouraged the local economy. MSF money seems to have stimulated both road repairs and new building."

"I agree. There's a lesson there, but I'm not sure what it is," I told her. "People need roads and a good economy to survive, so it can't be bad, but we encourage dependence when we stay too long. I know now that we should have balanced our immediate help with a long-term strategy, but without prior knowledge, we can only do our best."

"I prefer to think only in terms of helping the people in front of me. We come into this work to help, where and if we can. That's enough for me," Maria concluded.

I agreed with her in principle, but I couldn't help asking questions. Now that the emergency was over, I knew we should have handled it better. It seemed to be a constant theme of my work, wisdom only after the event. Maria and I had both learned from the experience, but how could this knowledge be transmitted to new staff?

Bundibugyo was too new for me to evaluate and the team were still finding both the conditions and the work extremely difficult. In fact, it had been agreed that each team member should come out to Fort Portal for a break, every three weeks. Seventy thousand displaced people were now living there and the serious risk of epidemics seemed set to continue. Food and shelter were less of a problem, so it should have been a simple matter to focus on clean water, improved hygiene and re-establishing the various dispensaries. But this population would not understand our concern for their situation. Whatever we did, they continued to disregard our advice. Unhelpful authorities exacerbated the situation, so that the team experienced lots of self-doubt at their apparent failure. I was just as frustrated at they were, but at least I wasn't up against the problem every day. Whatever MSF did, these IDPs didn't want to know about the problems of drinking dirty water, but if they didn't stop, they would eventually become ill.

But why should we expect a society, which has been living in a particular way for hundreds of years, to adopt the hygiene practices of a group of strangers? Europeans lived together under very crowded conditions after the Industrial Revolution, yet they took many years to develop an effective system of public health. And this was only after suffering the devastating illnesses, which resulted from bad hygiene. Public health medicine considers benefit to the population as a whole, but even educated communities may not choose this approach. We still pollute our environment and indulge in destructive personal habits like smoking, at huge cost to our systems. In Bundibugyo, people did not understand the risks, so that the team constantly found their work undermined and their advice ignored. Eight months later, during the Ugandan cholera epidemic, Bundibugyo was particularly badly affected.

Omugo, however, was progressing well. The mobile teams were still working their way around the county, screening as many people as possible. Our results now suggested that it would take two years, if we continued to use just one vehicle, so I began to look for another. The closure of Kitgum released extra vehicles, so I suggested that Omugo receive two of these. Our objective remained unchanged, that of reducing the prevalence of sleeping sickness below one in two hundred of the population.

I seemed to be moving seamlessly towards my departure, when at the beginning of December 1997 (on a routine visit to Adjumani) the morning radio contact with Kampala announced,
"Il y a le choléra dans le coin" (There's cholera around here).
With that, Jean-Luc cut contact and all I could do was imagine him

racing off to begin a hundred things, all at once. Luckily, he had great experience of cholera and loved this kind of challenge. Urgency, panic, working twenty hours a day: that was his forte. I returned to Kampala as quickly as possible, to hear that the first cases had been identified at Gaba Beach, a port, five kilometres outside the city. This was surprising, as we had predicted that any cholera that did arrive in Uganda would come from the east, by way of Tororo.

The seventh Cholera Pandemic had been passing from country to country, since 1970. Like the previous ones, it had started somewhere in South East Asia and was now heading west. There had been a minor epidemic in Kenya, around Homa Bay, a port on Lake Victoria. As more cases were notified, I had visited eastern Uganda to see if any cases had been identified there. I spent ten days visiting all the dispensaries along the border, asking about any suspicious cases, but no one had seen any sign of it. In fact, no one could remember having seen cholera in his lifetime. I was so encouraged by this result, that I wrote a report to say all was well, but if an outbreak occurred, it would be along the trade routes, through Mbale and Tororo. I was totally wrong. Some cases of cholera had been spread by water, through the fishing industry, which had brought it across the lake. A few days after the announcement of the first cases at Gaba Beach, they were confirmed by the Public Health laboratory of Makarere Hospital.

But in Kampala, Yves and Dominique had begun to take action. As soon as I arrived, Yves explained what they had done.

"The Minister of Health phoned to ask MSF for help, so we have organised the team into four groups and now we'll check all the hospitals, to see if they have any cases."

"Okay. Which ones do you want me to do?" I asked.

"Could you go to the clinic in Gaba Beach first?"

I was excited, but nervous. This was one of my responsibilities – to manage the MSF response to such an emergency, but I was glad to have the support of Dominique and Jean-Luc, with their previous experience. By the end of the day, we had discovered twenty-five suspect cases, fortunately restricted to two areas of the city.

Cholera is a simple disease. It is a severe form of diarrhoea, which if untreated can have a death rate of anything between 10% and 50% and in densely populated areas (such as large crowded cities, or refugee camps) it can spread quickly. The treatment is also simple, but in a major epidemic, patient numbers often swamp the capacity of health structures. Organisation is the key to a successful response.

Although there were only twenty-five cases identified at the moment, MSF experience suggested that one case was enough to define an epidemic, since Uganda had not seen cholera for many years. It was bad luck that Yves was due to leave in a few days time, while I would follow three weeks later. We discussed the problem and I suggested that we should consider passing the project on to MSF Holland, who had still not identified a new project. Yves was visibly unhappy about my suggestion, but I insisted. The MSF Holland group was delighted and we began by initiating a joint working group to introduce the programme.

After receiving permission from the Ministry of Health, we worked together to establish the bases, since this MSF Holland team had no experience of cholera. The co-operative transition period ensured that the Ministry had a good impression of MSF and enabled us to get the programme under way in the shortest possible time. The best course of action when attacking any epidemic is for all the agencies and departments to work closely together. Unfortunately, this does not always happen.

The recommended response to cholera is threefold, namely: treatment of patients, hygiene education and a clean water supply. OXFAM agreed to chlorinate Kampala's water supply and the Ugandan Health Authority said they would organise publicity campaigns and produce TV and radio broadcasts, leaving the MSF teams to support the major treatment centres. Cholera must be isolated, and we had to find two new treatment camps, since we could not use existing hospitals. The children were on holiday, so we had identified two schools as the most appropriate structures for temporary use. There was one in the east of the city, with thirty beds and another in the west, near Makarere hospital, with eighty. Other hospitals and dispensaries would refer all cholera patients to these two camps and if they became overloaded, more would be built.

Cholera is a very rapid disease, which can become severe in two or three hours, although with adequate treatment it lasts only three days. In a population of one thousand people, even if all are infected by the bacteria, only one hundred will become ill. Of those one hundred, about twenty will be severely ill and need intravenous treatment. The rest will recover, if they drink a lot of water mixed with sugar and salts to replace the fluid lost by vomiting and diarrhoea. Thus the medical staff can have a quick rule of thumb calculation of expected needs. The 80% of patients who are assessed as "mild" or "moderate" are given oral re-hydration fluid (the salt/sugar mixture) in an observation area and then sent home with re-hydration sachets, perhaps after only four hours. Severe cases are admitted and treated intravenously with fluids. It's simple. It just needs to be kept under control.

Despite being in the recovery phase of a malaria attack, Jean-Luc set up the Makerere camp in two days and we began admitting patients immediately. The severe cases were so weak they could not walk to the toilet, so the beds had holes cut at an appropriate position, to allow the diarrhoea to flow, without the patients moving. Each bed was supplied with two buckets, one at the head for vomit and one under the hole. The diarrhoea was at times so profuse, that it became clear "rice water", with hardly any smell and in the treatment rooms the sound was like a series of running taps. Family members and other helpers emptied the buckets.

Although at times we seemed to be verging on the chaotic, the number of deaths remained low, these occurring in people in extremely poor condition, who presented very late. For me, the work was satisfying. Patients arrived on stretchers, skin hanging in folds and eyes sunken, due to lack of fluids. Four hours later they would sit up and start to drink again. The more severely affected adults could require around twenty litres of infusion, over a period of twenty-four, or forty-eight hours, but even these usually recovered. Everything must be kept constantly disinfected, to limit the spread of infection, so we set up foot-baths of chlorine solution at strategic points, with guards posted, to ensure that everyone used them. A clean and copious water supply is the main requirement for a successful cholera hospital. Sometimes antibiotics are needed, but they are not really important. Jean-Luc's experience meant that he knew the procedures well and under his frenetic guidance, the unit functioned smoothly from the first day.

Over the next two weeks, we tried to establish an epidemiological surveillance system that would provide us with information about the number of cases in Kampala, together with their origins. In fact, since almost everyone came to Makerere, we obtained a reliable picture from attendance at that unit alone. We watched the figures anxiously, calculating the number of cases. In one sense (rather selfishly) we were concerned that there should be cases, because we had spent a lot of money in preparation. On the other hand, cholera can explode and kill large numbers of people and we were nervous in case dramatic proliferation might swamp our facilities. Day by day, the number of new patients grew, ten, fifteen, twenty-five.

As Christmas approached, we found ourselves stretched to the limit, as admissions rose to one hundred and fifty per day. The school had no electricity, so the local staff from Makerere hospital had to work at night by oil lamps. Each classroom was crammed with beds and the entire area became littered with empty perfusion bottles and tubing, as the disposal team became overwhelmed. By Christmas Eve, our planned care was collapsing in on us and it required a frantic effort to keep up with the rush of new patients. As I dropped into bed, I noticed that my only two pairs of trousers had become permanently bleached into an odd polka dot pattern, by constant exposure to the chlorine spray. On Christmas Day, I spent fourteen hours rushing from patient to patient, changing bottles and desperately trying to set up drips (intravenous lines). Children were the most difficult, with their small, thin arms and no visible veins. Inevitably, there were some deaths.

By this time, MSF Holland had taken over responsibility, including negotiations with the Government to set up a National Task Force, because there was every chance that the epidemic would spread. As the numbers stabilised, I felt that I could begin to withdraw my input, recognising the need to clear my desk, before my departure in mid-January, when I hoped the epidemic would be under control. Then, reports began to come in, about cases in new sites, between Kampala and the Kenyan border. The main town, Mbale, was at high risk.

When notified of these cases at the end of December, MSF Holland recognised that they might need a new treatment centre, but they had no available staff, so I set off for Mbale on New Year's Eve. My role was to assess the level of need for MSF Holland and to advise the authorities about the establishment of a new cholera camp in the meantime. I found that there were already forty cholera patients in Mbale hospital's main ward, the patients not isolated, so that numbers were increasing dramatically every day. Since the majority of cases were coming from a town about fifteen kilometres to the north, I set off immediately, to try to establish a treatment centre there.

I found the ideal place, a large church with spacious grounds and its own water supply. I persuaded the local Health Inspector to ask the priest to lend us the church, but in the best Christian tradition he refused, suggesting that we instead use the surrounding land to install tents. The other possibility, was a local mosque, so I left the Health Inspector to negotiate for whichever centre of religion was prepared to care for the health of its people and returned to Mbale.

Here, they were now setting up a separate treatment centre in a local school. Things were going a little slowly since it was New Year's Day, but the staff recognised the need for urgency and promised to do their best. After another assessment of the situation, I returned to Kampala to meet with Ton, MSF Holland's Head of Mission.

"You must send a team quickly," I told him. "There is a high risk of the problem escalating. I don't think that setting up the unit in the north, will stop the spread into Mbale, as it has a large shantytown close to the town centre. There are too many people, a poor water supply, few toilets and houses that are too close together. It's a textbook description of the risk factors for cholera."

Ton accepted my recommendation and sent a request to Amsterdam for another three workers, to be sent out as soon as possible.

As I was due to leave in a few days, there was little more I could do. Anyway, I needed to prepare for my successor, having promised myself that he or she would learn from all my failures, as well as my successes. But although I now had much less involvement in the epidemic, I continued to attend evening meetings, to keep in touch with the way things were progressing. It was a little sad to be leaving at such an interesting time, but my contract was up and it was time to move on. I completed last minute details for each of the other projects and flew out of Kampala on the 10th January 1998.

I expected that MSF would now want to change my location, as it is their habit to move people around regularly. Reasons given are to broaden volunteers' experience and to avoid them from becoming too involved. In fact, this is seldom a problem since most only work for the organisation for six months, or perhaps one year. At any given time, 40% of the staff are on their first missions. Even those who have the desire to continue may not be able to afford (economically or socially) to invest more time in this type of work. People who stay longer may do so for a variety of reasons. Some are adrenaline freaks (like Jean-

Luc), people who adore the endless challenges, while some are lost souls, who have become locked into a relatively cocooned way of life. But only a few find themselves in a position to become long-term, humanitarian aid workers.

As a result, most of the people who work in the field never have the time, the opportunity, or the confidence, to communicate their ideas and experiences to their management. Power remains centralised and unchallenged. It may not be planned, but the result is a diverse and widely dispersed organisation with physical communication problems. This constant stream of new recruits also means that much of the practical experience learned in the field is lost and must be rediscovered by each wave of well-intentioned volunteers.

CHAPTER ELEVEN

Il y a le choléra dans le coin

Back in France, it was good to have time to relax and re-establish contact with the rest of the world. I went skiing with my son, did some DIY around the apartment and read the newspapers. Then I found myself wondering about how things were going in Uganda and as the attractions of the ordinary world began to pale, I became a little restless. That's the thing about aid work; it can become habit forming. For all its discomforts and stresses, I felt more alive, more useful, when confronted by its demands and challenges. And although the money was hardly a motivating factor, it was just enough to pay my standing orders.

So I telephoned Paris, only to find that MSF had nothing immediately available. To fill the gap, I made enquiries with similar organisations and the first to offer me a post was Médecins du Monde (MDM). I knew little about them, other than the fact that MSF regarded them as rivals and they had the reputation of being disorganised, "bordelique", even. But why not? I was ready for a change of scene. So I accepted their offer and waited patiently to hear news of my next posting. It would be nice to see somewhere different, I decided.

MDM offered me a three-month contract in Uganda, working with the cholera epidemic, which had continued to spread since I left. So much for a change of scene!

It seemed a little strange going back to Uganda to work for another organisation, but I was curious to see how things were progressing. MDM gave the impression of being more relaxed and friendly, so I was pleased when they invited me to attend their headquarters in Paris for a briefing. However, I discovered that they were even less informative than MSF. Each organisation seemed to feel that it's just fine to pick things up as you go along, something I had now decided was neither respectful of, nor useful to, the host country! Later, I discovered that each of them had occasionally denied me information, presumably in case I changed my mind about accepting a position. This was to be one such time.

I travelled to Paris and spent a pleasant hour with Gael (the Secretary of the Desk). She gave me general details and asked me to come back the following day for a ten o'clock briefing. I arrived promptly, but it was 11am before the rest of the group assembled. As time passed, I could feel myself becoming a little irritated by the general nature of the conversation, so I decided to move the discussion in my direction, in an effort to discover more about my role.

"What will I be doing in Uganda?" I asked bluntly.

"You will be the Medical Reference for the programme," one of them replied and that seemed to be that.

But what did "Medical Reference" mean? Would I be a practising doctor, or as in my last post, a medical manager? I wanted just a little more detail, but didn't want to appear too pushy. Perhaps if they gave me an idea of what everyone else would be doing, it would all become clearer.

"Who is the Head of Mission?" I asked.

"MDM has no Head of Mission," Eric, the Head of Logistics told me.

"Then who makes the final decisions and more importantly, who is responsible for security?"

Since I knew these were vital questions in any mission, I no longer felt the need to beat about the bush.

"You will share this responsibility with Lucille, the Administrator," I was told.

"Does that work?" I asked. "I'm very much a consensus person, but surely someone has to be in absolute charge, in case of conflict, or an emergency? I don't mean that it has to be me."

I went on to explain that despite the fact that I believe strongly in discussion and negotiation with colleagues, there had in the past been times when one person had to be in charge, particularly when security was at stake. My new colleagues seemed to resist this idea. In fact, they were now looking at me as if I was somewhat unusual, eccentric even, so I gave in.

"Okay, I will try. But I think it's a recipe for disaster," I speculated.

"Perhaps we should move on to discuss details of the programme itself," I suggested.

"We are involved with the cholera epidemic, working on an education programme in Lowero, south of Kampala. The plan is still changing, so you will get a detailed briefing from Carlos when you arrive. We prefer that you receive the specific information in the field."

This habit of providing only a vague task description had become uncomfortably familiar, but since I had been involved at the beginning of the cholera epidemic, I decided that it shouldn't be too hard to pick up the threads. And I could always get an update from Ton at MSF Holland, if he was still there.

I flew the now familiar route, spending a night in Nairobi, but this time there was no one to meet me at Entebbe. A taxi took me into the centre of Kampala, to the MDM address I remembered from a party during my previous mission. This was not the right place, however, since MDM now had two houses, one for its long-term AIDS programme and another for "the cholera". It seemed that there was little communication between these groups, but they did at least know the address of their co-workers. I finally arrived there, only to find them loading a lorry with furniture.

"Hello. I'm Stuart Evans," I introduced myself, relieved that I had not arrived a day later.

A lightly-built man of about forty-five, with a tiny sprig of plaited pony tail, turned and responded.

"I'm Carlos. Glad you're here. We're moving the base to Kasese. That's where we'll be working," he said.

"I thought you were organising a cholera education programme in Lowero," I said, not really worried about what I did, but surprised by the speed of change in these parts.

"Things have altered. There are many new cholera cases reported in Kasese and now there are none in Lowero. MSF asked for help, so we set up a joint programme three weeks ago."

I was pleased at the prospect of returning to Kasese and equally happy to help with packing and loading the lorry. As we worked, I was introduced to the rest of the team. This was the most relaxed briefing to date, I decided, wondering if it was just French aid organisations that worked in this way.

In addition to Carlos (the doctor), there was Lucille (the admin), her boyfriend Yves (the log) and Jean-Sebastian (the assistant log). Natalie, with her husband Rocco, were the two nurses. There was a meeting just before we set off, at which Carlos tried to outline a plan of what we would be doing. However, since he had arrived in Uganda only ten days before, it was more a case of drawing together our initial impressions of the situation. It was clear to me at least that we could not make any concrete plans until we arrived in Kasese.

This meeting did reveal a little of what had happened during the first month of the programme and it had not been entirely satisfactory. MSF had originally suggested that MDM concentrate on three areas, but the epidemic failed to materialise in these places. Of course, this was not MSF's fault, since cholera is very unpredictable, but a lack of work meant that the original team of young expatriates had too much time on their hands. Relationships had become strained and there were regular clashes between lively personalities. Unfortunately some of the young men found less acceptable outlets for their energies, picking up girls, professional or not, and bringing them back to the house. Not surprisingly, some other team members (most notably the women) were not impressed, and after a somewhat stressful time two of the men had been sent back to Paris.

Now I understood the lack of detail in the original briefing and I was a little annoyed that I had not been told more, although I understood the reasons. This was a new team, apart from Yves, who seemed a steady sort of chap and hopefully we would find enough work to ensure that we did not fall into similar bad habits. We travelled to Kasese in the three MDM vehicles, an eight-hour journey, because one of the Land Cruisers was in very poor condition. On arrival, Yves led us to the Virena Garden Hotel, which would be our base until he could rent a house. Two of the nurses from the Lowero team (Nadine and Sabine) had started the work, but they were due to leave, once they had given a handover briefing.

Sabine explained that MSF had initially established four large cholera treatment centres, which had stretched their resources to the limit and MDM had opened nineteen minor treatment units, located all over the district. This strategy was well adapted to the geography of Kasese, since the population was much more dispersed than in Kampala.

"What is the function of the MDM units?" I asked Sabine.

"They treat the simple cases and refer any serious ones to the MSF centres. We take basins, chlorine, sprayers and medical equipment for the treatment of up to twenty cases at a time. Then we spend half a day explaining the procedures: hygiene, re-hydration, isolation and disinfection. We then move on to the detail of treatment regimes and identify which cases should be referred to one of the larger units for specialist care. The staff are mostly competent and motivated."

"How did you choose which health centres to focus on?" I asked.

"We spoke to the DMO and he gave us a list," replied Sabine. "He's easy to work with. He's called Dr Andrew and although he can be tough when necessary, he is very good."

"Is he also the director of a nearby missionary hospital?" I asked.

"Yes that's him,"

Great! I had met Dr Andrew in Kampala, at the time of the ADF troubles the previous year. He had run out of chloroquine for some of the IDP camps and I had given him enough to treat five thousand patients. It was gratifying to know that here the authorities were represented by someone who really knew how to do his job.

During their final two days, I accompanied Sabine and Nadine on their visits around the health centres, discovering that these facilities were spread out over a huge area. Clearly, we could not have much of a presence in each, but this activity complemented the four MSF centres which maintained a full-time aid-worker's presence. We would be involved at community level and I was interested to see how effective was this combined approach. It was unusual to have one organisation running large central facilities, supported by a second organisation's smaller, feeder units.

The evening before Sabine's departure, a message came from Paris to say that we had only been funded for three more weeks. They even asked if there was a continued need for our presence, saying that if no more funds could be found, we would have to pack up and leave. I was completely bewildered. They had just sent me here and now they were talking about pulling us all out. I wondered what sort of organisation would send out a new team, without funding having been identified in advance!

"MDM is often like that," said Lucille, shrugging her shoulders in the habitual French way. "They will probably find a bit more money, at least enough to last us for a few more weeks."

And that was it. The rest of the team seemed quite philosophical about the news. In the meantime there was a job to do, so I tried to concentrate on the present and ignore the future.

Kasese is a town of about twenty thousand people, on the southern tip of the Ruwenzori Mountains. In years gone by, it had been a centre for cobalt mining. On my previous visit I had little time to look around, but now I saw that this was a lively community, serving as a transport link between Uganda and Zaire, whose border was about one and a half hours away. Recently, trade had been disrupted by the chaos of the civil war in Zaire and there was a large army presence, intended to combat ADF rebels in the mountains. Despite the fact that there had been several attacks on the town during the last year, we were told that it was now quiet. Remembering my previous visit, I thought this was unlikely to last.

The two logs, Yves and Jean-Seb, were kept busy supplying all the units with endless quantities of materials and setting up enclosures for isolation and teaching the use of chlorine solutions. I visited all the sites, accompanying both the logs and the nurses, trying to absorb as much as possible about the area and discovering that there were major differences between the nineteen units. They varied greatly both in size and activity, some with no cases, while others were hardly able to cope with the pressure. We had to use discretion and common sense in deciding how to treat such different sites, supporting each according to need. The larger ones were effectively mini-hospitals, known locally as Lazerets, with at least two treatment rooms, one for oral treatment, the other for intravenous therapy of more severe cases.

One vital issue emerged as I travelled around, the absence of night staff. If a patient has a drip in place, there must be a nurse, or at least an orderly present, to supervise replacement. But Ugandan nurses often have only six months training and are not always as rigorous as the aid nurses would like, so regularly there were no nurses in the hospitals at night. I had become used to this custom, but it is a particular problem when dealing with a critical illness of epidemic proportions. When it was explained that this emergency situation required their presence, most of the nurses agreed to work nights for the duration of the problem.

A typical cholera epidemic starts slowly, with just a few cases. Then, as each patient infects many more, the numbers can rise exponentially, like an atomic reaction. Finally, it explodes to a peak that often stretches medical services to the limit, but after two or three months numbers begin to fall, tailing off slowly. Three weeks after my return to Uganda, our local centres recorded a peak of one thousand, six hundred new cases per week. Providing supplies to cope with these numbers was a considerable challenge for the logisticians, but they had it reduced to a formulaic supply model. For every one hundred patients, we needed fifteen drip-sets, one hundred and fifty litres of intravenous fluid, five rolls of tape and specific numbers of gloves, bandages, syringes, needles, buckets, basins and all the other medical paraphanalia. But the major life-saver was the intravenous fluid. This was flown in from Europe, ten tonnes at a time, because Ugandan stocks had been exhausted in the first month of the epidemic.

The MSF team was also very busy and our joint action seemed to be progressing well, treating about the same numbers of patients in our differently sized units. Each MSF unit had about sixty Ugandan staff and at least one MSF volunteer. Our smaller units normally had only two or three local staff, supported by the occasional visit from an MDM worker. There were in total about three hundred health staff dealing with the epidemic, of which six were from MDM and five from MSF.

The two aid organisations also co-operated in identifying new pockets of infection. Since the MSF centres kept a record of all the patients' addresses, we could easily spot significant cases from a new area. Then MDM would visit, to decide if it was necessary to open another unit. As the local staff became more competent and confident, our existing workload decreased, leaving us free to tackle new areas. We gained an overview of the district, learning quickly to channel our efforts to the places of greatest need. Not only were we in control of the disease, it was heartening for me to see two major NGO's working successfully together.

Our regular study of the weekly medical registers revealed that one unit, to the north of Kasese, indicated double the number of cases, although only on two specific days a week. We dispatched Natalie to ask the head nurse if she could offer an explanation. These were market days and just as is classically described in the textbooks, people were buying food from the stalls and spreading the disease. I had a word with Dr Andrew and he closed down all the small stalls that sold snacks, reducing the number of cases dramatically.

Kasese was an exotic place to work. We were right in the centre of the Queen Elizabeth National Game Park, which in more peaceful times had been a favourite attraction for tourists and animal lovers. In this part of Uganda it was not unusual to see elephants, wart hogs, antelope, buffalo and even the occasional leopard, although usually at a distance. A particular road sign made me smile. It was a British-style, red, warning triangle, surrounding the image of an elephant. One evening, I discovered that the sign was genuine, when I found my path blocked by three elephants, forcing me to wait for their decision to amble off the road.

On a visit to the village of Katwe, situated on the edge of Lake Edward, I spent time with the doctor, discussing his experience of the cholera. He had recorded two hundred and sixty cases, but only nine deaths. This man was pleased, because the number of new cases was now diminishing and so few people had died.

Once we finished our medical chit-chat, I asked him about the local wildlife, for I had noted lots of animals in the vicinity.

"On the road coming in to the village, I passed many wart hogs and some elephants. Are they a nuisance for the farmers?" I asked.

"Not for farming," he explained. "Elephants prefer to eat trees and there are plenty of them. Hippopotamus and buffalo are dangerous so we cannot walk safely outside at night. We must take particular care around the hippo, who like to graze in the cool of the evening."

But wild animals and cholera were not Katwe's only problems. Three weeks after my visit, rebels came down from the mountains to attack this village, killing four people and injuring many more.

During regular meetings with MSF, we heard of cases from areas not covered by our existing programmes. One of those was particularly serious, with five deaths reported. Sick people had to walk for four or five hours from an isolated mountain village, which only had a small dispensary, so that they were often quite ill, by the time they arrived in the MSF hospital.

"Could you set up a cholera unit in the village?" asked Bronwen, the nurse in charge of the nearest hospital treatment centre. "I'm sure it would save lives."

"I'll visit the village tomorrow and see what's feasible," I told her.

The next day, we set off for the mountains, following a reasonably good road for an hour and a half, before turning off onto a narrow track, that wound upwards into the hills. The scenery was marvellous and as we climbed we looked south, across the National Park, to Lake Edward. Northwest lay the Ruwenzori Mountains, and the valley between led directly into the highest peaks. We passed several isolated villages, where we had already set up cholera units. Since they were subject to frequent attacks, we normally kept our visits short, to diminish the risk to staff.

Our target village had a small dispensary, consisting of two tiny rooms. It was perched high on a ridge, from where we could see the local hospital, far below in the valley. The dispensary was run by a young, male nurse; in theory it was supported by the church, just a short distance further along the next ridge.

"They have very little money, so they cannot help me much," he told me.

After I had introduced our project, I asked if he had many cases of diarrhoea.

"I have had some, but now it is getting worse. There is no water here and I have no materials," he added.

"Where is the nearest water?" I asked.

We walked with him to the edge and followed his finger, as he pointed, way down the slope.

"You can just see the source. It is the small concrete lip, over there."

"How long does it take you to fetch water?" I asked.

"Thirty minutes there and fifty minutes back, because it's so heavy."

He explained that when patients came to him with cholera, they often needed hospital treatment, many hours away on foot. To survive this journey, they needed lots of water and the weakest of them were just not making it.

It was not ideal, a dispensary without water, but we could hardly expect the young man to spend his days walking up and down to the spring. I considered the problem. We could explain to villagers that anyone with diarrhoea must bring lots of water up with them when they came for treatment. But it might take a long time for people to get this message and in the meantime there would be more deaths. Since the problem was acute, we decided to supply the water ourselves, transporting half a tonne each week, using empty perfusion bottles from the major centres. They were ideal for the patients to carry, if they had to walk to the hospital. It was clearly a makeshift solution and I seriously wondered if I was choosing the right approach. But there were no more deaths recorded from that village.

Two weeks later, we heard from Dr Andrew that there were cases reported in the village of Mayhoro, on the other side of Lake George.

"Could you have a look?" he asked.

It was a Sunday when we set off, first crossing the Businga Channel, linking Lake Edward to Lake George. Almost immediately, we turned left onto a rough track and after thirty minutes I asked our driver to check on the route. I needed to know how long it would take to get to the other side of the lake. When we came to a small village, he asked someone for information.

"The bridge was washed away last month and has not been repaired," was the unfortunate response. "You can only cross on foot and it will take you four hours to get to Mayhoro, after the bridge."

Clearly, this was not feasible, because we were carrying supplies, so we returned to the Businga Channel to try to find a boat. There was none available at the lakeside village, although they assured us that the Park Safari Lodge had one for hire. At the Lodge gate, the attendant blocked our way.

"We have been told that there are cases of cholera in Mahyoro and we need to hire a boat to take some medical supplies to them. We believe there is a boat at the Lodge."

"I am not allowed to let anyone into the park without paying."

"Look, this is really important. You can see from our car who we are. Could you phone the person in charge? I'm sure he will agree."

It was no use. He wanted us to pay thirty dollars, each! Since even this did not guarantee a boat at the Lodge, we moved on to the village on the other side of the channel, where a fisheries' protection boat was rumoured to exist. As it was Sunday, we had to find the manager's house, but at least he was aware of the cholera problem. He was pleased that we were trying to help and immediately sent for the boatman, who loaded us into a sixteen-foot craft, with an outboard motor. It would take us three hours to get to Mahyoro, but we could carry most of our medical supplies with us.

As we loaded up, there were several hippo feeding at the jetty, about two metres from the shore and in my opinion, not quite far enough away. It was difficult to know exactly how many there were, as they regularly submerged, reappearing randomly all around us. I struggled desperately to keep track of their movements, counting them out and then back in again. Despite my anxiety, children played nearby, unconcerned, suggesting that the community had learned to live peacefully with their huge neighbours. Slowly, we moved up the channel between the two lakes, glimpsing elephant on the banks and large birds that I imagined were eagles, although the local boatman did not know their English name. It was like being on a small, select safari—an extremely hot and exposed safari, as we soon discovered. We began to burn under the relentless sun and spent the rest of the trip scooping up water, to drench ourselves.

On our arrival at Mayoro, we were cheerfully welcomed by the local children. Here, the beach was littered with rubbish and busy with scavenging Maribou storks, ugly, prehistoric creatures, the stuff of nightmares. Their thick-set bodies, were crowned by bald heads, with red, wrinkled skin hanging down in folds. With raucous cries and clumsy movements, they fed with impunity.

The health staff were pleased to see us.

"There are no cases of cholera in this village, but the next one has many sick people," they told us.

Unfortunately, it was now too late for us to travel further, so we asked if we could have a training meeting with the health unit staff immediately. This, they quickly arranged and we gave our teaching session to an enthusiastic audience, leaving the group with a fair stock of materials. I spoke to the nurse in charge.

"If you do have any cases, let us know and we will return to help. Please pass on our message to the next village."

We set off a little later than planned, but the captain assured us it was okay to travel in the twilight, although he was not really equipped to sail in the dark. It was more than okay, it was magnificent. The sun set gloriously on the lake, making us feel it had been a day's holiday, rather than a long day's work.

The epidemic was gradually declining, although there were always new, hot spots appearing. It was rather like a bush fire; as soon as you beat out one section, it leapt over to a new area, apparently without rhyme or reason. The following week, at the planning meeting, we heard that there were many new cases at Mahango, a dispensary in the mountains, directly behind Kasese.

"Could you establish a Lazaret hospital there?" Dr Andrew asked. "I must warn you, it's a bit remote. There are two ways to approach, but one of them has not been used for some time, so it may be difficult."

I listened to his instructions, planning to explore the route with Yves. So the next day, we took the route into the mountains, driving towards the Kilembe mines for six kilometres, before turning off the road. At first the track was not too bad, but gradually, it became steeper and then steeper. At a particularly bad patch, with a lot of loose gravel and shale, I had to engage four-wheel drive, but even with this we could not continue. I tried several times more, without success, finally handing over to Yves, who had no more luck. Then a local man (who had been entertained by our efforts) came over to the truck window, offering his help. I wasn't sure that someone who had never driven a truck before could help, but I listened politely anyway.

"You must put some weight in the back and then it will move without difficulty," he told me.

We were considering this excellent advice, wondering how long it would take us to shift some gravel into the back of the truck, when our helper shouted to some women and children, further down the path. Before we could say a word, they were installed in the back of the pick-up and as the man had predicted, we had little trouble in ascending the hill. Gradually, we dropped our passengers off at their own houses, so that everyone was pleased with the outcome. Finally we climbed up sharply on a firmer road, until we reached the ridge. There, we looked south to Lakes Edward and George with the Businga Channel between, lying about 1600 metres below, before going on to Mahango, about seventy five minutes from Kasese, (although only one kilometre as the crow flies).

"Where is the dispensary?" I asked the first boy we met.

"It is down there."

He pointed down the hill on the Kasese side, to a building that was just visible in the distance, between the trees.

"How long will it take us to walk there?" I asked.

"Not long," he replied, somewhat unhelpfully, before running off. It looked challenging, more so, I imagined, when carrying supplies.

Before we set off, we arranged with the village elders to run a training session when we returned the following day.

"But we would like to visit the dispensary now. Can someone take us?" I asked one of the elders.

"Of course," he replied, speaking to a young man in the crowd. Under a baking sun, the three of us then set off down the hill and as I had suspected, "not long", turned out to be more than an hour. We were also nervous, as we scrambled sweatily along the route, for although there had been no recent raids, this area was not a safe zone and any unusual movement in the hills could easily be construed by the rebels as a threat. I wondered how I could walk in a way that might be perceived as unthreatening, but since it was necessary to concentrate on not slipping down the slope, I forgot about the possible risk, in favour of the likely one.

This dispensary was built on a small shoulder of land, about twenty by thirty metres. Currently, it held eighteen cholera patients. We found the registers to be well kept, indicating there had been twenty-eight cases that week, so Dr Andrews' anxieties had been well founded. Although the head nurse was not available to meet us, her assistants confirmed that there was a shortage of materials and that there were no contingency plans for a sudden influx of cases. Yves began to work out the layout of a cholera isolation centre, while I asked the assistants a few medical questions, to get an idea of the dispensary's capacity. The assistants were fairly well informed, explaining that they had been to a training session in Kasese, three weeks before, but the promised delivery of materials had not arrived in the dispensary.

"Is there any way to drive here?" I asked.

"It is possible to come up from this side of the mountain, if you drive along the lake road and turn right."

"Is it a good road?" I asked hopefully.

"Someone came up in a four by four, just a few months ago." I was not convinced. That path looked more suitable for a mountain goat.

Two days later, we made an attempt to reach the dispensary by road, a local health assistant acting as our guide. He said he had been up several times on his motorbike and assured us that we would have no trouble at all. We approached from the south and as we turned off the tarmac, I saw a faint line threading up the side of mountain. This was our road! Use of the word "road" turned out to be something of an exaggeration. We crossed a dry riverbed and wandered through the scrub, doubting our guide's assurances that this was indeed the right way. When we finally found the rough track, clinging to the side of the mountain, we engaged four-wheel drive. We had climbed about two hundred metres, when, disturbingly, the truck began to slip and slide. Then, it lost most of its grip and we lost most of our confidence in its ability to get us up safely. The last thing we wanted was to turn ourselves into casualties, so we arranged to come back the following day, with our own Land Cruiser.

On this occasion, we made better progress. However, when we got scarily close to the precipice, we undid our seat-belts and opened the doors, so that we could jump out, if the vehicle started to slip. All the while the local driver remained unconcerned. We thought him quite mad and said so, but he simply laughed at our wimpish, Western attitude to risk. As we climbed higher, the track gradually diminished to a footpath, no more than fifty centimetres wide. Fortunately, there were very few trees, so we drove where we thought the path should be, until we were within two hundred metres of the dispensary. The "road" was indeed passable, although I didn't like the thought of making this trip on a regular basis. Familiarity might easily lead to a fatal loss of concentration.

Approached from this new direction, the dispensary still looked precarious, as if it might at any moment tumble down the hillside. Since our last visit, the workers had begun to prepare an isolation room and spraying facilities, to disinfect everyone coming in and out. These simple measures, together with our supplies, would make all the difference. Over my next few visits, the number of cholera cases increased, but there were only two deaths after our intervention. Prevention may not be as prestigious as some front-line emergency work, but it can be both strenuous and rewarding and it is a pleasure to arrive to hear the words, "no more deaths".

Our MSF colleagues in the larger hospitals were now reducing their team, as the local staff gained confidence. We too had begun to think of reducing our numbers, when MSF had news of the first outbreak in the north, beyond Fort Portal. When they decided to transfer their local team to deal with this problem, they asked if we could take over Fort Portal hospital, so we sent two people north. For some reason, which no one understood, there had been relatively few cases although this area had been at risk of cholera. When we arrived, we found the hospital had already tried to establish an isolation unit of sorts, with about twenty patients. In comparison with our other units, this was well stocked and staffed, but there was an unusually high death rate. In fact, they had the worst record in the area.

Almost all the deaths happened at night, because the nursing staff went home and even the doctors refused to come out when called. Whereas it was true that they were already over stretched on the existing wards, this did not excuse leaving patients to die, when they could so easily be saved. I did everything I could to try to persuade the staff to work at night, but all my efforts were in vain. Then I visited the hospital Director, at first being very diplomatic and then bluntly pointing out that this centre had the worst figures in the region.

"You have a death rate of 9%," I said. "It's inexcusable!"

"Yes, I see what you mean, but we have staff problems, particularly with the nurse in charge. I will see if I can do anything," he promised smoothly.

But nothing happened. It was a classic case of weak management, an administrator refusing to deal firmly with staff, but in this situation it was killing people. And there was no reason for them to die. All that was required was for the staff to do their jobs! At our next evening meeting, Rocco, always the most outspoken, was very direct.

"They are disgraceful," he said. "They have the best facilities, plenty of equipment and a good staffing level. They just don't care if their patients die. It's outrageous!"

Natalie chimed in,

"I try to be there as much as possible, but when I arrive in the morning, there are no nurses and anyone who needs a drip is just lying there, completely dehydrated. Then I put up the drips myself and the patients are feeling better by the time I leave, but the staff won't do it. There are plenty of them and I can't be there all the time."

"I have tried talking to the Director, but he says the right things when I'm there and then he does nothing," I told them.

"We should just leave and let them take the consequences," said Rocco.

"We can't do that — it's the patients who will suffer and there will be more unnecessary deaths," said Natalie.

"There will not be many more deaths if we leave, than if we stay," Yves chipped in. "We are already achieving almost nothing. Anyway, they have enough staff and we aren't there to do the bits of the job they don't like."

If the people wouldn't take our advice and no one would intervene, there was nothing more we could do. It was all very disheartening, in fact one of my most disagreeable experiences in Uganda. I kept up the pressure on the Director and the hospital matron and Natalie spoke to the other nursing staff. Whatever else, I was convinced we shouldn't abandon the patients, just because of the staff's bad practices.

We were relieved to hear that Paris had approved six weeks additional funding for our programme. This time would allow us to plan a seamless hand-over to our Ugandan colleagues. (So much better than telling them at the last minute that our money had run out!) The Red Cross had already left once, only to return later when more money was found. We had seen first-hand the problems that had resulted. My main hope was that we would leave behind something resilient enough to last, until the epidemic died out naturally.

Apart from the Fort Portal hospital staffing problem, we were very pleased with the results of our work. The number of patients in Kasese was approaching twelve thousand, yet the mortality rate was only 1.6%. It is sometimes possible to achieve less than 1%, but that is in ideal conditions, such as a closed environment like a refugee camp, where there is more control. In Kasese, the patients came from a large catchment area and transport was a problem, so we felt pleased with our accomplishment. Although interpretation of such statistics is fraught with problems, I made an effort to evaluate what we had achieved during the five-month project, so that I could pass on concise records to any future group.

There had been only one hundred and ninety five deaths in Kasese. Without intervention, there could have been one thousand or more. Working together, the local people, the local authorities, MSF and MDM, had saved at least one thousand lives. As I told the team, this was something to be proud of.

Later, when I spoke with Ton, he told me that thirty-seven of Uganda's fifty districts had been affected by this cholera epidemic. The three areas most affected had been Kasese, Kampala and Mbale and throughout the country there had been more than fifty thousand cases, with a mortality of two thousand. However, as I congratulated myself over the cholera intervention, I was reminded of Uganda's malaria problem and its estimated one hundred thousand deaths annually from that disease.

But malaria is a much harder disease to master and cholera is, in essence, a short-term problem. We had been privileged to help Dr Andrew and his staff. They could not have coped alone, because they already had such a heavy workload and were desperately short of materials. Once, when I visited Dr Andrew to discuss the cholera problem, I found him in the operating theatre, repairing a man who had been badly hacked by a rebel machete. He was a special kind of person, someone I admired a lot.

Then, just as we thought we might leave Uganda on a high note, there was news from the North. ADF rebels, commanded by a woman, had raided a residential college near Fort Portal, attempting to persuade students of between twelve and twenty years to join them. The students had refused, barricading themselves in their dormitory.

With extraordinary cruelty, the rebels blocked the doors and windows and set fire to the building. Thirty-nine students were burned alive, some of the bodies found melted to glass windows. I was haunted by this image, finding it hard to believe that human beings could do such a thing.

CHAPTER TWELVE

Iran and ideology

"Can you come to Paris on Wednesday? We need someone urgently, for Iran." As usual, I said "Yes" instantly and then turned to study the map of the world, now a permanent part of my living room decoration. I had wanted a short contract and I didn't mind where it took me. Iran sounded as good a destination as any.

Iran had been in the newspapers a lot in recent years, yet I knew little of what to expect when I got there. I could remember the revolution and the American hostages, the Ayatollah Khomeini and the war with Iraq. It was well known that the Islamic Republic adhered to strict Muslim codes, with severe punishments for anyone who broke the rules and I knew that women were forced to wear black, all-covering garments. There was also a complete ban on alcohol! Iran would be a totally different experience for me, but as an aid worker and a man, I assumed that my life would not be too severely curtailed. In the short term, I didn't really mind about the alcohol.

So I caught the sleeper train from Marseilles to Paris a few days later and after a leisurely breakfast of coffee and croissants at the Gare de Lyon, set off for my meeting with the Head of Desk. In best MSF tradition he was not currently in Paris, so instead I met his deputy, Pierre, a lawyer by training, specialising in International Law and Human rights. Realising that he would be unlikely to offer an in-depth medical exposition of my mission, I settled down for what would no doubt be a detailed geopolitical analysis. Pierre was very enthusiastic.

"At the moment, there are three MSF workers in Iran: Marie-Pierre, Head of Mission, Geneviève, the nurse and Salah, the log. Marie-Pierre is based in Teheran and the other two are working in a refugee camp at Sarvestan, in the south of the country. Apart from the earthquake in 1991, NGOs have not been allowed into Iran for years, so we're very pleased to have a foothold, however small. Although the authorities are anti-Western, they recognise the need to improve their relations with the rest of the world, but to date MSF is the only international aid organisation to gain access," he finished proudly.

"Which emergency provoked this current involvement?" I asked, for I imagined that it must have been something quite significant, to open a door that had been so firmly closed to Western influences.

"There is no emergency. We are working in two refugee camps for the moment, but that's not really the point. MSF wants access to Iran because of the country's poor record concerning women's rights, in fact human rights in general. We want to see for ourselves what's going on there."

"That sounds a bit like spying to me," I said, not really sure if this was what I had envisaged myself doing for MSF.

Pierre looked a bit surprised at this response, so I tried to explain.

"I'm more a hands on sort of chap, pleased to leave the politics to those who like that sort of thing."

"But Stuart, only by being present in a country, can we really help its population. MSF is interested in helping people to achieve change, especially where their human rights are at risk. Change requires international pressure, which is why we need to witness what is going on. We call it "témoignage" (witnessing). It's an integral part of MSF philosophy. You must have heard of it."

Of course I had read about the word. I'd even heard other people use it, but as I listened to what Pierre was saying, I found its message difficult to absorb. What's more, I had not thought of témoignage in this context, where it appeared to be quite divorced from my medical remit. I thought it meant speaking out against atrocities, seen in the midst of medical work. Perhaps if we concentrated on what I would actually be doing in Iran, I might understand what it was MSF wanted to achieve.

By now, our meeting was constantly interrupted by people poking their heads round the door, either to ask questions, or to hand out snippets of news. So it seemed wise to jog things along, before one of our visitors decided to stay and join in. The casual French way of holding meetings is for me, a little disturbing, since I retain a more formal, British liking for an agenda and minutes.

"Could you give me any specific details about what I will be doing?" I suggested, without too much hope. I had been here before.

"You will be working in a refugee camp in Arak, close to the border with Iraq. The refugees are Iraqi Marsh Arabs, who have been forced to flee from Saddam Hussein. I am not "medical", so I can't go into the details of your job, but Marie-Pierre is a doctor and she will brief you fully when you arrive in Teheran."

And that was that. Actually, the mission didn't sound too bad. I was to work in a refugee camp, the sort of thing I expected to do for MSF. Témoignage, I imagined, would simply take care of itself.

After the meeting, I found my way to the "Bureau de Depart", eager to acquire all the things I needed for my trip, feeling rather an old hand at the game now and confident about what would happen next. However, this time there was no plane ticket, since I had not yet been allocated a visa. Marie-Pierre was required to prepare documents for the Iranian Embassy in Paris, before my application would even be considered.

"There is always a delay in Teheran," Natalie said.

"Is it likely to be a very long wait?" I asked, anxious to be off.

"With Teheran, we can never tell. It's different each time."

"Should I just go home and wait for news there?"

"It's up to you, but sometimes they want to see you at the embassy in person, if the visa comes through quickly."

So, I would stay. After all, how long could it take to process a visa for a humanitarian aid doctor? I decided to spend my unexpected break exploring Paris and researching Iran in the MSF library.

The library had a reasonable stock of newspaper articles and political analyses, which occupied my time, when I wasn't being a tourist. There was even a fairly recent guidebook. Anti-American feeling had continued to run high after the revolution and it appeared that all Westerners were lumped together as "undesirables", (particularly aid workers, if the speed of my visa was anything to go by). Yet it was also clear that in recent times some things had begun to change and Iran was cautiously trying to improve its relations with the West. Unfortunately, there was no information about the project itself, so there was little more I could do in preparation.

Glad of my anorak, I plodded resolutely around the chilly streets, getting to know Paris. At least Iran would be warm, I told myself. Paris is a beautiful city and it was gratifying to have this opportunity to explore its hidden corners of charm, way beyond the customary tourist attractions of the Eiffel Tower and Notre Dame. Each quarter has its own fund of history and there are wall plaques that tell the story of important streets and significant buildings. However, as the days passed, I began to regret my decision to hang around, for endlessly marking time is ultimately frustrating, however beautiful your surroundings.

Then, after three weeks, my visa was finally delivered to MSF and I set off from Roissy Airport, catching a direct flight to Teheran. As I emerged from the baggage reclaim area, I immediately spotted Marie-Pierre, looking quite incongruous, beside all the other women in the place. Tall, well-built and fair-complexioned, she wore a long, dark grey coat and training shoes, with a scarf tied round her head that only vaguely hid short, light brown hair. Somewhat disturbingly, her long oval face showed a pained expression, but I later discovered that she had that look whenever she went outside in Iran, because of the way she had to dress. It was for her, a constant irritation and affront to be forced to shroud herself in this manner.

"Hello and welcome," she greeted me pleasantly in English.

As we left the airport behind and made our way into town, she began to explain about life in Iran. Unusually for MSF, here we had no cars of our own, using taxis most of the time. It was the weekend, so we headed straight for the MSF house in Elahiyah, a residential suburb on the north side of Teheran, where the land begins to climb steeply up towards the Alborz Mountains. As the taxi wove in and out of heavy traffic, Marie-Pierre pointed out the landmarks that she felt were important, talking enthusiastically all the while, about the country and the work.

Our MSF house was the lower half of a property, which belonged to a family that had managed to retain some of its wealth, after the 1979 fall of the Shah. Behind an unusually high wall, there lay a pleasant, landscaped garden, where heads of blue and yellow crocuses pushed through a light covering of snow. I was fascinated by the height of the wall, which Marie-Pierre explained was necessary, to enable women to remove their coats and scarves, without being seen by men. But the temperature and the snow surprised me most. It was freezing. In fact, it was even colder than Paris!

"Where is all that heat I've been reading about?"

"Don't worry Stuart, in about six weeks, Teheran will be a furnace of hot traffic fumes and dust. It will be forty degrees in the shade and still there will be snow on the mountains, since they rise to well over four thousand metres. Don't worry about the heat. It'll come. You'll wish it hadn't."

I stowed my things into one of the three bedrooms, somewhat surprised to see such incongruously poor furniture in this spacious, well-built house. Then Marie-Pierre suggested a walk around the local area, so that my briefing could be integrated with an initial exposure to Iran and its people.

"Is it okay for us to walk together in the street?"

I had read that mixing of the sexes is not allowed in public, except for husbands and wives.

"That's a problem for young people, but I think I look sufficiently foreign and given our age, I don't think anyone will bother us," she replied. "But it's good to be aware of these things. BAFIA is very suspicious and they are liable to be watching us all the time."

"What's BAFIA?" I asked, bemused by this new piece of information.

"They are the Bureau of Foreign Affairs and Immigration, but they are also the real power in the country—the secret police. As foreigners, we must deal with them all the time. They take precedence over the Ministry of Health. In fact, they control everything we do and they're always there, watching us."

Iran was now beginning to sound decidedly reminiscent of George Orwell's "1984", but despite this, we strolled unaccosted in one of Teheran's many parks, where I was surprised to find that even in winter, there were lots of people walking around: men in pairs, and in larger groups. There were also a few families. The whole scene seemed quite mundane, so I presumed Marie-Pierre had probably been exaggerating, with all her talk of relentless Iranian espionage. She was now explaining that there were few outdoor activities allowed, in this strict Islamic regime, so walking and picnicking were extremely popular pastimes, even when it was really cold.

We paused to look down from the park over Teheran, to the desert beyond. I saw a tremendous, sprawling city, much bigger than I had expected.

"They say Teheran has fourteen million people," Marie Pierre explained, "but with so many refugees and itinerants, no one is really sure. Though we are fortunate to be able to see so much of it today. It's usually obscured by smog, especially in summer."

It was certainly an incredible sight and we sat for a while on a bench to absorb the panorama. It was too cold however, to stay still for long.

"At the moment, MSF has only one established base in Iran, a small refugee camp at Sarvestan. Salah and Geneviève work there, with about three thousand Iraqis. We travel by plane, since it's about one thousand kilometres away and flights are incredibly cheap in Iran. In a couple of weeks, they will visit Teheran, so you will have a chance to chat with them about what they are doing. You will be working on your own, in a refugee camp at Arak, southwest of here."

"How soon do I start?"

"I will come with you to Arak, on Monday, to introduce you to the authorities. We'll travel by car this time, because I have to return immediately, for another appointment. By car it is about three hours, but by bus, five and a half hours."

"Is that how I'll travel normally?"

"There's no precedent, since you are the first MSF person to work in Arak, but I thought that you could try the bus, to see if it's practical. I suggest you come back to Teheran each weekend. You would be too isolated if you stayed there alone all the time."

"Have we rented an MSF house in Arak?"

"I haven't had time to look for one, but you can stay in a hotel, until we decide what is best. In fact, none of the details has been worked out yet. The refugee camp is forty kilometres from Arak and you will travel there daily by taxi, since we can't get permission to buy cars. You should talk with the doctor in the camp, to see what you can do for the refugees. Of course, you won't be dealing directly with patients."

"If I'm not seeing patients and there are no defined needs, then what on earth am I doing here?"

My question might have been a little blunt, but it reflected my feelings. Although I had been warned that this was an unusual mission, one that involved "témoignage", I had expected to have a few specific goals, even if I wasn't going to have any patients. Marie-Pierre tried once more to explain.

"Stuart, MSF wants to be in Iran, but we are very constrained about what we can do here, because of the authorities. They are suspicious of anyone from the West and they have never worked with an NGO before. You will have to be flexible and we will discuss things each weekend in Teheran, to see how it goes. Of course, we must also see what BAFIA allows us to do."

So, despite the fact that my mission was about to begin, I still knew little about the specifics of the assignment; indeed, I felt increasingly bemused by the situation. But at least I knew a bit more about the refugees. They were Iraqi Arabs, who had fled their homes in the marshy south of the country, following repeated attacks by Saddam Hussein. Iranians are not Arabs, but in the main they show sympathy towards their neighbours and now there were several refugee camps set up along the border with Iraq. For whatever reason, the Iranian government had decided that the camps at Arak and Sarvestan should be the target for MSF support.

On Sunday night, I met my interpreter. It was difficult to judge her age, as she was wearing the regulation scarf and black coat, which did the requisite job of hiding most of her shape. Ameneh was a part time English teacher in a Teheran primary school and during the current three-week holiday it had been agreed that she would stay with me in Arak, until we found someone more permanent. She had been born in England, where she had lived until the age of twelve, so her English was perfect, although she confessed that her written Farsi was not so good. Her parents had been wealthy factory owners, who had fled the country just before the revolution. Later the family had returned, feeling that it was once more safe to live in Iran and presumably content to accept the new regime.

The three of us arranged to meet at 8am the following morning for our journey to Arak. We set off punctually, but Teheran suffers from huge traffic jams, so it took nearly an hour to leave the city, although this did give me time to look around. The buildings in the centre were classic brick, or modern constructions of no particular architectural, or historical interest, but as we moved south, we began to encounter, older, single-storeyed houses, often with a mattress or carpet hanging over the roof edge.

"Why do they do that?" I asked.

"Teheran is so dusty, that they have to be cleaned regularly," Ameneh told me.

Several kilometres outside the city, we passed a huge mosque still under construction, a shrine to the Ayatollah Khomeni. The four main minarets were in place, but the domes were not yet finished and it looked impressive, if rather modern and functional. Then at last, we moved out into the desert, travelling on a good tarmac road. We passed low mountains on the right, while on the left, empty desert stretched into the distance. There were pastel colours of endless variety in the rocks, the cliffs and the sand: green, ochre, yellow, red, even blue. It was extraordinarily beautiful. I was spellbound and didn't notice time passing, until Marie-Pierre pointed out the holy city of Qom.

In Iran, Qom is the centre of Islam, home to all the religious colleges and the town where Ayatollah Khomeni studied, during the years before he went into exile. We did not pass through the city, stopping instead for tea on the ring road, at the Iranian equivalent of a service station, which comprised about thirty modest shops and teahouses, all in a row. A melancholy litter of plastic bags and food wrappers were caught up on low, thorny plants, for 100 yards around the periphery. People stood chatting, drinking cups of hot, strong tea and munching on a dry cake, which I tried, but didn't much like.

Back in the taxi, we turned west, climbing slowly up into low hills. The bare, dry desert was beginning to show evidence of small scrub plants, but there were still no trees and the road climbed monotonously upwards until we reached Arak, which was lightly dusted with snow. Bizarrely, one of the first sights was a funfair, perched on a hill just behind the bus station, Ferris Wheel and roundabouts oddly incongruous, yet strangely familiar. But then, why not? It was nice to know Iranians had some form of enjoyment. Three kilometres further on, we turned off the main road, entering what looked like a Stalinist housing estate, quite at odds with anything I had expected to find here. It was Ameneh who explained this rather odd phenomenon.

"During the years of prosperity, there was a thriving Japanese aluminium plant on the other side of the road and the company built this estate for its workers. The factory hardly functions at all now, but there is still a hotel for visiting business men. BAFIA says you must use it."

The estate was an ugly jumble of depressing, grey concrete shapes. Red, checked tablecloths peeking out through the hotel's restaurant windows were the only cheerful things to be seen. Later, I realised that this was the best hotel in Arak, but the bleak reception area, drab walls and the threadbare carpet, gave a less than welcoming first impression. Behind the reception desk was a short man in an open necked shirt, with old trousers, tousled grey hair and a three-day growth of stubble; this image marginally improved by a huge, beaming smile. Ameneh told him that I would be staying for some time and I learned later that she had negotiated the Iranian rate, since I was not a tourist (seven dollars a night, instead of thirty-five!). The man spoke no English, but seemed to recognise the international terms for both taxi and money.

Upstairs, the somewhat dreary bedrooms were almost devoid of furniture. Mine had two beds, a small table and one chair, with a large floor to ceiling, metal-framed, French window, from which a small balcony allowed me to glimpse a tree-lined park, with a running track. But the electricity worked and there were both hot water and heating, the latter essential, since temperatures regularly dropped to minus ten degrees at night. Only two weeks earlier, Arak had recorded minus twenty-seven degrees centigrade, so it seemed that my fondness for heat was not going to be satisfied immediately.

Now, we set off to seek clearance from BAFIA. and I discovered that Arak was much bigger than I had imagined, with the same mix of old and new buildings that I had noted in Teheran. Ameneh told me that the city had a population of about one million people. When we arrived at BAFIA, I had what was to be the first of many meetings to gain "permission". In Iran, almost every activity requires someone's written authorisation, particularly if you are a foreigner. Each of these requires both formal meetings and time consuming negotiation. This meeting was much as I had anticipated, although possibly slightly shorter and even more frustrating. From the official's gestures and demeanour, not to mention Ameneh's responses, I could tell that he was not entirely thrilled by my presence. Not only that, I had the impression that Ameneh herself was being interrogated, as there were long periods of conversation in Farsi, with no mention of either my name, Marie-Pierre's, or even that of MSF.

Although at first very evasive, Ameneh later confirmed my impression, admitting that she had been grilled about her family connections and her motivation for the taking the job.

"He told me that I must relay all our conversations and activities back to him. He said that his agents would be always close by. I am afraid he doesn't trust you. Or me either," she concluded, rather forlornly.

I had the impression that BAFIA trusted no one. This engendered a feeling of isolation, which was intensified by my total inability to communicate. Although I had worked with a translator in Cambodia, this was my first experience of being completely isolated by language and I was surprised how strange it felt, to be quite so detached from everyone else. In Arak, very few people spoke English, or French and there were no other expats with whom I could relax and chat. The language of Iran is Farsi, which uses Arabic characters, and Arabs, I am told, can understand some Farsi. Strangely, it doesn't seem to work the other way around. The sounds are mostly quite alien to my Western ear and I learned to recognise very few words during my stay.

Eventually, we received our permission to work and BAFIA also proposed a permanent translator, to help me when Ameneh left. I was surprised when she said that this would be a bad idea, as he would certainly be a spy. Thinking she was being a touch too melodramatic, there seemed no good reason to cancel the forthcoming interview.

I said good-bye to Marie-Pierre, confident that I could now survive on my own in Arak and looking forward to my new job, although I still had no real idea what it would demand of me. Ameneh assured me that she would stay on, until I engaged a long term interpreter, although she had to return to her family in Teheran for the weekend of Naw-Ruz, Iranian New Year.

At 7am the next morning, we found ourselves the only patrons of the hotel dining room, staring at highly stylised pictures on the wall, while chatting in subdued tones over our meal. Above the door, a large photograph of the Ayatollah frowned directly down, reminding the world that he would tolerate no nonsense in Iran. It was not the most cheerful venue to start the day, although the breakfast menu was excellent, including bread, goat's cheese, carrot jam, and fried eggs. The bread was cardboard-thin wafers about two feet long and one foot wide. Ameneh explained that it came from an earthen oven and despite the cardboard texture, it has a dry savoury taste, which I grew to like. There were other types of bread too and later, one of my small pleasures was to walk to the bakery, join the queue and choose one of the varieties as a snack.

The first time that I went outside for a walk by myself, I ventured further into the estate, quickly becoming depressed by the lifeless, grey uniformity, with no advertising, no colour, nothing at all to catch the eye, or break the monotony. It seemed like the USSR, rather than the

Middle East. Eventually, I found some shops, tiny rooms selling a few essentials. Later, when I developed the habit of walking before sunset, I occasionally came across a few children at play. Laughter changed the character of the place a little, though not a lot and not enough.

The next day, Ameneh and I dutifully met with the two proposed interpreters and it took only about thirty seconds to recognise that whatever their skills as spies, neither of them had anything other than a rudimentary knowledge of the English language. They were quite useless to me, so I sent them packing immediately.

"Why don't we try the University? I have a relative working there," suggested Ameneh, politely omitting to add, "I told you so".

We spent the next two days trying to find someone else for the job, but this was not a good time, since it was now the start of the Naw-Ruz holiday, so we made no progress.

On Thursday we returned to Teheran, having achieved virtually nothing. I had now been in Iran for over a week and I hadn't even visited the refugee camp! The whole thing was becoming extremely frustrating. This time, however, we used the bus, which took longer, but was far better for sightseeing. I had always imagined the desert to be dull and uninteresting, but the very emptiness drew your eye to small changes of form and colour. It fascinated me. When we climbed out at the Qom service station for our regulation break, instead of the dry cake, Ameneh introduced me to Sohun, a biscuit made from compacted and sweetened pistachio nuts.

"It's delicious," I said, "although it may pull all my teeth out."

This sweetmeat was quite addictive and it became part of my routine to treat myself to a small box, whenever I made the long journey between Arak and Teheran.

The following Tuesday we returned to Arak, this time leaving from Teheran's Central Bus Station. It is a circular area, large enough to accommodate fifty or sixty buses, nose in, with another two hundred or so, stationed around in a large parking lot. I suppose a massive bus station is essential for a city of 14 million inhabitants, most of whom can't afford a car, but it was all a bit overwhelming for a newcomer who didn't speak the language. In fact, I came to the conclusion that most of Teheran's inhabitants had now moved into the bus station, so overwhelming were the crush and noise. Every walk of Iranian life was represented: smart businessmen, huge, extended families, endless numbers of black swathed women, swarms of children, old people, students and beggars. Rich and poor combined to produce a level of noise that was frightening. To top it all, since some of the buses were privately operated, many drivers touted their destinations verbally, each trying to shout louder than the next, in an effort to attract custom.

After an initial pause, Ameneh bravely leapt into the melee, asking people which counter sold tickets for Arak. None of the directions seemed to be right, so that we found ourselves in many wrong queues and on many wrong buses, before we could verify our tickets. As we sank gratefully into our seats, I asked Ameneh why it had all been such a problem and, to my surprise, she said that she had never used a bus before!

All the time we were in the bus station, I had tried to make a mental note of the layout and procedures, since later, I would have to navigate the route on my own. However, I was by now quite bewildered. It was a relief to discover that on leaving the bus station, we drove slowly round the perimeter road, with the driver's assistant shouting at the top of his voice, "Qom Arak, Qom Arak". Since he stopped for anyone who indicated they wanted a ride, I realised that I had an alternative to buying a ticket inside the bus station, if I could be sure of identifying the call "Qom, Arak". I also noted that the bus was now two and a half hours late. Since the trip itself took five to six hours, it became clear, that as long as I used the bus, two entire days a week would be taken up by travel. But the journey was as usual, quite enchanting and I asked Ameneh about some of the sights that we saw. Unfortunately, due to her English upbringing, she was quite poorly informed about her country.

So it was the second week before we visited the refugee camp. Our rickety taxi arrived outside the hotel at 7am, its toothy, cheerful driver chattering pleasantly to Ameneh, as he struggled to open the rear passenger door. Strangely, he had never heard of a refugee camp in the area and later I discovered that the authorities avoided publicising its existence. The camp was called Ali Abad and it was forty kilometres outside Arak, on the road leading back to Qom. When we turned off the main road on to a dusty track, two watchtowers loomed ahead, indicating the rear corners of a rectangular compound. Inside, we could see groups of buildings, surrounding a clear, central area. The camp was about seven hundred metres by four hundred metres and it housed five thousand refugees inside its barbed wire fence. As we approached, I was relieved to see that the towers were empty of soldiers and machine-guns, although there were armed guards on the gate. Despite the fact that the guards were just sitting around chatting, to my mind, the whole place looked like a prisoner-of-war camp from an old, Second World War film.

Ameneh said quietly, "It's awful. I didn't know anything like this existed in Iran."

Now, there was the inevitable hurdle of Iranian officialdom to overcome. We needed to speak to the camp commandant, but the guards refused to let us in, or even tell him we had arrived. It seemed ludicrous to sit here just looking at one another, but they didn't seem to mind in the least, however much Ameneh remonstrated. Finally, they telephoned the camp office, where someone authorised our admission, but by the time we were escorted into the commandant's presence, I was beginning to feel like a prisoner myself.

Mr Mir Shafi was a small, dapper man, with a hostile expression. Unlike many of his compatriots, he had a businesslike appearance, with a smartly trimmed beard, white shirt and neatly pressed trousers. In Iran ties are seldom worn, to avoid identity with Western culture. So for me formal meetings often seemed unusually casual, indeed almost bohemian, when you took into consideration the fact that most men either had a beard, or were in the process of growing one. The office was furnished with a long table and eight elegant chairs. Three other men were working in the room: one typing, one organising folders, while the third simply sat, watching.

Ameneh made the introductions and through her, I explained about MSF and our presence in Iran. I had to remain rather vague about our proposed activity, because I was rather vague about that detail myself. Then, despite having been forewarned of my arrival, Mr Mir Shafi insisted on telephoning the BAFIA office in Arak, to check that I was allowed to see the camp. When he received this official confirmation he seemed to relax a bit, so I asked if we could make a quick tour, to introduce ourselves to the refugees.

"You will not need to speak to the refugees. I have all the information you need, here," he told Ameneh. "My assistants will tell you anything you want to know."

It took me over an hour to persuade him that I must have access to the refugees themselves, in order to assess their needs and priorities. Whatever else MSF wanted, I knew that they would expect me to talk to the people, yet for Mr Mir Shafi, such a concept seemed quite unacceptable. Although it is always difficult to convey an argument through an interpreter, the commandant finally agreed to my demand, but it took a little more persuasion for him to agree to a specific start date. This was to be in two days' time. I never understood why delay was necessary, but throughout my contract in Iran postponement was the order of the day.

So it was that two days later we made our first walking tour of the camp, accompanied by an armed guard. My first impression was that the structure had probably been an Iranian military camp. It was built around three enclosed courtyards, rather like stables, two of which were encircled by perhaps eighty rooms, each accommodating a family of about ten people. To one side of the courtyards, there was a large open area with many tents. The health centre was arranged around a smaller square, separated from the rest by a large, iron gate and since the camp doctor was consulting with patients, we decided to view this area at the end of our visit. We returned to the main, central square for a more detailed appraisal, noting for the first time the additional buildings around its periphery: a bakery, the camp office complex and a garage workshop. There was also an area where a football pitch had been crudely marked out and a game was in progress. This activity gave the impression of a more conventional existence, but rows of tents beside the pitch belied this suggestion, since they were clearly homes for families. There was also a small market, with a few makeshift counters and basic goods, such as soap and cooking oil, laid out for sale.

Outside the tents, women were cooking on wood fires, while young children played around their feet. Beyond the barbed wire fence at the other end, someone was building houses, but I assumed these had nothing to do with the camp. Ameneh tried to talk to a few people and although one or two replied in Farsi, the majority did not understand. Even those who offered a few words were not too enthusiastic about saying much to strangers. We began to look for someone to hire as an Arabic interpreter, but each time we broached the subject with a Farsi speaker, our guard intervened. So we returned to speak to the doctor.

The medical facility consisted of six rooms, each with a different purpose: pharmacy, consultation, childbirth, health education, rest area and store. There was little furniture, several windows were broken and, although whitewashed, the walls were dirty. The staff comprised one doctor, two nurses, one pharmacist and two refugee helpers, who acted as interpreters, since the others spoke no Arabic.

Dr Shah was twenty-eight years old, small and neat. He listened patiently to my standard introduction and explanation of MSF and then told me that he had been assigned to Ali Abad, as part of his military service. Although he understood some English, he could not speak it, despite the fact that this had been the language of all his University textbooks. His lecturers, he told me, spoke Farsi.

"Things are difficult here," he explained, through Ameneh. "We have no equipment, we are short of drugs and I must work through an interpreter."

As we chatted, it became obvious that his education and knowledge were of the same standard as a British doctor and he was frustrated to be sent here, a place almost totally lacking in facilities, where most of his training was superfluous. We walked together back to the caravan that was his living quarters.

"I work in the camp five days a week and spend the weekends in Arak. There is nothing here and I am on call twenty-four hours a day. Even the nearby village of Ibrahim Abad has only three shops and one restaurant. Look around," he said, waving his arm in an arc, "desert and mountains."

Clearly, Dr Shah was not happy.

Before we left, I asked him to consider how we could work in collaboration, to help the refugees. As an afterthought, I enquired about the new buildings, at the other end of the camp. It seemed an odd place to construct new homes, on the edge of a refugee camp!

"These are new houses for the refugees, with electricity and hot water. It's very cold here at night and the tents are not good enough. Despite this new building, we still need help with our drug shortages and with the medical facilities."

In the taxi back to the hotel I was silent, as I tried to digest what I had seen and heard. Marie-Pierre had suggested in my briefing that we might refurbish the health centre and improve the drug supply. She had explained that since we were operating on MSF private money, there was no written proposal, so we required no authorisation for whatever we decided to do. It was up to me to devise a detailed plan, so I began to analyse what I had seen. As always, the first priority was to evaluate the camp's needs, in collaboration with the health staff and the refugees themselves. For this activity, interpreters were a priority. Yet my first impression was that the medical practice was doing very nicely on its own, apart from some drug shortages. Once more, I wondered what was expected of me. Now that I had seen the camp, I felt that Marie-Pierre needed to explain in more detail what MSF wanted to achieve. In the meantime, I would make an effort to develop relationships and gather information.

When I arrived in Teheran on the Friday night, I approached Marie-Pierre to arrange a meeting for the following morning. We travelled the short journey by taxi, because even with me for company, Marie-Pierre did not like walking beside the main road, as she felt that her appearance attracted attention. Clearly, living in Iran was a much bigger issue for her than I had realised. I felt free to wander around without fear or hindrance, but just walking to work had become an issue for her, because of the way she looked. I didn't mind in the least however, because Iranian taxis were interesting.

The first type is like the European model; you phone for a taxi to pick you up and pay the fare. The second (much more popular with the locals) follows a route like a bus and you flag it down. There is a drawback with this cheaper version; it does not take you precisely to where you want to go. It is your responsibility to get off at the nearest point to your destination. Flagging down consists of standing by the roadside, waving hopefully at any passing yellow car. When you find the right sort of yellow car, it slows down and you shout your destination through the window. If it is going in your direction, it stops and you climb aboard. If not, the driver makes a marvellous gesture to signify "no". He nods lightly, blinks simultaneously (allowing his lower jaw to drop slightly open) and accelerates away, without a word.

This second type of taxi can squeeze in as many as six passengers and it's only an ordinary saloon car. I found this particularly amusing, since for some reason, men and women can travel in the same vehicle. With four people in the back, you get interestingly close to the women, in a complete contrast to the Iranian custom of segregation. Even in liberal Europe, sensibilities would be offended. Later, I met one young

Iranian male, who cruised up and down the standard taxi routes in his yellow car, stopping only to pick up unaccompanied, attractive, young girls. He had not been caught as yet and more significantly, none of his passengers had complained publicly. I wondered how he knew when to stop, since I had difficulty guessing the age and appearance of women cloaked in black. Of course, young girls did occasionally indicate individuality, even rebellion, pushing scarves far back on their heads, to display their hair to best advantage. But as soon as an older person, or a policeman appeared, the scarf was tugged quickly to the front, to avoid trouble. Although difficult teenagers are a universal problem, in Iran they are severely punished for their rebellion, so it's not just the simple game that it is in the West.

Sometimes it was embarrassing, this inability to recognise women out of their black garments. Once, I apologised profusely for arriving at the wrong room, only to discover when the woman spoke, that it was Ameneh and I had not recognised her without her scarf. Even though I wore a uniform at school and a different sort of uniform at work, I don't believe that I really understand what such enforced covering feels like, or how significant it is to many women, to be obliged to hide their individuality. Of the expatriate women with whom I have worked, half found the Muslim style of dressing intensely upsetting and constraining. The others tolerated it.

However, there were some admirable Iranian traditions. As soon as we arrived in the office each morning, someone was allocated the task of preparing tea, Iranian style. This Saturday, I was quite happy to be the one to set it all out, while Marie-Pierre dealt with the post and briefed our secretary, Rashi. Every morning, a hugely strong brew of tea was prepared in a small teapot, while a samovar of hot water was used to dilute it, throughout the day. When I discovered that brucellosis was endemic in the country, I quickly learned to take my tea without milk.

Once Marie Pierre was seated with her cup, I got straight to the point.
"Look, I've seen the camp, but I'm still not sure why MSF is in Arak and what you want me to achieve there. Can you explain our strategy in more detail?"
Marie Pierre thought for a moment and then began to explain.
"Iran is very important to MSF, Stuart. It was 1990 before they first allowed us in and that was only for a few weeks, to deal with the worst

earthquake in the 20th century. Ever since then we have wanted a more permanent base here and the refugee camps are the first step."

"But why should MSF insist on being present, if there's no obvious need? I don't even get the impression we're wanted here."

Again, my colleague thought before she spoke, this time much more passionately.

"You must realise that Iran is considered to be the power behind much Islamic fundamentalism and terrorism. It is also suspected of human rights' abuses and they treat their women very badly."

Marie Pierre was echoing Pierre in Paris, but even now that I was here, it made no more sense than it had before. Once more, I tried to express my doubts.

"But all that has nothing to do with medicine," I began. "We are MSF, Doctors Without Borders, not Amnesty International, or Human Rights' Watch."

"Yes, but how can we help people, if we don't know what's happening to them? We have to be here, to see the situation for ourselves. It's necessary to listen to the people's story, for only then can we decide if they need us. We need to find out what's going on here, so that we can tell the outside world. That's what témoignage is, Stuart. Témoignage is something we believe in."

This explanation didn't make me feel any better. If anything, it made me even more uncomfortable with the project. It appeared that I was supposed to be a mixture of secret agent and evangelical reformer.

"Look, all that makes me feel like I'm here to be a spy," I tried to explain. "I'm just an aid doctor, remember, and as far as I can see, there are no glaring medical problems in the camp that need my help. The people don't have a high standard, but they're not in any particular need."

"There are always medical problems—what about the lack of drugs, or vaccinations?"

"Yes, but that isn't the point. I've talked to the doctor in the camp and had a quick look at the health centre in the nearest village. The doctor expressed no exceptional need and Ali Abad camp already seems to have better facilities than some of the surrounding population. What are our terms of reference? Do we improve the place until it is up to European standards, or do we try to do something that is coherent with the rest of the country? I thought that was always MSF's objective. " In my frustration, I could feel myself getting a little heated. Maire-Pierre frowned, sighed and thought for a while.

"I agree with you in part, but when Iran relaxed their attitude to aid work and said they would allow a single NGO into the country to help with refugees, we were nominated, so we had to seize the opportunity. BAFIA suggested these two camps and we accepted them, as a base to become established. They will allow us to see what else is needed. It is an opportunity."

"And what does Iran want? Why did they invite us into the country?"

"In part, it's a political game, but there is genuine need. Iran has nearly three million refugees, in a population of around sixty million. The country's economy is in a mess because of the mullahs, who insist on running everything, despite the fact they know nothing about economics. They have a reputation as a country that trains terrorists and they are still engaged in a kind of cold war with the United States. Iran needs to improve its image in the West and get some economic help. Besides, they really care about the refugees. They want a credible agency to pass on the message that they're not beyond the pale. MSF is it."

"Don't you feel MSF is allowing itself to be manipulated?"

"No, MSF has taken a conscious decision to accept the conditions imposed by BAFIA, in order to have access to the people. We want to find out what is really going on. There is no one else here, Stuart! And there's no risk that we will keep quiet about anything, just to stay here. We have a record of being expelled from countries, for that very thing and there's no way we would prejudice our principles. If we're not here, we can't find out what's going on."

"It wasn't very honest to send me here, without making all that clear," I grumbled.

It was only later that I remembered joining MSF, without being too explicit about my own objectives and motivation. Even now, my main objection was the comparative lack of need. But I had never insisted on knowing any political detail before, so why demand the right to criticise here? For the moment, I decided to accept that MSF's objectives might be open to question and get on with the job.

"OK, I'm here. What should I do next? I've met the authorities and I've seen both the camp and its doctor."

"You could begin by setting up the drug supply system in the camp, so that they don't keep running out of things. Then you could write a report on what to do for the health centre, to make it completely functional. After that, we will meet to re-evaluate your programme."

A few days later, it was time for Marie-Pierre to take a short leave. She was combining this with her attendance at MSF's AGM and Co-ordinators' week in Paris, where all Heads of Mission meet with the central organisation, to discuss their projects and their ideas. This absence meant that for the next few weeks, there would be no opportunity to discuss the programme with anyone. From now, I was on my own, something to which I am not in the least averse.

In Arak, Ameneh had managed to find a replacement interpreter, a young woman who had recently finished an English degree. Zorei arrived for her interview in the standard outfit of black coat, black headscarf, with brilliant white training shoes, peeking out from underneath her coat. Although at first nervous, she spoke good English and was extremely enthusiastic, since she felt this job would improve her grasp of the language. Iranian access to Western media sources is strictly forbidden and with few Europeans allowed into the country, it had become increasingly difficult to find native English speakers. Despite this, Zorei had driven a hard bargain on salary. I agreed to give her a try, as she was by far the best English speaker we had met so far and it was imperative to have a good interpreter, when negotiating with the authorities. The three of us worked together during Ameneh's last few days, to enable Zorei to learn her role.

Following my weekend in Teheran, my new assistant was waiting at the bus station in Arak. This time, I had made the trip on my own and was ridiculously pleased with my ability to negotiate the mysteries of the bus station successfully. There had been one small incident of note when the man at the counter, who spoke a few words of English, had been unable to explain where I should find the bus. At first he had simply beckoned me to follow him, then, as we pushed our way through the crowd, he took me by the hand. Despite having frequently observed such behaviour between Iranian men, I was extremely uncomfortable to be in this position. My instinct was to pull away, but I managed to resist, as this considerate man guided me towards my bus. I just hoped that hand-holding wasn't a habit that I would be expected to take up on a regular basis.

That evening, I spent some time discussing details of the job with Zorei and the following morning, we set off for Ali Abad camp with what I now considered to be "our" taxi, with its cheerful driver. Yet this morning, I could feel that Zorei was not quite herself. She was, in fact, quite subdued. During previous taxi rides she had chattered incessantly, asking lots of questions about England and her English. I was a little hesitant to ask if anything was wrong, as it might have represented a breach of etiquette and she could just be having a bad day, so the silence continued for a while. Then she came out with an explanation that left me feeling slightly disturbed.

"While you were away this weekend, the police from BAFIA came to my house and interviewed my family".

"What did they want?" I asked, not a little startled.

"They asked my father about his life and his business activities, if he had connections with other countries, or if he had been a member of a political organisation. Then they asked me why I had taken the job with you," she concluded miserably.

Zorei was very uncomfortable about these revelations, admitting that she had never seen this side of her country before. It had both shocked and frightened her, not to mention the upset it had caused to her family. I too was surprised, for I could not imagine why someone like me merited such intense scrutiny. What did they hope to find out?

"Look, do you want to carry on working for me? There is nothing secret about my work. If they ask you to keep an eye on me, don't worry. I have no objection and won't be doing anything wrong."

At the same time, I felt a little foolish not to have realised that this sort of thing might happen. Later, I found out that the staff at the hotel had been put through the same routine and they were all faithfully reporting my every movement back to BAFIA. All I can say is they must have been very bored, listening to repetitive accounts of daily walks and carrot jam breakfasts. Luckily for the assorted spies, I went to bed early, partly because there was nothing to do and partly because I was woken at 5am by a call to prayer from the mosque next to the hotel. After a couple of weeks of this morning alarm call, I decided that it was unfair that they used a tape-recording. If the mullah wanted the faithful to get up and pray at that hour, in my opinion, he should be up and about himself.

My days began to develop a regular rhythm. At 7am, the taxi to the camp arrived and at 4pm, it took me back to the hotel. The time until my 9pm bedtime dragged a bit, so once I had eaten my evening meal of lamb kebabs and herb salad (a menu that repeated itself with few variations), I took to walking into Arak, to explore both the town and its surroundings.

When the weather changed dramatically, with hot days and pleasant evenings, I found that even Arak looked better bathed in sunlight. The midday temperature climbed to over forty degrees, but people have learned to adapt to the heat. The bazaar closed for several hours, so that the locals could stay inside, during the warmest part of the day. All the bazaars I saw in Iran were enclosed, covered streets, dimly lit and bustling with crowds. Arak's bazaar is one kilometre long, lined by stone arches, which lead to other streets, exits, or to small shops. These have their merchandise piled to the ceiling: carpets, aluminium cookware, electrical goods, spices, herbs, cloth, meat, vegetables, everything imaginable which can be bought in the bazaar and all at the lowest prices. Shop owners sit at tiny tables, or crouch beside their wares, drinking tea and pausing only to cry out the day's bargains. It's noisy, colourful, stimulating and endlessly fascinating.

Different types of goods tend to be grouped together, so that the meat stalls, with more flies than meat, were located in one area, close to all the other foodstuffs. Each stall emitted a different smell, some enchanting, others decidedly less so. In another sector, there were bolts of cloth and rolls of carpet, which the assistants enthusiastically rolled out in front of you, if you paused. My favourite were the spice shops, each with hessian sacks, filled with earthy coloured spices, piled high into neat cones at the neck. Another area specialised in kitchen utensils, the artisans perched amongst their stock, hammering loudly at kettles or pans, over a makeshift anvil, creating gadgets, often quite unknown to me. I never bored of wandering and watching the people.

One weekend, I decided to stay in Arak, to allow myself more time to explore. Directly behind the hotel was a hill, the beginning of the mountain range that separates Iran from Iraq. Naïvely, I asked Zorei if she would like to go for a walk this Saturday, to act as my guide.
"I couldn't possibly do that. To take a walk with a man is completely forbidden."
She sounded quite affronted and I was annoyed with myself that I had completely forgotten the rules. I apologised.

"Perhaps your brother would like to come with us as well?" I suggested.

"No, it would still be most improper."

Her tone left me under no illusion about continuing with this line of discussion, but I wondered what she thought I was suggesting? All I wanted was some company on my walk. But since this was not to be, I went alone, taking biscuits and water, as it was now quite hot in the afternoons.

Getting out of the estate proved harder than I had thought. There was an endless succession of fences, ditches and stagnant ponds to navigate, before I reached open country. The mountain I intended to climb was black and treeless, although a few goats grazed on lower slopes, nuzzling small, dusty, almost invisible succulents. It was not in the least pretty, reminding me of slagheaps that I had seen in Scotland. I climbed steadily for two hours, gradually shedding layers of clothes, but finding the view to be worth the effort. To my right, I could see a long way back down the valley towards Qom and to my left, Arak spread away over the valley, into the foothills. I sat down on a rock, both to recover my breath and to drink some water and noticed a sea of tiny, enchanting red flowers in the shape of tulips, their exotic colour appearing out of place in this black wilderness. Then, as the sun went down, I made my way home. It had been a relief to get away for the day, remote from crowds, from restrictions and spies, for I was fairly sure that BAFIA had not followed me here. There was no vegetation to hide behind and the goats all looked quite genuine!

Fortified by my day of freedom I returned to my task of rehabilitating the health centre buildings and improving the drug supply, the latter reported to have frequent "ruptures de stock" (shortages). The rehabilitation itself was relatively simple: restoration of the hot water supply, repainting the grubby walls, mending broken windows and the digging of a drainage well. Mr Mir Shafi advised me about reputable contractors and to speed up the whole process a bit, I went into Arak myself to buy materials. Zorei found this idea a bit odd at first, but she soon got the hang of dealing with the traders and even began to enjoy herself. Salah, (the MSF log) was fully involved in Sarvestan, but I felt reasonably confident, telephoning him occasionally with technical questions, but otherwise proceeding as I thought best. For the main contractor I suggested a tender system, but this idea seemed totally unknown in Iran. Anyway, the person identified by Mir Shafi asked an incredibly low price.

The work went ahead fairly smoothly, if exasperatingly slowly. The only problem was the drainage well, whose depth I calculated, using the MSF standard logistic reference book. I thought the hole should be about four metres deep, but the builder assured me that it had to be at least twenty metres! I knew from experience in England that four metres was enough there, but I was nervous about going against local knowledge. Surely no one digs a twenty-metre hole, if four metres will suffice? Then it occurred to me, that perhaps there was some problem with the soil, the land drainage, or some other factor of which I was unaware. After two weeks, we were still arguing the toss, so I telephoned Salah. He confirmed, with great conviction, that four metres was enough. Despite the contractor's continued doubts, I insisted that he dug no further, hoping that after my departure, the camp yard did not become a running sewer.

Resolving the drug supply, proved to be more difficult. I talked at length to the pharmacist and the other medical staff, in an effort to clarify the nature of the problem. Marie-Pierre had assumed it was simply a matter of bad management, suggesting that we introduce MSF's system of stock control. MSF's drug policy is sensible; donating drugs, rather than money and insisting that health centres use the organisation's stock control system, to keep track of what happens. However, such a simple plan did not address the problem in Arak.

Although Iranian doctors are highly trained and familiar with most modern drugs, the authorities permit them to use only a limited number of products. Furthermore, medical centres can only keep smallish stocks, in an effort to avoid expiry and waste. It is this policy that leads inevitably to shortages, as some drugs disappear when there is a run on them, or new supplies are held up. Furthermore, if Iran produces a specific drug itself, no import licence will be granted, which would be fine if the supply of the Iranian drug was guaranteed. Iranian factories often have problems sourcing raw materials, so there are regular shortages of locally produced drugs.

MSF's stock control system allows a few months stock in reserve, in case of delivery failures. Here, the Iranian government would have to change its policy guidelines, to allow this system to work. Without such a change, it was obvious that any drugs given by MSF, would be added to the existing stock and used until they were finished, which would put the situation right back where we started. We could hardly ask the pharmacist to go against his government's policy, so the problem seemed to me to be insoluble. The pharmacy procedure used at the camp was not one approved of by MSF, but it seemed to work well enough. I explained our approach to the pharmacist, but neither of us believed that a new system was the solution.

To resolve immediate supply problems however, I found out where we could buy drugs locally. Some had to be purchased in Teheran, but quite a few suppliers had offices in Arak, or Qom, although I needed an official code to buy directly from them. I went straight to the Ministry of Health office in Arak with my request, only to be told that this application would take months. Using the hospital code was also impossible, as this would disturb their accounts. Finally, the official proposed that I return in two or three days, to enable him to discuss the problem with the Minister.

The necessary two days passed and this time, I was told that the Minister would like to see me himself. Zorei and I were ushered into his sanctum and after asking her to welcome me, he came straight to the point.

"Why don't you give the money directly to the pharmacy and they will buy the drugs, using their system?"

This is a difficult issue, since MSF fund-raising advertises that it will spend its money only on personal contact. It guarantees not to hand over cash to foreign governments. This policy is designed to prevent money from disappearing into unidentified accounts, (or pockets) but it sounds rude, when you have to explain it to someone you have just met in a foreign country.

"Our auditors in France require that we have all the suppliers' receipts for any foreign expenditure, including records of drug donations to pharmacies. I can't get round the rules, I'm afraid. I have to buy everything myself."

I made a stab at sounding apologetic, in an effort to erase any hint of a lack of trust, but a bureaucratic reason is completely acceptable in a bureaucratic state, so the Minister seemed to be satisfied. He said he would give me a letter of authorisation that would probably satisfy the suppliers. I did find it strange, however, that in such an authoritarian state, he only said "probably".

Drug buying proved to be a laborious business, since each of Arak's six companies produced only two or three drugs. To complete the pharmacist's list, I also had to visit Qom, although for this I had to find yet another interpreter, as Zorei thought it would be improper for us to travel together, during an hour and a half taxi ride. Eventually she found someone and we set off early, our taxi even more decrepit than usual. It was a bumpy, uncomfortable and dusty journey. After about an hour, the driver spoke and my interpreter said "He wants to know if you have cars like this in England?"

"I certainly hope not," I replied, which my interpreter found very amusing. Then he translated for the driver, who did not.

My dealings with all the companies were amicable and the transactions passed without incident, although locating the entire list took nearly six weeks. Because of internal supply problems, there were a few items that I could not find, but in the main I managed to stock the pharmacy, so that it could work effectively. I tried to remind the pharmacist of the MSF system when I handed the boxes over, but I was quite sure that he wouldn't (or couldn't) pay any attention to what I was saying. In a short period of time, the medical centre would use up all the drugs and the shortages would return. In the end, we were making a donation of cash into an existing system, with little or no hope of long-term change.

This was part of my problem with the mission, the feeling that what I was doing made no real difference–for the refugees, the doctor, or the medical staff. However, in my individual contacts with Iranians, I never had the impression of dealing with a single corrupt person. Perhaps I was naïve, but Iranians seemed to me to be a patient and highly principled people, all working under intense pressure from their own regime.

CHAPTER THIRTEEN

What am I doing here?

During the time I worked on the drugs issue, I was away from the camp a great deal, but still I made a point of keeping in touch with the medical staff. Over time, they relaxed and began to talk about their individual views of the camp's medical problems. One issue, which troubled them all, was the range of difficulties they encountered in introducing preventive health procedures, such as child vaccination, health education and contraception. When I asked if they thought I could help, they referred me to Dr Mousavi, the head of Arak public health, so I duly made an appointment to see him.

Dr Mousavi was about forty years old, small, fair and clean-shaven. Like the camp doctor, he understood English quite well, although he spoke none. After I had explained my presence, he said he was delighted to see me and began to explain the difficulties that the camp presented for him.

"I am responsible for Arak and the surrounding area, as well as for Ali Abad. We are understaffed and under-funded, so anything you can do to help will be most welcome," he said.

This was a good start. Dr Mousavi could have seen my presence as interference, a foreign doctor meddling within his territory. However, even with his permission, more information was necessary, if I was to make progress in such a short period of time.

"Before I try to do anything, I would like to speak with some of the refugees myself, but the camp commandant does not want me to use a refugee as my interpreter. Can you suggest someone?"

"That could be a problem. Since the war with Iraq, Arabic speakers are not popular here. It might take a little time to arrange, but I will see what I can do."

Then I explained my intended strategy. I hoped to tap into existing social structures within the camp, locating recognised elders, so that they could advise me and help with any plans I formulated. Since I was aware that the mullah visited the camp fairly regularly, he would be my next target. Finally, I would conduct a survey of the refugees

227

themselves, to find out what they thought they required. But I needed his help to persuade Mr Mir Shafi that this was a good idea. I explained that the commandant was horrified at such a radical notion and was adamant that I could make a balanced judgement on the basis of his officers' information. It would be unfair to be over critical of Mr Mir Shafi, however. Iran was a state where the sole criterion for decision-making was the mullahs' wishes.

"I would also like to discuss my findings with you first, if that's all right?" I asked Dr Mousavi. " It's essential that I don't misunderstand anything."

"You must be careful about what you do," he warned me. "There is already tension, because local people feel that some of the facilities at the camp are better than in the nearby village of Ibrahim Abad. Some of them are not pleased with such an idea."

I had already formed that impression by myself, but I asked him for specific examples of conflict.

"In Iran, our normal ratio is one doctor, for twelve thousand people. The camp has one doctor for just five thousand refugees and there will soon be a second one, to give even more assistance. Then there is the MSF presence with whatever you bring, not to mention the new houses with their electricity and running water. Many poor people in Ibrahim Abad lack such things."

"And this is widely known in the area?" I asked.

"Yes, of course. You must have seen the poverty in the surrounding villages. My medical staff feel uncomfortable, because they know the local health centre is more impoverished than the one in the refugee camp. It is difficult to try to defend two different standards, when Iranian people are the ones who are losing out," he finished.

I had encountered the same attitude in Britain, when local people felt that immigrants had better access to social services, than they did themselves. Here, MSF was contributing to the feeling of inequality and tension, so Dr Mousavi's words added to my existing discomfort with my work.

Then he added something unexpected.

"The refugees are our brothers. They are Shia Muslims, as we are, and we must help them. Because of Saddam Hussein and the Sunni Ba'ath party's actions, they lost everything in Iraq and thousands were killed. It is our duty under Islam to help them. The mullahs are clear about this."

He paused and seemed to think carefully before he spoke again.

"But there are other issues concerning Ali Abad. BAFIA is keen to present a positive image of Iran to the visiting authorities and foreign dignitaries, who are to be brought here, from Teheran."

"So Ali Abad is to be something of a show camp?" I suggested.

"Yes, but please understand, we do want to help these refugees," Dr Mousavi insisted.

I already suspected that the camp was some sort of political pawn, but the information concerning the conflict between the two forms of Islam was new to me. Later, I was to understand that Sunni and Shia Muslims often faced the same sort of problems as different branches of Christianity.

The show camp idea was confirmed about four weeks later, when Mr Mir Shafi arrived, accompanied by a group of smartly dressed men in big Mercedes cars. The German Ambassador to Iran was visiting the camp nearest Teheran, to see the situation of refugees. He made it abundantly clear to me that he understood this particular camp had been specially prepared for him. If, however, MSF was working here without comment, he assumed that all must be well. Everyone seemed to accept that it was just a political game.

Eventually, I found a non-refugee, Arabic-Farsi speaker, who satisfied Mr Mir Shafi's demanding standards. Naserzadeh, an Iraqi, was married to an Iranian and had lived in Arak for twenty years. At last I could conduct my interviews and start to gather genuine information, although my problems were not quite over, since she could understand neither English, nor French. Working with two translators made communication a total nightmare.

Our first task was to prepare suitable material for the questionnaire, to be sure that I obtained the information I wanted. So, I would pose a question to Zorei, who would translate it for Naserzadeh, who would discuss it with her and then Zorei would convey their conclusion back to me. By the time this happened, what they had to say often bore no relationship at all to the question I had asked in the first place. It was frustrating, like a bizarre game of Chinese whispers. Nevertheless, we battled on, finally completing a set of questions that seemed to be worthwhile. The majority related to the history of health care that the refugees had received while in the camp, all fairly standard issues, like how many children people had, how many vaccinations the children had received, if there had there been any serious illness or death in the family, and whether they had access to contraception.

Then I had to persuade Mr Mir Shafi that replies must be anonymous and this concept seemed to be beyond his understanding. We argued at some length and only when he realised that I would not give in, did he relent, although clearly with grave misgivings. Naserzadeh then began to interview a random sample of refugee families, trailing slowly round the camp with Zorei and myself in tow, a weird little flotilla of strangers, invading their privacy.

I had intended that the replies would help medical staff to plan future services, but to our surprise, we received some unexpected responses. The refugees urgently wanted us to express the fact that they had no ill feeling towards the staff and, more importantly, they were anxious to gain a voice in the running of the camp. Mr Mir Shafi had become much more relaxed and co-operative in his dealings with me, so I decided to convey this information to him, and was astounded when almost immediately he agreed to form a camp committee to help with internal affairs. The questionnaire provided a fund of useful data, both for myself and the other medical workers. These results, together with the information I had gained from the medical staff, enabled me to write a short proposal for a health education programme in the camp. I discussed the draft with Dr Mousavi and the final version was accepted as a plan for the future. My current remit seemed almost complete.

But life in the camp was like an onion. Every time you thought you had revealed a little of the truth, you found another layer of fascinating information, hidden beneath. While visiting the refugees at home, I had been surprised to find that almost all the men left the camp during the day. When questioned, Dr Mousavi told me they were, "out looking for work". It appeared that the men could get either a day pass, or one for a longer period, if it was a really good job. So why was there a refugee camp, if the people in it were able to come and go? Why didn't the authorities just encourage these Iraqis to settle in Iran?

"The war with Iraq lasted for eight years," he told me. "It was a terrible experience, costing Iran much of its wealth (about 90 thousand million $US!), not to mention a total Iran / Iraq death toll, of approximately one million. The scars are still raw and people do not trust Iraqis. Anyway, there are too many of them to assimilate and some of them are rumoured to be spies, sent to destabilise Iran. In the long run, we would prefer if they all went home."

In a very short time, I had changed my attitude to Iran. Before, I had believed (because I had been told) that it was an obsessively religious, backward looking place. Instead, I met sophisticated, intelligent people, many of whom were involved in their own daily struggles with the state. True, I had encountered BAFIA, whose members seemed to embrace the state line wholeheartedly, but it seemed to me that most people were afraid of them. Of course, I have no idea how much Islamic fundamentalism is funded from Iran, but the ordinary Iranian people that I encountered were peaceful and generous, clearly disturbed by their image abroad. Many explained that they were upset to see themselves portrayed as fundamentalist terrorists, pressing on me the need to explain to my friends that Iranians do not all behave like BAFIA. Because so few Westerners currently travel to Iran, it is particularly difficult for ordinary Iranians to communicate with the outside world.

Since my work in Arak was nearing completion, during a weekend visit to Teheran Marie-Pierre suggested I visit the Sarvestan refugee camp, to see if I could offer the MSF workers there any medical help. I agreed enthusiastically, hoping to combine this with a visit to the nearby ancient city of Shiraz. There was also a message that Paris had agreed with my modest plans resulting from the questionnaire and I could go ahead with them when I returned.

This weekend, we were also invited to a party, my first since arriving in Iran and as I showered and dressed, I wondered what such an event would be like, in a fundamentalist Islamic state with no alcohol, no mixing of the sexes, no dancing and no modern music. When we set off, my hopes were not high. We had an address, written in Farsi on a bit of paper, but when the taxi decanted us, there was no light or sound, and no evidence of other people. We knocked and waited, beginning to suspect that this was the wrong place, a feeling that grew as we stood in the dark, listening to a series of bolts being drawn, as if in a scene from a Boris Karloff film. Marie-Pierre hesitantly said the name of our host to the young man who appeared, then much to my surprise, he beckoned us to follow him along the dimly lit corridor. Through a second door and down a flight of stone steps we went, arriving unexpectedly at a 1960's student party. I tried not to look totally amazed, as I took in loud pop music, mini-skirts, make-up and yes, alcohol! Such was the generation gap between ourselves and the rest of the group, that we felt completely out of place, but it was a revelation to discover these remnants of the old regime, rich families, whose children aspired to a different way of life.

Back at the MSF house, I expressed my amusement at these young people enjoying their rebellious party, conducted with the greatest of decorum. Perhaps the state was not as strict as I had imagined, if this was going on regularly? Marie Pierre assured me that these party-goers were taking a great risk, for the state could severely punish both them and their families, if they were caught. Recently, the Secret Police had raided a twenty-first birthday party for one young man, who had somehow then fallen from a fifteenth floor balcony. Boys and girls risked fifty lashes for such crimes and even if the punishment could be bought off, the family would have to pay several thousand dollars, a huge sum in Iran. I remembered hearing that physical punishments were not unusual and sometimes people were hanged in public for their crimes. Suddenly, this rather mundane party acquired greater significance and I was sharply reminded that here, rebellion was not just a game.

The flight to Shiraz was delayed by three hours, yet Geneviève and Salah were both waiting at the airport. Salah, the log, of Berber origin was short and dark, while Geneviève a tall, slim nurse came from the Basque country, near the Spanish border. Her dark colouring meant that she looked almost Iranian, and she seemed much more at home in the black coat and scarf than Marie-Pierre had done. I took to them both immediately. In the car park they introduced me to their driver / interpreter, Jamshed, who despite a willingness to please, was clearly not the brightest of souls. Salah explained that the most important consideration when hiring him had been that he owned an old Land Rover and his salary included the hire of the vehicle.

"We plan to visit the camp tomorrow and Thursday. On Wednesday and Friday we will do some sight-seeing," suggested Geneviève. "I hope that's okay."

I assured her, that after a couple of months on my own in Arak, this plan sounded quite hedonistic.

"How is the rehabilitation coming along?" Salah then asked. "I'm sorry I've not been able to come over and have a look myself."

"There were no major problems, apart from the debate about the depth of the well."

"Four metres is fine," he assured me.

The team had not found a suitable house in Sarvestan, so they were living in Shiraz, a lovely old city, dating in its present form, from 700AD. Today, its suburban streets are wide and tree-lined and MSF was renting a three-bedroom bungalow, with a small, well-kept garden and a swimming pool (alas empty). This luxury was due in part to the fact that in Iran, unmarried men and women are not supposed to live together, so a secluded house with no overlooking neighbours, was necessary to avoid scandal. The interior of the house was much more comfortable than anything I had experienced so far and sitting in the luscious, green garden that evening, it occurred to me that life lacked only a cold beer, to attain perfection.

Next morning, Jamshed and his ramshackle Land Rover arrived at 7am and we set off on a long, slow, dusty drive. The road wound its way through bare hills, almost devoid of vegetation and lacking the richness I had so admired on my trips between Qom and Teheran. Suddenly, we came upon a very colourful group of about fifty people, walking parallel to the road.

"Who are they?" I asked Jamshed.

"They are Baluchi nomads," he told me proudly. "My ancestors belonged to the same tribe, but we gave up the nomadic life several generations ago."

All the women wore brightly coloured headscarves and full skirts, like ball-gowns, seemingly quite out of place in this hot dusty landscape and a complete contrast to the sombre apparel of other Iranian women. The group were accompanied by a few sheep, goats and camels and I was surprised that there was enough grazing for all these animals. It was also fascinating for me to discover that such an incongruous lifestyle should have survived in Iran to this day.

Sarvestan itself was very small and dusty and it was easy to see why Salah and Geneviève were more than content to live in Shiraz. On the way in, Salah said, "We won't go through the town centre today, since they hanged a young man in the square on Friday. I think it was for theft, but I'm not sure. They leave the body on the scaffold for two or three days, pour encourager les autres."

Although I was content to agree, I was surprised and disturbed to find in myself, a ghoulish interest to see the hanged body.

It was a further fifteen minutes to the camp, which appeared much less organised than Ali Abad. There were guards on the gate, but here the perimeter fence had several breaks, through which children happily passed back and forward and adults came to throw away rubbish. All the refugees here lived in tents, although there were a few permanent administrative buildings. The medical centre was similar to Ali Abad, but the doctor here was present less often, forcing the refugees to come to Geneviève for medical advice, which she admitted she was not always qualified to give. I was introduced to Hajji Birmani, the commandant, whom Salah described as being reasonable, or difficult, depending on what they wanted. Geneviève explained that the title Hajji is a form of respect and means, "someone who has made the pilgrimage to Mecca".

As I had suspected, the team had no real need of my medical abilities, although there was a problem, while I was there. One of the local nurses came in to say that a young woman had been in labour for thirty-six hours and was now becoming exhausted. It was her first baby and she was not sure about the pains. I offered to see her, although my knowledge and practice of obstetrics were now years out of date. The communication through Arabic and Farsi was as usual, unhelpful and forgetting, where I was, I found myself saying,
"I'll need to examine her. Do you have any gloves?"
The silence that followed this innocent remark was deafening.
"That's impossible; you cannot examine a woman." I was told sharply. There was no debate. The idea was simply "out of the question," whatever the woman's condition. But that didn't help the patient.

After a little more thought, I made a suggestion.
"Geneviève, you examine her and tell me what you find."
She looked alarmed, saying, "I'm a nurse. I've never done obstetrics."
"But you must have had the basic training."
"No. In France, midwives have a completely separate course."
"Look, I'll draw you a diagram and explain what to do. You can tell me what you find."
Geneviève looked a bit doubtful, but finally she agreed. I explained the dilatation of the cervix during labour and drew a sketch of the cervical rim at normal, two cm, six cm and fully dilated.

"It should feel like.." (I was lost for words. I had never thought about teaching obstetrics.) "a half-peeled grapefruit," I added inaccurately, but I couldn't think of any other comparison at the time. All went well however, and with Geneviève's description, I felt we could send the woman home, where she delivered normally, two days later. I was extremely relieved, Geneviève was proud and the patient was happy. Obstetrics can be very rewarding.

The next day, I left the world of refugees behind to become a tourist. With Geneviève and her friend Yashema, I entered Shiraz. It was considered to be safer, even in this tourist environment, not to appear obviously a man and woman alone together, so our guide was to be both translator and chaperone. First, we visited the King of the Lamp Mausoleum, built for the brother of Emam Reza, the eighth grandson of the Prophet Mohammed. Yashema thought that I would be allowed inside and she hoped that they might gain entrance too. The guard inspected us for correct attire, before directing us to the appropriate doors: to the right for me and to the left for the women.

Most mosques have a central dome and tower minarets. Here, the outside was decorated in blue tiles, each inscribed with the word Allah in elaborate, white script. I left my shoes in the entrance hall, feeling a bit silly to be wandering around in socks, when most of the men had bare feet. At first, this mosque seemed a little garish, but inside it was unbelievably grand, being completely covered in triangular pieces of glass mirror, which created astonishing, multiple reflections. We passed from room to room, each vaulted ceiling lined in glass. In the smaller side rooms, prayer was individual, but in the main area, rows of men knelt together on the carpeted floor, praying in unison. I felt very welcome, unnoticed and privileged to be here. Geneviève, who had been brought up a Catholic, was equally moved.

The next day we were back in camp, where I listened to Geneviève discussing family planning with the women. I could tell that she was becoming frustrated by their cultural resistance to talking about this topic, especially the influential, older women and I guessed she was probably attempting too much, too soon. It is hard to alter traditional behaviour and Iraqi women normally have large families. One of the helpers told me that she became a grandmother at the age of twenty six! She remembered playing in the street with the other children, just after the birth of her daughter. She had been thirteen years old, just as her daughter was now.

This lunch-time we were treated to a picnic, arranged by Hajji Birmani. Salah and Geneviève were pleased by the invitation, seeing it as a breakthrough in relationships and Yashema was asked to come along as interpreter. We travelled by car, climbing to a spot where three isolated trees stood beside a fast-flowing, noisy stream, that bubbled unexpectedly out of the hillside. Although small, the stream was an astonishing and unexpected sight, in the midst of the barren landscape. It made an attractive backdrop, as we sat chatting under the trees, while the food and cutlery were produced.

Then, as we began to eat, I noticed that Yashema had neither plate nor food, so I gave her mine and waited. Hajji Birmani immediately told one of the men to bring me a plate, but said nothing. I never found out if it was a mistake, but when I asked Yashema, she said that it was probably intended to remind her of her place and I could tell by her manner that she was annoyed. It was a trivial incident, but it raised a recurring question in my mind. Intervention in another culture is a difficult issue. At the time, I was unsure about whether I should speak or not. Yet I could not ignore my own values, pretending not to notice that someone else had no food.

One of the founders of MSF coined the phrase, "le droit d'ingérence," the right to interfere, and that is part of what MSF does. It believes that it has the right to speak out against any perceived injustice. But to be fair, it's not just MSF. Interfering is what most aid organisations do, however well-intentioned. The problem is that this philosophy infers that there are universal values and these are ours. Some argue that we should let other people see our ethics at work, so that they understand them, but such an attitude to another culture is surely insulting, even dangerous. This issue troubled me, all the time I was with MSF. It is an issue that troubles me still.

On my last day in Shiraz I visited Persepolis. It dates from 500 BC and is extraordinarily well-preserved, parts of the bas-relief looking almost newly sculpted. There were very few visitors, so we spent a leisurely two hours marvelling at the skill and the majesty of the work. By now, although I felt extremely privileged to be able to see the site, I was beginning to feel uneasy, when I thought of the criticism that aid work can be more "tourism, than altruism".

I then assuaged my conscience by devoting the next two weeks to writing the preventive health programme for Ali Abad, with the help of

Dr Mousavi. It pleased us both, when the mullah was receptive to the idea of using the mosque as a meeting place for health messages and teaching sessions.

Then, out of the blue, we arrived at the camp gate one morning to find that Zorei was refused admission, although the guards said I could go in as usual. Since there was no explanation, I naturally refused to enter and there we stood, until Mr Mir Shafi came to the gate. The commandant simply explained that BAFIA had forbidden Zorei's return. There was nothing he could do, so I had no option but to visit the BAFIA office myself.

"We are making enquiries," was all they would say.

After two more days, the decision was reversed without explanation. I was glad that the end of the project was in sight, for I was now bored by the lack of work and irritated by the delays, conspiracy and intrigue. More and more, I felt I was wasting my time.

Before leaving Shiraz, I had arranged a final excursion, to Esfahan. On this occasion, the bus journey took nine hours, but it was all new and very interesting. On arrival, I found Geneviève and her friend Lia installed in a comfortable, European-style hotel. We ventured out before it became dark and with Lia's help, we found the famous 16th century Se Pol Bridge, with thirty-three arches and a teashop built at water level, within one of the arches. It was a marvellous, smoky, whimsical place, festooned with scarves, artefacts and curiosities. We sat in an alcove on embroidered cushions, and drank tea from small hot glasses, that were difficult to hold. The girls experimented with a hookah, but when I tried, it made me cough. In the days of the Shah, the hookah sometimes contained opium, but today only tobacco.

The next morning, armed with our tourist guide, we set off to see the sights. In suffocating heat, we made our way round the mosques, museums, gardens, parks and of course, the bazaar. This bazaar is a huge central square, the Meidun-e Shah, reputed to be the largest of its kind in the world. As we wandered, I was attracted to the metal-workers emporium, filled with samovars, kettles, pots, silverware and in a corner, my perfect souvenir. I drink a lot of tea, especially in the mornings and here was a copper teapot, more than a metre high! Then I remembered that transport home would be difficult; so perhaps next time? Esfahan is famous for its carpets, but although I would have liked to buy, the good ones were well beyond the pocket of an MSF aid worker.

On the second day, as we walked along a crowded shopping street, a white car pulled up suddenly alongside. One of the passengers called us over. Lia looked frightened, saying it was the police.

"They are searching for drugs and as foreigners, you are suspect. They want you to go over to the car. You had best do as they say."

We complied and the man asked to see inside our bags. I demanded to see his identity card, but since I couldn't read it, this was rather an empty gesture. Furthermore, I was carrying the equivalent of three thousand dollars of MSF money, which I had no intention of handing over, so I stood there, pulling notes out of the bag and stuffing them into my pockets until there was no room left. The whole scene was becoming quite farcical, since Iranian currency is extremely bulky and some of the notes even fluttered gently to the ground.

"I don't want your money, just show me your bag," the policeman said gruffly.

He repeated the process with Geneviève, before driving off, leaving us nervous and upset. I then had to stand in the middle of the crowded street, stuffing wads of notes back into my bag, a less than subtle activity, that reminded me of all the warnings I had been given, about not drawing undue attention to one's wealth in public! Eventually we resumed our sightseeing, but thirty minutes later, Geneviève discovered that all her money had disappeared, so we spent the rest of the afternoon in the police station, reporting the incident with no hope of recovering the money. We never found out if it had been dishonest policemen or thieves and although it was not really a major issue, it detracted somewhat from the pleasure of the trip.

In Arak, the closure of the project was a low-key affair. The drugs had been delivered, the last wall had been painted and the preventive health programme was well under way. I invited Mr Mir Shafi for tea, along with some other staff and said a few words. Then I took the taxi back to town, where I had been summoned to the BAFIA office. I wondered what on earth they had to say to me now. It wasn't as if there was anything left to forbid! The face of the thin, expressionless man who spoke to us hardly moved, as he made a long speech and I began to worry about what it was we had done now. It would be a pity to have destroyed MSF's credibility, whatever I personally felt about the job. Eventually Zorei explained that all was well. This new head of BAFIA in Arak was pleased with our work and he intended to present me with a gift, to support these sentiments. I was surprised and pleased at the pretty decanter and four glasses, all in traditional Iranian style. Together with small gifts given by Naserzadeh and Zorei, they continue to remind me of the positive elements of my stay in Iran and of the kindness of the Iranian people.

My last task was to look after the office in Teheran for a few days, while Marie-Pierre investigated a potential new project, this time at Mashhad, in the East. On her return, she was very enthusiastic, asking me to extend my mission for two further weeks, to make a detailed evaluation. I was pleased to accept, because exploratory missions are interesting and challenging. We flew to Mashhad together, so that she could introduce me to the BAFIA authorities and the people from the Ministry of Health. Her initial contact had come through the United Nations High Commission for Refugees (UNHCR), which was facing a lot of difficulties, so we decided to remain as independent as possible. UNHCR was, however, able to recommend an interpreter, a young girl with an English degree, who was on holiday from her job in a bank. Mayah was small, birdlike, cheeky and very inquisitive.

My objectives for this project were to confirm and quantify needs and evaluate the feasibility of any MSF intervention. For this, I must first discover as much as possible, about the state of the target population's health, whether there had been any epidemics, or if there were any specific needs, such as malnutrition. I must also find out about the availability of housing for MSF staff, information about telephones, transport and access; everything that would avoid nasty surprises for a new team. At first sight, two weeks seemed to be plenty of time, but as usual there were public holidays and BAFIA bureaucracy to be considered. In the end, I had to work hard to meet my deadline.

The people identified as requiring help were Afghan refugees and illegal immigrants, who lived together in a small southern suburb of Mashhad, called Gulshar. Although there were some recent arrivals, many of these people had been in Iran since the 1979 Russian invasion of Afghanistan. There were perhaps sixty thousand refugees, but this was little more than a guess and many were second generation, some with good jobs. Most were now completely integrated into the local culture and economy, and held valid identity cards, with permission to reside in Iran. (Only men have identity papers in Iran). These Afghans had no desire to go home to a country where conditions were very poor and the Mujahadeen and the Taliban were still fighting.

But the Iranian government felt that it must do something about its refugee population. Three million was currently insupportable. So the first step was to expel the Afghans and the procedure was simple. They would stop all men and examine their papers, and any Afghans would have their papers torn up, turning them immediately into illegal immigrants. Everyone knew there were many Afghans in Gulshar and although denied by the authorities, here the policy was being pursued vigorously. Not surprisingly, Afghan men were now in hiding, while simultaneously continuing to search for work.

There was one government health clinic in Gulshar and MSF planned to reinforce this unit, in an effort to ensure that the Afghan population still had access to basic health care. The problem was that we could not target Afghans specifically, without arousing BAFIA's suspicions, or for that matter those of the refugees. My role was to evaluate this element of the programme and make recommendations.

Having found accommodation and gained permission from BAFIA to work, Mayah and I began to make enquiries. It was forty degrees centigrade and incredibly dusty, so the task soon became exhausting. Gulshar was an extremely compact and crowded district, with narrow streets that formed a grid between mud-brick houses. Resolutely, we knocked on doors, asking the people straightforward questions about economic conditions and health problems.

"Do you have any income?

"Where do you go if you become ill?"

"Have your children been vaccinated?" and so on.

At first there was much suspicion and the work was gruelling in the hot sun. No one invited us inside and some people did not want to talk at all. We hardly saw any men, since those with papers were at work and those without would not show themselves. By the third or fourth day, however, we were invited into a few homes, where we discovered that some people had radios, electric fans, cookers and the like, while others had nothing at all. Gradually, a picture emerged of a relatively well-knit community, composed of old and new refugees and poor Iranians. There was a general feeling that it would not be good to go back to Afghanistan, even if one were Afghan, which of course one was not.

After work, I took the opportunity to explore Mashhad itself. The city was clean, with wide streets and mostly low, traditional buildings, interspersed with occasional modern structures, like shopping malls and banks. I spent several evenings wandering round the bazaar, attracted as usual by the cool interior, the noise and the panoply of goods for sale, buying several items as souvenirs, including a prayer mat and some beads.

My first weekend, I set out to visit the Shrine of the 8th Imam, Reza Shah and as I walked towards it, I became aware of a faint drumming noise, like some large, slowly turning machine. Gradually, the sound became louder and louder, until I could distinguish voices. Finally, I turned a corner and there stretched in front of me, a procession of thousands of men, dressed in formal black trousers and black shirts. They took over the whole road, as they marched towards me, rhythmically beating their chests with the palms of their hands, creating the huge booming sound. Many were chanting and some were flagellating themselves symbolically, with wooden-handled cat o' nine tails, which they flicked over their shoulders to beat their backs as they walked. This was only a gesture; no one was hurting himself, but still I was nervous, until I saw that many men were walking hand in hand with their sons.

Certainly, this was not an English football crowd and there was no alcohol to fire them up, but I did wonder if my presence might be unwelcome. Was I an infidel, perhaps contaminating an important religious moment? No one paid any attention to me, however, and I watched this amazing spectacle in absolute peace. The shrine itself was marvellous, with circular walls enclosing many buildings, including mosques, colleges, museums and libraries, some with gilded towers. Most of the site is accessible to tourists and I returned several times, privileged to sit and stare in this tranquil and atmospheric place.

But I was in Mashhad to assess health needs, so when the interpreter was available, we worked. The health centre in Gulshar was located in a run-down shopping centre. It was in reasonable condition, apart from some leaks in the roof, yet despite the fact that there were patients most days, it was certainly under-utilised. When I met the doctor, a young woman from a rich family, she made it clear that she was only there as part of her military service. Although she was always perfectly pleasant to me, I didn't get the impression that she was outstandingly well-motivated.

"These people are primitive and dirty," she complained, "and I cannot understand the Afghans at all."

Her hours were a problem too. She worked only from 8am to 1pm, after which she returned to her home in the city. Outwith that time, emergencies had to go to one of the two religious hospitals, located some distance away, between Gulshar and Mashhad. Although the medical care was good, they charged a small fee, which excluded the poorest refugees from their services. When I visited, they were busy and said that people from Gulshar were only about 10% of their work.

In my evaluation of the situation, I identified that Afghan men were definitely excluded from health care. However, it was a very difficult issue. If we encouraged the men to visit the MSF clinic, they might be caught and deported by the police. For their wives and families it was less of a problem, since they had no papers. Everything hinged on the men. A second factor, that of increasing poverty related to the men's diminishing opportunity to work, highlighted the need for good health care. And I was still not sure why so few women used the clinic, apart from the attitude of the doctor. Without fully understanding the cause, it was difficult to say with any confidence that we could bring about an improvement.

Another problem was that I could not accurately evaluate the number of Afghans in the community, something that would become even more difficult if the political climate deteriorated further. The precise number of refugees was in itself of no great importance, but MSF had to have some idea of figures. There was also the complication that this was a diverse population; containing people with disparate living standards, who had been in Gulshar for different lengths of time. We had to ensure that any improvements in the clinic were not sufficient to attract patients from outside the area, as this would overload facilities. The main difficulty, however, was how to target Afghans, without luring them into a trap. We could solve the potential problem of attracting outsiders to our clinic, by ensuring that we offered only a minimum of basic care. But, try as I might, I couldn't see a medical solution to the problem of increasing risk to the Afghan men.

I indicated in my report both the dilemma and the risks for MSF. They would have to decide whether to choose the option of delivering very basic care. If Paris got it wrong, they might end up with as many Iranian patients as Afghans. Marie-Pierre was in favour of taking this risk and we duly sent the proposal to Paris. In time, I heard that it had been accepted and after several months and many difficulties with BAFIA, the mission opened as proposed. Some years later, when I was working in Afghanistan, I discovered that the project was still functioning. These two weeks in Mashhad had been a rewarding and stimulating way to end my Iranian mission.

Before leaving Teheran, I completed my final reports and once more took the opportunity to discuss my feelings with Marie-Pierre.

"I have enjoyed my time in Iran," I began, "but I am still not sure that it has been all that useful, except to me."

Marie-Pierre was not really surprised, but I wanted to record my feelings formally.

"Tell me why you think that," she said.

"Well, let's look at Arak. In three months, I bought some drugs, made some minor changes to the buildings, sorted out the water supply and set up a preventive health proposal. Within three months, they will have used up all the drugs, which are unlikely to be replaced. The changes to the building will make life more comfortable for the staff, but they will not directly help the patients and the preventive health programme will probably not continue to be implemented, because there is no one to see it through. So I achieved very little."

"That's far too negative," Marie-Pierre responded vigorously. "The water supply will improve hygiene and the availability of drugs will probably save some lives. They will both ease suffering in the meantime."

"Yes," I said, "and I forgot the camp committee, which may last and produce a real improvement to the refugees' well-being, but that's not really a health issue, is it?"

"I agree, but although we are a health organisation, we are much more than that," she went on. "There are the intangibles to consider."

Of course, I couldn't let that go. Intangibles were like a red rag to a bull!

"What are the quantifiable benefits, Marie Pierre? If MSF analyses the cost, can it really say that the money was well spent?"

In Britain, my time in the NHS had made me painfully aware of the need to balance costs with benefits. This principle had ruled my life. Surely MSF had similar criteria?

Marie-Pierre thought for a moment.

"Stuart, this has been a very cheap mission for MSF, compared to the emergencies that make up so much of our work. You must remember, non-quantifiable elements have a value too. You have too much of an Anglo-Saxon, business-like approach to aid work. Some of the things we do can't be measured. MSF accepts that. We have made contact with the refugees and we have shown them that someone cares and knows that they exist. Equally importantly, we have demonstrated to the Iranian Government what we do and we have generated sufficient trust to keep working in Iran for the moment."

"So we sit around here, doing small things of little value, in case something important comes along?"

I still couldn't see it. This was tinkering with trivia, when there was so much genuine need in the world.

Marie Pierre answered my question.

"In a sense, yes. We stay here and wait. Twice in the last six years, Iran has experienced major earthquakes and the last time we tried to help we were too late. We had to make contacts, gain permission, learn about the country and get to the site. If we are already here, we can respond quickly."

"Surely you don't feel that justifies using money, volunteers and time, simply to be strategically positioned, in case there happens to be another earthquake?" I asked.

Now, Marie Pierre changed the subject.

"And you are forgetting about témoignage. Women have no kind of life here. I am the one who suffers from wearing the scarf and that horrible coat all day, not you. You can't imagine what that's like."

"I don't see how we are helping these women by fiddling around with unimportant medical projects. Anyway, Geneviève doesn't find the clothes all that bad. Surely it's not the end of the world, to have to wear a coat when you go outside!"

We were getting into a fight and I was losing sight of the main issue, which wasn't whether or not women had to wear raincoats. I tried to get the argument back on track.

"Look, although I agree that there are some needs, even Gulshar is not an emergency. Perhaps there should be a longer evaluation phase before MSF commits itself to places like Ali Abad or Gulshar. If it's not an emergency, perhaps we should think before we jump in and interfere."

"I agree that Ali Abad was quite political and that Gulshar is a risk, but we won't learn very much until we are in there, working with the community. Then we will gain insight through contact with the people. Only if we are here can we say if human rights are being abused. The non-quantifiable elements of MSF are just as valuable to us as all the rest. You must try to see that. Perhaps you should discuss your problem with Pierre and Pierre-Pascal, when you get back to Paris."

Marie-Pierre seemed to be finished and since I didn't much like the suggestion that the problem was mine, I gave up. It was both frustrating and intriguing, to feel that there was something out there, something I couldn't grasp, but I resolved to make an effort to discuss things in more depth when I got back to Paris. I wanted to understand what it was that MSF was doing. Most of all, I wanted to understand témoignage.

I returned to Paris early in June and arranged an appointment for my official debriefing. As before, I spoke to Pierre.

"How was your mission?" he began pleasantly.

"A fabulous country and I really enjoyed my time there, but I am still doubtful about my role and what MSF was trying to achieve.

He looked surprised.

"But you did a lot. You refurbished the health centre buildings and improved the drug supply. Marie Pierre sent me a report that you introduced a preventive health programme, just before you left. How can you have any doubts?"

"That is a very positive view of my work. The refurbishment was largely the repair of a hot water boiler and the installation of water pipes to each clinical room in the health centre, although there was also a bit of paint and a drain. At the other end of the camp, the Iranians were building five hundred new houses, each with hot and cold running water! It would have been simple for them to do my bit of rehabilitation. It doesn't take a doctor to organise some painting and the replacement of a few windows.

As to the medicine supply, that amounts to about five thousand dollars worth of drugs, which will be used up in two or three months. Then the pharmacy will revert to its old ways and shortages will reappear.

The preventive health programme is unlikely to continue, because the public health doctor has no time to follow it through. Anyway, the camp now has better facilities than the local Iranian village and this is causing its own problems."

"Do not forget the value of témoignage" said Pierre. "You were in contact with the people and let them know they were not alone. Solidarity is important," he continued. "Our objective is to help those in need and sometimes we do this simply by bearing witness to their situation. Being there raises awareness and spreads the message. If we are there, we can speak out, should we see something wrong."

He had finished his catechism and that was that. I had enjoyed talking with Pierre, an intelligent man who was clearly convinced of his beliefs, but he failed to persuade me.

"Témoignage", "Solidarity", I understand the meaning of these words and the fact that they are important for the French, but I am still not sure what they mean for me. Do I really have the right to tell other people what it is they should do and how they should live?

I don't think I believe that at all.

CHAPTER FOURTEEN

Helping or harming?

When I worked in Afghanistan in 2000, people told me of the anarchy, murder and fear that existed before the Taliban, when their country was ruled by rival warlords and there was a climate of lawlessness. Everyone was at risk and afraid to go out, especially women. Then the Taliban took over, disarming rival groups and bringing order and security, making them popular with almost all the Afghans I met. The production of heroin poppies was outlawed, reducing its international supply. But in the new fundamentalist state, girls were not educated, women could not work and widows were forced to beg to survive. Men also had to obey a host of new laws, music was banned and both flogging and public execution were conspicuous.

American "interference", following September 11, was supposed to make things better for the people, but the warlords have reclaimed their positions, everywhere except Kabul. There are kidnappings, armed robberies, beatings, extortion, and rape. Fundamentalism is returning, with the reinstatement of the religious police. Most women still wear the Burqua and the education of girls is limited, particularly outside Kabul. The economy is in tatters and malnutrition is rife. Heroin is widely available: in Afghanistan, its neighbouring countries and on the streets of Europe. The situation for many is no better than before. For others, it is worse.

From the moment I began to work as an aid doctor, I was disturbed by an undercurrent of doubt about the purpose and appropriateness of some of the work I was doing. It took me time to realise that the problem was a clash between my personal philosophy of "helping," and the way I was working. All that I had learned in my career as a GP taught me the value of being passive, of waiting and listening, until patients told me what was wrong (or what it was they wanted). Of course there are times when passivity is inappropriate, such as when faced with a heart attack, or a broken leg, but surprising amount of medicine involves listening. And there was not enough listening in the aid work that I now saw.

Finally, I realised that I was troubled by the intrusive things being done *to* populations, rather than *for* them. An aggressive example of this behaviour is the French concept, "le droit d'ingérence" (the right to interfere), which is linked to "témoignage". I feel that, when taken together, these ideas constitute a form of crusade, which may become an end in itself, rather than a means to an end. MSF is not alone in this type of thinking, but its success seems to make it think that it has earned unquestionable rights on the international scene. This feeling apparently empowers MSF to go anywhere they perceive human rights abuses, to denounce them and, by definition, "resolve the problem".

However, while speaking out is understandable in genocides like Rwanda, or Srebrenica, témoignage can become both exaggerated and inappropriate. When you decide to denounce something publicly, you must be sure that you understand the context; not always easy when you are a foreigner, with limited awareness of another society. Should you then decide to interfere, you must endeavour to predict the long-term consequences. Hippocrates' medical aphorism, "First do no harm", applies particularly to humanitarian aid work. Despite the fact that I believe in emergency aid, I consider that intervening in another culture, or country should be done only with great caution. While action or reaction may be justified, interference never is.

Our intervention in Kitgum, although well intentioned and useful at the beginning, became destructive when it discouraged people from returning to their traditional, self-sufficient ways. As often happens, aid supplies leaked into the local economy, generating corruption and internal strife. A poor strategy was implemented by hard-working and well-meaning aid workers, who lacked experience of both the country and the situation. During the ensuing years, I was to see this type of "mistake" repeated again and again.

In the Iranian refugee camp there was no authentic medical need; instead, a desire to search for human rights' abuses. Worse still, the improvement in the refugees' conditions caused tension within the local Iranian population. I was perturbed to find myself involved in an unnecessary medical mission that masked quite a different purpose.

The Ugandan sleeping sickness project, although worthy in its intent, illustrates a range of problems facing aid providers. The numbers of patients estimated by the project planners did not materialise in Omugo, so we employed too many nurses. Later, we had too few vehicles because emergencies took precedence over our needs. When

I began to negotiate the hand-over to the Ugandan medical authorities, I discovered that they had a quite different perspective of our work. Against a backdrop of crippling, endemic health problems, we were investing huge sums of money on one minor illness, while the country could barely provide minimum health care for most of its inhabitants. Even without the unfortunate need for expensive drugs, the amount of money spent on this project seemed disproportionate.

In Cambodia, I was not sure that I did much harm, but neither was I convinced that MSF maximised the "good" that might have been achieved from the presence of a nurse and doctor in Kroch Mar. The desire to be in touch with the people, to witness their true condition, meant that we were sent to a remote mission, with insufficient work and an inadequately researched role. Sadly, as long as NGOs lack accountability, they will continue to interfere, without adequate research and analysis. This could cause great harm.

But interference is not the only dilemma facing the aid world. There is also a disturbing tendency for agencies to compete. When I was in Cambodia, there were 300 different NGOs and in Afghanistan today there are even more. Although lip service is paid to co-ordination, aid organisations regularly fail to work in partnership, because they need to fight for their "market share". Even within MSF, the French, Belgian, Swiss, Spanish and Dutch Sections compete with each another for work, a fact most puzzling and confusing for host nations. Worse still, competition gives rise to duplication, omission and waste. More co-operation, communication and co-ordination are essential, if we are to maximise the funds given by countries, donor agencies and individuals.

Competition for funding is made worse when success is measured by either the amount of money collected, or the media profile achieved. Less attention is then paid to performance and long-term evaluation. To make matters worse, the independence of many NGOs can limit accountability. In the case of MSF, I gained the impression of an organisation that is very successful at fund raising, but which pays scant attention to using these funds wisely, or efficiently. Perhaps this is not entirely their fault. How many people, who donate money, follow up on what is done with it?

Aid given in crises and catastrophes, is in many ways simple to deliver. The need is obvious and immediate. The methods used are less important if the result is good, since the clear objective is to save lives. Both MSF and MDM have set up infrastructures that cope well, sometimes spectacularly well, with emergency responses. It is rewarding to be part of a well-structured emergency reaction like Uganda's cholera epidemic programme.

The emergency culture of both organisations causes me unease. This approach stems from their 1970's origins, but it does not reflect the reality of much of their current work. On average, MSF has been present for twelve years in the countries in which it works. Ninety percent of its projects are not crises, but the organisation continues to rely on emergency methods and planning. This they excuse, by perceiving most of their activity as emergencies. So in the field, we regularly see volunteers on short-term contracts (on average five months), with little training or preparation, people who lack an in-depth knowledge of the task, the host country, or even the organisation for which they work. There is great reliance on expatriates and often the use of disproportionate resources.

Regularly, I saw the damaging effects of the overnight loss of both staff and vehicles from long-term missions, because of the latest emergency. Having an existing base or project in a country, enables an NGO to get in first in an emergency, to claim ownership and to display its presence on the world's television screens. I now wonder how many long-term missions are simply a convenient, local reservoir of resources, for an aid organisation's core business, the "media-genic emergency".

In non-emergency situations, I regularly found myself without an adequately planned role. Although I am more than willing to create my own solutions for problems, perhaps such ad hoc responses, however enterprising, are neither respectful nor the best answer to a country's needs. Aid workers need time to learn about new cultures, unfamiliar diseases and their project's long-term objectives.

Development aid is a response to inherent situations like poverty, endemic disease or recurrent food shortages and may require many different types of help. Unlike emergency situations, the methods used for this kind of aid are extremely important and the aims and objectives can be difficult, both to define and fulfil. Furthermore, it is essential that objectives should be generated by the host nation, without external coercion. Co-operation, consultation and listening are vital, as are reviews of progress and ongoing assessment.

MSF and MDM are not alone in finding development work difficult. The World Bank states that over the last fifty years they have used three or four different strategies and all have proven unsuccessful. Currently, for all programmes, they advocate three elements: the economic, the social and the environmental. The World Bank seeks to promote greater co-ordination between involved agencies, intending to consult more and to work in partnership with aid recipients. This, they currently admit, does not always happen.

Despite the fact that there are problems, it must be remembered that positive results are achieved. Much good work is done and many lives are saved, due in no small part to the unstinting efforts of an army of enthusiastic, mainly young, volunteers. But NGOs must look objectively at what they are doing, so that they maximise the results of these efforts. Poorly planned humanitarian work can promote dependency, encourage corruption and ultimately delay development.

Yet neither external nor internal evaluation of aid organisations is common. In fact, in France where I now live, criticism of MSF is regarded by many as a heinous crime. Of course I know that MSF, MDM and all the rest, must persist in their attempts to help. It is unthinkable that we would not respond to emergencies, no more than I could have walked away from the two boys who were shot in Omugo. But there should be nothing second-rate about the quality of any help we give. Helping begins by listening carefully and long, to ensure that the "diagnosis" is correct; that the problem is understood in depth.

Organisations must carefully and co-operatively plan all longer-term projects. If it is not an emergency, they must move at the pace of, and in the direction defined by, the host country. Some objectives may take decades to achieve. It may even be appropriate not to intervene, to avoid making matters worse.

Success will improve the quality of life of some of the three billion people, who currently exist on less than two dollars per day. These are men, women and above all children, for whom adequate health care is currently only a dream.